T0200338

ADVANCED TOPICS
IN SCIENCE AND TECHNOLOGY IN CHINA

ADVANCED TOPICS
IN SCIENCE AND TECHNOLOGY IN CHINA

Zhejiang University is one of the leading universities in China. In Advanced Topics in Science and Technology in China, Zhejiang University Press and Springer jointly publish monographs by Chinese scholars and professors, as well as invited authors and editors from abroad who are outstanding experts and scholars in their fields. This series will be of interest to researchers, lecturers, and graduate students alike.

Advanced Topics in Science and Technology in China aims to present the latest and most cutting-edge theories, techniques, and methodologies in various research areas in China. It covers all disciplines in the fields of natural science and technology, including but not limited to, computer science, materials science, life sciences, engineering, environmental sciences, mathematics, and physics.

Zengchang Qin
Yongchuan Tang

Uncertainty Modeling for Data Mining

A Label Semantics Approach

With 61 figures

ZHEJIANG UNIVERSITY PRESS
浙江大学出版社

Springer

Authors

Prof. Zengchang Qin
Intelligent Computing and Machine
Learning Lab, School of ASEE,
Beihang University, Beijing, China
E-mail: zengchang.qin@gmail.com

Prof. Yongchuan Tang
College of Computer Science
Zhejiang University,
Hangzhou, Zhejiang, China
E-mail: tyongchuan@gmail.com

ISSN 1995-6819   e-ISSN 1995-6827
Advanced Topics in Science and Technology in China

ISBN 978-7-308-12106-4
Zhejiang University Press, Hangzhou

ISBN 978-3-642-41250-9   e-ISBN 978-3-642-41251-6
Springer Dordrecht Heidelberg London New York

Library of Congress Control Number: 2013949181

Printed on acid-free paper

Springer is a part of Springer Science+Business Media (www.springer.com)

This book is dedicated to my parents Li-zhong Qin (1939–1995) and Feng-xia Zhang (1936–2003)

Zengchang Qin

Preface

Uncertainty is one of the characteristics of the nature. Many theories have been proposed in dealing with uncertainties. Fuzzy logic has been one of such theories. Both of us were inspired by Zadeh's fuzzy theory and Jonathan Lawry's label semantics theory when we both worked in University of Bristol.

Machine learning and data mining are inseparably connected with uncertainty. To begin with, the observable data for learning is usually imprecise, incomplete or noisy. Even the observations are perfect, the generalization beyond that data is still afflicted with uncertainty; e.g., how can we be sure which one from a set of candidate theories that all of them explain the data. Though Occam's razor tells us to favor the simplest models, this principle does not guarantee this simple model is the truth of the data. In recent research, we have found that some complex models seem to be more appropriate comparing to simple ones because of our complex nature and the complicated mechanism of data generation in social problems.

In this book, we introduce a fuzzy logic basesd theory for modeling uncertainty in data mining. The content of this book can be roughly split into three parts: Chapters 1-3 give a general introduction of data mining and the basics of label semantics theory. Chapters 4–8 introduce a number of data mining algorithms based on label semantics and detailed theoretical aspects, and experimental results are given. Chapters 9–12 introduce prototype theory interpretation of label semantics and data mining algorithms developed based on this interpretation. This book is for the readers like postgraduates and researchers in AI, data mining, soft computing and other related areas.

Zengchang Qin
Pittsburgh, PA, USA
Yongchuan Tang
Hangzhou, China
July, 2013

Acknowledgements

First of all we would like to express sincere thanks to our mentors, colleagues and friends. This book could not have been written without them. Special thank goes to Prof. Jonathan Lawry, our mentor who introduced label semantics theory to us. The first author thanks Prof. Lotfi Zadeh for his insightful comments and support during his two year stay in BISC at UC Berkeley. Many people have helped in our research and providing comments and suggestions, including Trevor Martin (Bristol University), Qiang Shen (Aberystwyth University), Masoud Nikravesh (UC Berkeley), Marcus Thint (BT), Zhiheng Huang (Yahoo!), Ines Gonzalez Rodriguez (University of Cantabria), Xizhao Wang (Hebei University), Baoding Liu (Tsinghua University) and Nam Van Huynh (JAIST). Weifeng Zhang, my student at Beihang University, helped to develop the algorithm of data and imprecise clustering. The first author would also like to thank Prof. Katia Sycara for hosting him at Robotics Institute, Carnegie Mellon University. This visit gave him more time to focus on this book and think more deeply about the relations between linguistic labels and natural language.

This work has depended on the generosity of free software LATEX and numerous contributors of Wikipedia. Zhejiang University Press and Springer have provided excellent support throughout all the stages of preparation of this book. We thank Jiaying Xu, our editor, for her patience and support to provide help when we are behind the schedule.

This book is funded by Beihang Series in Space Technology and Applications. The research presented in this book is funded by the National Basic Research Program of China (973 Program) under Grant No. 2012CB316400, and National Natural Science Foundation of China (NSFC) (Nos. 61075046 and 60604034), the joint funding of NSFC and MSRA (No. 60776798), the Natural Science Foundation of Zhejiang Province (No. Y1090003), and the New Century Excellent Talents (NCET) program from the Ministry of Education, China. Finally, we would like to thank our families for being hugely supportive in our work.

Contents

Acronyms

AI Artificial Intelligence
ANN Artificial Neural Networks
AUC Area Under the ROC Curve
AVE Average Error
BLDT Bayesian LDT
BP Back Propagation
CAD Computer Aided Diagnosis
CW Computing with Words
D-S Dempster-Shafer
DT Decision Tree
EM Expectation-Maximization
FDT Fuzzy Decision Tree
FLDT Forest of LDTs
FOIL First-Order Inductive Learning
FPR False Positive Rate
FRBS Fuzzy Rule-Based Systems
FRIL Fuzzy Relational Inference Language
FSNB Fuzzy Semi-Naive Bayes
GTU General Theory of Uncertainty
IBL Instance-Based Learning
ICMM Information Cell Mixture Model
ID3 Iterative Dichotomiser 3
IG Information Gain
ILP Inductive Logical Programming
KDD Knowledge Discovery in Database
k-NN k-Nearest Neighbors
LD Linguistic Data
LDT Linguistic Decision Tree
LFOIL Linguistic FOIL
LID3 Linguistic ID3

LLE Locally Linear Embedding
LLR Locally Linear Reconstruction
LPT Linguistic Prediction Tree
LS Least Square
LT Linguistic Translation
MB Merged Branch
MLP Multi-Layer Perceptrons
MSE Mean Square Error
MW Modeling with Words
NB Naive Bayes
NN Neural Networks
PDF Probability Density Function
PET Probability Estimation Tree
PNL Precisiated Natural Language
QP Quadratic Programming
ROC Receiver Operating Characteristics
SNB Semi-Naive Bayes
SRM Structural Risk Minimization
SVM Support Vector Machines
SVR Support Vector Regression
TPR True Positive Rate

Notations

$\lvert A \rvert$	Absolute value of A when A is a number or cardinality of A when A is a set
DB	Database with the size of $\lvert DB \rvert$: $DB = \{\mathbf{x}_1, \ldots, \mathbf{x}_{\lvert DB \rvert}\}$
$\mathbf{x}_i$	n-dimensional variable that: $\mathbf{x}_i \in DB$ for $i = 1, \ldots, \lvert DB \rvert$
$\mathbb{L}_x$	Set of labels defined on random variable x
LE	Logical expressions set given $\mathbb{L}$
$\mathbb{F}_x$	Focal set of random variable x
T	Linguistic decision tree that contains $\lvert T \rvert$ branches: $T = \{B_1, \ldots, B_{\lvert T \rvert}\}$
$\mathbb{B}$	A set of branches: $\mathbb{B} = \{B_1, \ldots, B_M\}$ $T \equiv \mathbb{B}$ iff: $M = \lvert T \rvert$
B	A branch of LDT, it has $\lvert B \rvert$ focal elements: $B = \{F_1, \ldots, F_{\lvert B \rvert}\}$
$\mathbb{C}$	A set of classes: $\mathbb{C} = \{C_1, \ldots, C_{\lvert \mathbb{C} \rvert}\}$
m_x	Mass assignment of x
$m_{\mathbf{x}}$	Mass assignment on a multi-dimensional variable $\mathbf{x}$
$\mu_L(x)$	Appropriateness degree of using label L to describe x
$\mu_\theta(x)$	Appropriateness measure of using logical expression θ to describe x where $\theta \in LE$
$p(x\lvert y)$	Conditional probability of x given y
$Bel(\cdot)$	Belief function
$Pl(\cdot)$	Plausibility function
$\lambda(\theta)$	λ-function to transfer the logical expression θ into a set of labels
$\mu_\theta x$	Appropriateness measure of using logical expression θ to label x
$IG(\cdot)$	Information Gain function
FD	Fuzzy database $FD = \{\langle \theta_1(i), \ldots, \theta_n(i) \rangle : i = 1, \ldots, N\}$
$\hat{x}$	Estimated value of x based on a training database
$\tilde{p}$	Updated value of p at iterative updating process
$P(x\lvert m)$	Conditional distribution of x given mass assignment m
$pm(\cdot)$	Prior mass assignment
$\mathscr{LP}$	Information cell mixture model $\mathscr{LP} = \langle \mathbb{L}, Pr \rangle$

1

Introduction

So far as the laws of mathematics refer to reality, they are not certain. And so far as they are certain, they do not refer to reality.

— *Albert Einstein (1879–1955), "Geometry and Experience"*

1.1 Types of Uncertainty

Our nature is uncertain. Given this fact, there are two main streams of philosophy to understand uncertainty. First, the nature is incomplete and is full of uncertainties. Uncertainty is an objective and undeniable fact of nature. The second stream implies that the nature is governed by orders and laws. However, we cannot perceive all these laws from our limited cognitive abilities. That is where the uncertainties come from. The existence of uncertainty is because of the lack of information. Following these two streams of philosophy, uncertainty can be roughly classified into the following two categories:

(1) Epistemic or systematic uncertainties are due to things we could in principle know but don't in practice. This may be either because we have not measured a quantity sufficiently accurately, or because our model neglects certain effects. The uncertainty comes from an imprecise nature which is involved with mixture of truths. As gray is a mixture of black and white.
(2) Aleatoric or statistical uncertainties are unknowns that differ each time we would make the same experiment. We assume there exists an ideological and undeniable fact which is the reason for a phenomenon. However, it cannot be perceived due to the limitation of human cognitive abilities. Each experiment is actually the observable evidence of this "fact" from which we can know better about this fact by conducting repeated experiments.

Vagueness or ambiguity is sometimes described as "second order uncertainty", where there is uncertainty even about the definitions of uncertain states or outcomes. To quote Lindley[1]:

There are some things that you know to be true, and others that you know to be false; yet, despite this extensive knowledge that you have, there remain many things whose truth or falsity is not known to you. We say that you are uncertain about them. You are uncertain, to varying degrees, about everything in the future; much of the past is hidden from you; and there is a lot of the present about which you do not have full information. Uncertainty is everywhere and you cannot escape from it.

Philosophically, uncertainty is ubiquitous. However, in the practice of science and engineering, what we are concerned with is how to predict future events by using uncertain information with a proper measure. Probability is a way of expressing knowledge or belief that an event will occur or has occurred using uncertainty information. Generally, there are two broad categories of probability interpretations: frequentists and Bayesians. Frequentists consider probability to be the relative frequency of occurrence from repeating games. Bayesians use probability as a measure of an individual's degree of belief. Such belief can be updated by new observable evidence from a prior [2]. In the last few decades, Bayesian probability has been widely used in probabilistic reasoning and statistical inference [3,4]. Many successful algorithms have been proposed and applications have been used in real-world practice. Bayesian probability theory assumes that uncertainty exists because of the limitation of our cognitive abilities and lack of information [1]. Some other uncertainty theories have been proposed to assume that the nature itself is uncertain and independent from the limited abilities of acquiring this information. Among them, Fuzzy Logic is the most successful and widely-used theory of modeling such a type of uncertainty.

Proposed by Zadeh in 1965 [5], fuzzy logic is a superset of conventional Boolean logic that has been extended to handle the concept of partial truth (an interpretation of the uncertainty of being true) — truth values between "completely true" and "completely false". Three hundred years B.C., the Greek philosopher, Aristotle, came up with binary logic of true and false, which is now the principle foundation of mathematics. Two centuries before Aristotle, Buddha, had the belief which contradicted the black-and-white world, which went beyond the bivalent cocoon and sees the world as it is, filled with contradictions. Such beliefs are popular especially in oriental cultures, such as the Chinese Yin-Yang concept which is used to describe how polar or seemingly contrary forces are interconnected and interdependent in the natural world, and how they give rise to each other in turn [6].

Both fuzzy logic and probability theory can be used to represent subjective belief. Fuzzy set theory uses the concept of fuzzy set membership (i.e., how much a variable is in a set), and probability theory (Bayesian) uses the concept of subjective probability (i.e., how probable do I think that a variable is in a set). While this distinction is mostly philosophical, there is no such situation where this variable is partially in the set; the variable is either in the set or not, absolutely. However, we do not have such absolute belief because of the lack of information. The

---

① According to Jaynes, probability is an extension of logic given incomplete information [2].

fuzzy-logic-derived possibility measure is inherently different from the probability measure; hence, they are not directly equivalent[7]. The work presented in this book actually uses both fuzzy logic and probability for modeling uncertainty and making predictions based on observable evidence. The nature of uncertainty is modeled by fuzzy labels and the reasoning for using evidence is probabilistic.

A prediction or forecast is a statement about the way things will happen in the future. A basic difference between a good predictor and a random guesser is that a good predictor always uses the previous experience or embedded knowledge when making predictions. We human beings are using such a way for making wise decisions or predictions. The research of studying how to effectively use machines to make predictions using given historic data is referred to as machine learning[8]. In this information age, we are buried by a tremendous amount of data. How we use machine learning algorithms to exploit the data for discovering useful patterns is called *data mining*.

Machine learning and data mining research has developed rapidly in recent decades. As one of the most successful branches of artificial intelligence (AI), it has had a tremendous impact on the current world ②. Many new technologies have emerged or been reborn with its development such as bioinformatics[9], natural language processing[10], computer vision[11], information theory[12], and information retrieval[13]. Traditionally machine learning and data mining research has focused on learning algorithms with high classification or prediction accuracy. From another perspective, however, this is not always sufficient for some real world applications that require good algorithm transparency. By the latter we refers to the interpretability of models; that is, the models need to be easily understood and provide information regarding underlying trends and relationships that can be used by practitioners in the relevant fields. Transparent models should allow for a qualitative understanding of the underlying system in addition to giving quantitative predictions of behavior. The intuition behind this idea is the way of human reasoning with imprecise concepts. It has been a well-accepted fact that computers have beaten the human being in numerical calculations in both accuracy and speed. However, the capability of imprecise reasoning is still Achilles' heel for machines.

Uncertainty and imprecision are often inherent in modeling these real-world applications and it is desirable that these should be incorporated into learning algorithms. In this book, we shall investigate the effectiveness of a high-level modeling framework from the dual perspectives of accuracy and interpretability. The reasoning is that by enabling models to be defined in terms of linguistic expressions we can enhance robustness, accuracy and transparency. We need a higher level modeling language which is to be truly effective and it must

---

② In 2011, IBM's *Watson*, an artificial intelligence computer system capable of answering questions posed in natural language, beat other human competitors on a famous American quiz show *Jeopardy* and became the biggest winner. Its core algorithm, *DeepQA*, basically uses advanced machine learning and information retrieval technologies. This is a big event for attracting people's attention to the long lasting human-machine competition since the last breakthrough by *Deep Blue*, the world champion chess player, also from IBM.

provide a natural knowledge representation framework for inductive learning. As such it is important that it allows for the modeling of uncertainty, imprecision and vagueness in a semantically clear manner. Here we present such a higher level knowledge representation framework centered on the Modeling with Words (MW)[14] paradigm.

We need to notice that the underlying semantics of our approach is quite different from computing with words (CW) ③ proposed by Zadeh[15]. In this book, the framework is used mainly for modeling and building intelligent data mining systems. In such systems, we use words or fuzzy labels for modeling uncertainties and use probabilistic approaches for reasoning. Therefore, the framework we will introduce is an achievement of the research of modeling with words (MW) rather than CW. The new framework we shall use in this book, label semantics[16], is a random set based semantics for modeling imprecise concepts where the degree of appropriateness of a linguistic expression, as a description of a value, is measured in terms of how the set of appropriate labels for that value varies across a population. Different from traditional fuzzy logic, fuzzy memberships are viewed as being fixed point coverage functions of random sets, themselves representing uncertainty or variations in underlying crisp definition of an imprecise concept. Also, label semantics allows linguistic queries and information fusion in a logical representation of linguistic expressions. Therefore, label semantics provides us with an ideal framework for modeling uncertainty with good transparency.

1.2 Uncertainty Modeling and Data Mining

Since the invention of fuzzy logic, it has been widely applied in engineering especially in control problems by handling the uncertainty information as a set of expert rules. However, in this information age, we are facing some new challenges. Nowadays, a tremendous amount of data and information has flooded us. Contributing factors including the widespread use of the World Wide Web (WWW) and other digital innovations in electronics and computing, such as digital cameras, intelligent mobile phones, PDAs and new portal computing devices such as iPad, Blackberry, Kindle, and etc. Most importantly, all the classical communication tools such as papers, books, photos, videos are digitalized and have never been so easily accessed as today. We are in the age of overwhelming information. The ability to find the useful information has never been so important in history. Valuable information may be hiding behind the data, but it is difficult for human beings to extract this without powerful tools. We have already been living in a "data rich but information poor" environment since the invention of these innovative IT infrastructures and devices. To relieve such a plight, data mining research emerged and has developed rapidly in the past few decades.

---

③ CW is focused on developing a calculus of using linguistic terms directly for reasoning based on a fuzzy logic framework. More details on modeling with words are available in Reference [14], in which Zadeh pointed out the differences between CW and MW in the foreword of this book.

Data mining has become one of the most active and exciting areas for its omnipresent applicability in the current world. Approaches to data mining research mainly include three perspectives according to Zhou[17]: databases, machine learning, and statistics. Especially from the perspective of machine learning, many data mining algorithms have been developed to accomplish a limited set of tasks and produce a particular enumeration patterns over data sets. But more theoretical and practical problems still block our way to gain knowledge from data. Among these obstacles, uncertainty is one of the most intractable. The traditional data mining algorithms, such as decision trees[18,19] and K-means clustering[20], are crisp and each database value may be classified into at most one cluster. This is unlikely to satisfy everyday life experiences where a value may be partially classified into one or more categories.

Probabilistic approaches for data mining have been the main stream of this research for handling the statistical uncertainties. We generally assume some prior probabilities in the hypothesis space, by inference on observations, to yield the best hypothesis that can explain the observations best. Form another perspective, systemic uncertainties are not well handled in such a probabilistic reasoning framework. Imprecise data, missing data, and human subjectivity, all could cause such uncertainty. Fuzzy logic is a good means for handling these uncertainties, and also provides an inference methodology to enable the principles of approximate human reasoning capabilities to be systematically used as a basis for knowledge-based systems. In contrast to a classic set, the boundary of a fuzzy set is blurred. This smooth transition is characterized by membership functions which give a fuzzy set flexibility in modeling linguistic expressions. The appearance of fuzzy logic becomes an important milestone in not only mathematics and logic but also scientific philosophy — it is complementary to our classical 0-or-1, black-or-white view of the nature[21]. Interpretations of membership degrees include similarity, preference, and uncertainty[22]: they can state how similar an object or case is to a prototypical one, they can indicate preferences between suboptimal solutions to a problem, or they can model uncertainty about the true situation that is described in imprecise terms. Generally, due to their closeness to human reasoning, solutions obtained using fuzzy approaches are easy to understand and apply.

Uncertainty may exist in data mining models in various different ways:

(1) The model structure, i.e., how accurately a mathematical model describes the true system for a real-life situation, may be known only approximately. Models are almost always only approximations to reality.
(2) The numerical approximation, i.e., how appropriately a numerical method is used in approximating the operation of the system. Most models are too complicated to solve exactly. For example, the finite element method may be used to approximate the solution of a partial differential equation, but this introduces an error (the difference between the exact and the numerical solutions).
(3) Input and/or model parameters may be known only approximately due to the noise of data.

(4) Input and/or model parameters may vary between different instances of the same object for which predictions are sought. As an example, the wings of two different airplanes of the same type may have been fabricated to the same specifications, but will nevertheless differ by small amounts due to fabrication process differences. Computer simulations therefore almost always consider only idealized situations.

In recent years, a new framework of label semantics that was proposed by Lawry[23] has become an alternative approach to dealing with two types of uncertainties in inference problems. In contrast to fuzzy sets, label semantics encodes the meaning of linguistic labels according to how they are used by a population of communicating agents to convey information. Label semantics contest that the efficiency of natural language as a means of conveying information between members of a population lies in shared conventions governing the appropriate use of words which are, at least loosely, adhered to by individuals within the population. Following this idea, a new approach based on random set theory to interpret uncertainty is discussed in this book. Based on these semantics, several new algorithms are proposed. In such models, linguistic expressions such as *small, medium, large, tall, short, hot, cold, young* and *old* are used to learn from data and build linguistic models. These models are modified from the traditional models in accordance with the label semantics. These models not only give comparable accuracy to other well-known data mining models, but also have higher transparency and robustness, which are all considered important properties of a data mining algorithm.

1.3 Related Works

Fuzzy logic provides an approximate yet effective means for describing the characteristics of a system that is too complex or ill-defined to admit precise mathematical analysis. A fuzzy approach is based in the premise that key elements in human thinking are not just numbers but can be approximated to a set of fuzzy rules. Fuzzy logic implements this idea by introducing membership function which is gradual rather than abrupt — which agrees with some eastern philosophy of smooth transition. Much of the logic behind human reasoning is not the traditional two-valued or even multi-valued logic[24]. This fuzzy logic plays a basic role in various aspects of the human thought process[25].

For the above advantages of fuzzy methods, fuzzy logic can play an important role in uncertainty modeling, so that there is a rich literature of fuzzy logic based data mining algorithms. Particularly, fuzzy logic has already been used in the data selection and preparation phase for modeling vague data in terms of fuzzy sets[26,27]. Another possible application of fuzzy logic in data mining is the induction of fuzzy cluster analysis. Clustering methods are among the most important unsupervised learning techniques. In data mining, they are often applied as one of the first steps in order to convey a rough idea of the structure of a data set. Clustering refers to the process of grouping a collection of objects into classes such that objects within the same class are similar in a certain sense, and objects from different classes are dissimilar. In standard clustering, each object is assigned to only one cluster. Consequently, the clusters have sharp boundaries. However, in practice, such boundaries are often not very natural or even counterintuitive. In fact, the boundary of single clusters and the transition between different clusters are usually "smooth" rather than sharp. This motivates researchers to extend fuzzy logic to clustering algorithms. In fuzzy clustering an object that may belong to different clusters is usually assumed to form a partition of unity. Fuzzy clustering has proved to be extremely useful in practice [20].

One of the most frequent applications of fuzzy logic in data mining is the induction of rule based models. Linguistic modeling which is now an important area of application for fuzzy logic is accomplished by descriptive Fuzzy Rule-Based Systems (FRBSs). At present, FRBSs are becoming more and more important. These kinds of systems constitute an extension of classical rule-based systems, because they deal with fuzzy rules instead of classical logic rules. In order to enhance the robustness in classification or prediction, many fuzzy rule induction algorithms have been proposed. Some are simple fuzzy logic rules in the form of IF-THEN, e.g., Reference [28] and some are fuzzy associate rules [29]. There are also fuzzy rules from semi-supervised learning [30]. Drobics et al. [31] proposed a fuzzy FOIL based on traditional fuzzy logic. Lawry et al. [32] also applied fuzzy rule induction algorithms in hydrological modeling.

A fuzzy rule base is the key procedure in constructing FRBSs. A large quantity of methods has been proposed for automatically generating fuzzy rules from numerical data. Usually they make use of complex rule generation mechanisms such as neural networks [33,34], genetic algorithms [35,36], fuzzy clustering [37], and etc. And all these learning algorithms could be categorized into three kinds: cluster-oriented approaches, hyperbox-oriented approaches, and structure-oriented approaches. Cluster-oriented rule learning approaches are based on fuzzy cluster analysis [20]. Hyperbox-oriented approaches use a supervised learning algorithm that tries to cover the training data by overlapping hyperboxes [38]. The main problem of both approaches is that each generated fuzzy rule uses individual membership functions and thus the rule base is hard to interpret. Cluster-oriented approaches additionally suffer from a loss of information. Structure-oriented approaches avoid all these drawbacks, for they do not search for clusters in the data space. Among these algorithms, a family of efficient and simple methods, called "ad hoc data-driven methods", has been proposed in the literature [39–41]. One of the most known and widely used ad hoc data-driven methods is Wang and Mendel's method (WM-method) [41]. By providing initial fuzzy sets before fuzzy rules are created the data space is structured by a multidimensional fuzzy grid. A rule base is created by selecting those grid cells that contain data. One important criterion used to evaluate the interpretability of a fuzzy system is that there are few fuzzy rules in the rule base. And in addition, to improve the performance, the membership function is usually trained after the rule base has been generated.

After decades of developments of fuzzy methods, their application in data mining has made a great progress. But there is still a problem: What is a good solution from the point of view of a user in the field of data mining? Of course, correctness, completeness, and efficiency are important, but there is a constantly growing demand to keep the solutions conceptually simple and understandable. Unfortunately, it is extremely hard to develop a formal theory to evaluate the so-called "simplicity", because for complex domains it is difficult to measure the degree of simplicity and it is even more difficult to assess the gain achieved by making a system simpler. Nevertheless, this is a lasting challenge for the fuzzy community to meet [42].

Another big area for applying fuzzy logic is decision tree learning. As pointed out by Quinlan [43]:

> The results of (traditional) decision trees are categorical and so do not convey potential uncertainties in classification. Small changes in the attribute values of a case being classified may result in sudden and inappropriate changes to the assigned class. Missing or imprecise information may apparently prevent a case being classified at all.

To overcome this problem, some probabilistic or soft decision trees were proposed. The first fuzzy decision tree (FDT) reference was attributed to Chang and Pavlidis in 1977 [44]. Since then more than 30 algorithms were proposed. Generally, these algorithms can be divided into two categories according to Olaru and Wehenkel [45]:

(1) Enable the use of decision trees to manage fuzzy information in the forms of fuzzy inputs, fuzzy classes or fuzzy rules;
(2) Use fuzzy logic to improve their predictive accuracy.

One of the representative FDTs is the one proposed by Yuan and Shaw [46]. They proposed a model based on the reduction of classification ambiguity with fuzzy evidence. They argue that there are two kinds of uncertainties, which are statistical uncertainties and cognitive uncertainties, in real-world applications. In some real-world classification problems, the feature values are actually vague and with involved cognitive uncertainties. For example, given a rule such as "If the weather of tomorrow is sunny, then I will go to play football", the term "sunny" has the inherent cognitive uncertainties. They use fuzzy membership functions to represent these uncertainties and try to build a fuzzy decision tree that gives the best partitioning of classes given the fuzzy data. Wang et al. [47] also extended this model by considering branch merging. Most of the fuzzy decision trees use fuzzy membership functions to model uncertainties. Baldwin et al. [48] proposed a fuzzy decision tree based on mass assignment theory which is another interpretation of imprecise concepts based on Shafer-Dempster theory [49]. Elouedi et al. [50] directly used belief functions in decision trees.

Fuzzy logic can also be applied to Bayesian estimation. Fuzzy logic can enhance the robustness of the model by using soft boundaries rather than sharp boundaries in the problems with numerical attributes. For example, Naive Bayes classifiers proposed by Zhang and Tang[51]. Di Tomaso and Baldwin[52] also proposed a fuzzy Bayesian network model. Label semantics, as an alternative interpretation of vagueness and uncertainties to fuzzy logic and belief functions, has a nice probabilistic property and the advantages of modeling with linguistic (or fuzzy) labels. Using label semantics for Bayesian modeling is still a new research field. Randon and Lawry[53,54] proposed a semi-Naive Bayes algorithm. A comprehensive study of this algorithm can be found in Reference [55]. Chipman *et al.*[56] proposed Bayesian treed models, where they used a binary tree to identify partitions of a data set and the tree will be used for finding and fitting parametric treed models using a Bayesian approach. In this book we will use a different approach to combine Naive Bayes and decision trees.

References

[1] http://en.wikiquote.org/wiki/Dennis_Lindley, accessed on March 19, (2011).

[2] Jaynes E. T.: Probability Theory: The Logic of Science. Cambridge University Press, (2003).

[3] Bishop C. M.: Neural Networks for Pattern Recognition. Oxford Uni. Press. (1995).

[4] Jordan M. I.: Learning in Graphical Models, MIT Press. (1999).

[5] Zadeh L. A.: Fuzzy sets, Information and Control, 8: pp. 338-353. (1965).

[6] http://en.wikipedia.org/wiki/Yin_and_yang, accessed on March 29, (2011).

[7] http://en.wikipedia.org/wiki/Fuzzy_logic, accessed on March 29, (2011).

[8] Mitchell T.: Machine Learning, McGraw-Hill, New York. (1997).

[9] Rogers S., Girolami M., Campbell C., and Breitling R.: he latent process decomposition of cDNA microarray data sets, ACM Trans. on Computational Biology and Bioinformatics, 2(2), April-June. (2005).

[10] Manning C. D., Schuze H.: Foundations of Statistical Natural Language Processing The MIT Press, Cambridge, Massachusetts. (1999).

[11] L. Fei-Fei, Perona P.: A Bayesian hierarchical model for learning natural scene categories. Proceeding of IEEE Computer Society Conference on Computer Vision and Pattern Recognition, pp. 524-531. (2005).

[12] Mackay D. J. C.: Information Theory, Inference, and Learning Algorithms, Cambridge University Press. (2003).

[13] Manning C. D., Raghavan P., Schuze H.: Introduction to Information Retrieval, Cambridge University Press. (2008).

[14] Lawry J., Shanahan J., Ralescu A.: Modelling with Words: Learning, fusion, and reasoning within a formal linguistic representation framework. LNAI 2873, Springer-Verlag. (2003).

[15] Zadeh L. A.: Fuzzy logic = computing with words, IEEE Transaction on Fuzzy Systems. 4(2): pp. 103-111. (1996).

[16] Lawry J.: A framework for linguistic modelling, Artificial Intelligence, 155: pp. 1-39. (2004).

[17] Zhou Z. H.: Three perspectives of data mining, Artificial Intelligence, 143(1): 139-146. (2003).

[18] Quinlan J. R.: Induction of decision trees, Machine Learning, 1: pp. 81-106. (1986).

[19] Quinlan J. R.:C4.5: Programs for Machine Learning, San Mateo: Morgan Kaufmann. (1993).

[20] Bezdek J. C., Keller J. M., Krishnapuram R., Pal N.: Fuzzy models and algorithms for pattern recognition and image processing. The Handbooks on Fuzzy Sets, Netherlands, (1999).

[21] Kosko B.: Fuzzy Thinking: The New Science of Fuzzy Logic, Hyperion/Disney Books, (1993).

[22] Dubois D., Prade H., Yager R.R.: Information engineering and fuzzy logic. Proceedings of 5th IEEE International Conference on Fuzzy Systems, pp. 1525-1531. (1996).

[23] Lawry J.: Modelling and Reasoning with Vague Concepts, Springer. (2006).

[24] Gabbay D.: Classical vs non-classical logic'. In Gabbay D. M., Hogger C. J., and Robinson J. A.(Eds), Handbook of Logic in Artificial Intelligence and Logic Programming, 2, Oxford University Press.

[25] Hullermeier E.: Fuzzy methods in machine learning and data mining: status and prospects, to appear in Fuzzy Sets and Systems. (2005).

[26] Laurentm A.: Generating fuzzy summaries: a new approach based on fuzzy multidimensional databases. Journal of Intelligent Data Analysis, 7(2): pp. 155-177. (2003).

[27] Viertl R.: Statistical methods for non-precise data. CRC Press, Boca Raton, Florida. (1996).

[28] Baldwin J. F., Xie D.: Simple fuzzy logic rules based on fuzzy decision tree for classification and prediction problem, Intelligent Information Processing II, Z. Shi, Q. He (Ed.), Springer. (2004).

[29] Xie D.: Fuzzy associated rules discovered on effective reduced database algorithm, To appear in the Proceedings of IEEE-FUZZ, Reno, USA. (2005).

[30] Klose A., Kruse R.: Information mining with semi-supervised learning, Soft Methodology and Random Information Systems-Proceedings of the 2nd International Conference on Soft Methods in Probability and Statistics (SMPS'2004), Springer. (2004).

[31] Drobics M., Bodenhofer U., Klement E. P.: FS-FOIL: an inductive learning method for extracting interpretable fuzzy descriptions, International Journal of Approximate Reasoning, 32: pp. 131-152. (2003)

[32] Lawry J., Han D., Cluckie I.D.: Fuzzy rule generation in hydrological modelling, Soft Methodology and Random Information Systems–Proceedings of the 2nd International Conference on Soft Methods in Probability and Statistics (SMPS'2004), Springer. (2004).

[33] Jang J. S. R., Sun C. T. and Mizutani E.: Neuro-Fuzzy and Soft Computing, Prentice-Hall, Inc. Simon & Schuster. (1997).

[34] Nauck D., Klawonn F., Kruse R.: Foundations of neuro-fuzzy systems. United Kingdom. (1997).

[35] Cordón O., Herrera F.: A three-stage evolutionary process for learning descriptive and approximate fuzzy logic controller knowledge bases from examples. International Journal of Approximate Reasoning, 17(4), pp.369-407. (1997).

[36] Thrift P.: Fuzzy logic systhesis with genetic algorithms. Proceedings of the 4th International Conference on Genetic Algorithms, pp. 509-513. (1991).

[37] Chiu S. L.: Fuzzy model identification based on cluster estimation. Journal of Intelligent and Fuzzy Systems, 2(6), pp. 267-278. (1994).

[38] Berthold M., Huber K. P.: Constructing fuzzy graphs from examples. International Journal of Intelligent Data Analysis, 3(1), pp. 37-53. (1999).

[39] Bárdossy A., Duckstein L.: Fuzzy rule-based modeling with application to geophysical biological and engineering systems. CRC Press. (1995).

[40] Nozaki K., Ishibuchi H., Tanaka H.: A simple but powerful heristic method for generating fuzzy rules from numerical data. Fuzzy Sets and Systems, 86(3), pp.251-270. (1997).

[41] Wang L. X., Mendel J. M.: Generating fuzzy rules by learning from examples. IEEE Transactions on Systems, Man, and Cybernetics, 22(6), pp. 1414-1427. (1992).

[42] Kruse R.: Information mining. Proceedings of the International Conference of the European society for Fuzzy Logical and Technology, pp.6-9. (2001).

[43] Quinlan J. R.: Deciion trees at probabilistic classifiers, Proceedings of 4th International Workshop on Machine Leanring, pp. 31-37, Morgan Kauffman. (1987).

[44] Chang R. L. P., Pavlidis T.: Fuzzy decision tree algorithm, IEEE Trans. on Systems, Man and Cybernetics, 7(1): pp. 28-35. (1977).

[45] Olaru C., Wehenkel L.: A complete fuzzy decision tree technique, Fuzzy Sets and Systems, 138: pp. 221-254. (2003).

[46] Yuan Y., Shaw M. J.: Induction of fuzzy decision trees, Fuzzy Sets and Systems, 69: pp. 125-139. (1995).

[47] Wang X. Z., Chen B., Qian G., Ye F.: On the optimization of fuzzy decision trees, Fuzzy Sets and Systems, 112(1): pp. 117-125. (2000).

[48] Baldwin J. F., Lawry J., Martin T. P.: Mass assignment fuzzy ID3 with applications. Proceedings of the Unicom Workshop on Fuzzy Logic: Applications and Future Directions, pp. 278-294, London. (1997).

[49] Shafer G.: A Mathematical Theory of Evidence, Princeton University Press. (1976).

[50] Elouedi Z., Mellouli K., Smets P.: Decision trees using the belief function theory. Proceedings IPMU-2000 1: pp. 141-148. (2000).

[51] Zheng J., Tang Y.: One generalization of the Naibe Bayes to fuzzy sets and the design of the fuzzy Naive Bayes Classifier, IWINAC-(2005), LNCS 3562, pp. 281-290, Springer-Verlag. (2005).

[52] Di Tomaso E.: Soft Computer for Bayesian Networks, PhD Thesis, Department of Engineering Mathematics, University of Bristol. (2004).

[53] Randon N. J., Lawry J.: Linguistic modelling using a semi-Naive Bayes framework, IPMU-(2002), Annecy, France. (2002).

[54] Randon N. J., Lawry J.: Classification and query evaluation using modelling with words. Information Sciences, 176, pp. 438-464, (2006).

[55] Randon N. J.: Fuzzy and Random Set Based Induction Algorithms, PhD Thesis, Department of Engineering Mathematics, University of Bristol. (2004).

[56] Chipman H. A., George E. I., McCulloch R. E.: Bayesian treed models, Machine Learning, 48: pp. 299-320. (2002).

2

Induction and Learning

Learning is any process by which a system improves performance from experience.

— Herbert Simon (1916–2001)

2.1 Introduction

Induction is fundamental to the acquisition of human knowledge. Twenty-four centuries ago, Plato raised the point that people have much more knowledge than what appears to be present in the information to which they have been exposed. Chomsky referred to it as Plato's problem to describe the gap between knowledge and experience[1]. Induction can be regarded as an important property of intelligence. Human beings have the ability of generalizing from already known cases to new unknown cases with which they share similarities or patterns. Actually, people have been seeking patterns in data throughout human history. Hunters seek patterns in animal migration behavior in order to hunt for survival, farmers seek patterns in crop growth in order to feed themselves and their families, businessmen seek patterns from markets to make profit, and politicians seek patterns in voter opinions in order to be elected. A scientist's job is to make sense of observed evidence (or data) in order to discover the patterns that govern how the physical world works and encapsulate them in theories that can be used for predicting what will happen in the future. Scientists are the first group of people who woke up and dared to argue with the followers of the Almighty on the issues such as the earth is not the center of the universe and human beings, like all other species, have evolved to what they are today. The powerful tool they have been employing, so called science, is based on such a hypothesis-evidence paradigm. With the development of new measuring tools, we can always find more new evidence about the nature and our hypothesis spaces have been updated again and again by those giants like Copernicus, Newton, Maxwell, Darwin and Einstein.

The problem of how to make machines learn like human beings is a key issue of artificial intelligence research. This research has been developed rapidly with the advance of computing technology. It has grown into a new research field called machine learning. Machine learning is about how to build algorithmic or mathematic models that can be trained from data in order to make correct decisions or predictions. The learning processing can be to consider a search through the hypotheses space in order to find what can explain the evidence best. In other words, we need to find an algorithmic "theory" to explain the "observations" and use it to make predictions. A theory is good if it can be validated by observations and predictions. For more than two thousand years, philosophers have debated the question of how to evaluate scientific theories, and the issues are brought into a focus by inductive learning because what is extracted is essentially a "theory" about the data. Machine learning and the philosophy of science share a lot of similarities and are regarded as an experimental philosophy of science, though the methodological skills employed in science are non-algorithmic [2]. In this chapter, we are going to introduce some basic ideas about inductive learning and some classical algorithms that will be used in the following chapters.

2.2 Machine Learning

Learning, a main feature of intelligence, covers such a broad range of processes that is hard to define precisely. Based on dictionary definition, learning is the process by which we "gain knowledge or understanding of, or skill in, by study, instruction, or experience" and results in "modification of a behavioral tendency by experience" [3]. To quote Herbert Simon[1], "learning is any process by which a system improves performance from experience". Usually, human learning involves the following steps:

(1) Observation;
(2) Analysis in order to find out the regularities or patterns among the observations;
(3) Formulation of a theory to explain the observations;
(4) Prediction of new phenomena according to the theory.

Can machines follow the same steps of learning[2] and if so, how? This is a central question in machine learning research originated from early research on

---

[1] Herbert Simon has made important contributions in many areas including cognitive psychology, cognitive science, computer science, public administration, economics, management, philosophy of science, sociology and political science. He received the Turing Award in 1975, the Nobel Prize in Economics in 1978, National Medal of Science in 1986, the Von Neumann Theory Prize in 1988, the American Psychology Association's Award for Outstanding Lifetime Contributions to Psychology in 1993. With almost thousands of high cited publications, he is regarded as one of the most influential social scientists of the 20th century [4].

[2] It still remains controversial for machines to have human intelligence. For example, Penrose argued that the human intelligence is inseparable from his physical structures. Since the machines (or specifically, computers) have the different physical structures, it is infeasible to recreate the human intelligence in silicon structures [5]. The *Chinese Room thought* experiment by Searle proposed another philosophical problems of machine's

game playing, letter recognition, abstract concepts and verbal memory in the mid-1950s[7], and developed into an area of artificial intelligence research. According to Reference [8], similar to human learning, the machine learning process can be divided into the following steps:

(1) Observing and exploring interesting phenomena;
(2) Generating hypotheses;
(3) Formulating a model to explain phenomena;
(4) Testing predictions made by the theory;
(5) Modifying theory and repeating (at step (2) or (3)).

Machine learning is not a single area. It combines computer science, mathematics (especially probability theory, statistics and information theory), cognitive science, biological sciences and even linguistics. It is regarded as a computational approach to understanding the mechanism of learning and used as a powerful tool in many areas. As an engineering field, machine learning has become steadily more mathematical and more successful in applications over the past 30 years. Learning approaches such as data clustering, probabilistic classifiers, and nonlinear regression have found surprisingly wide application in the practice of engineering, business, and science. We can say that, machine learning is the study of computer algorithms capable of learning from experience to improve their performance on some special tasks. Thus, if machine learning is a science, so is it a science of algorithms[7].

Today machine learning algorithms are being applied to many kinds of problems and developed into some new fields by emphasizing the different aspects of the problem, including knowledge discovery in databases (KDD) or data mining, natural language processing[12], computer vision[13,14], information retrieval[12], biometrics, bioinformatics[15], robot control[16] and crime location prediction[17], as well as to more traditional problems such as speech recognition, face recognition, handwriting recognition, medical data analysis and game playing[18,19].

AI researchers can roughly be divided into two groups: one group is trying to combine current mathematical and computational techniques with cognitive science and neuroscience with the aim of understanding the essence of intelligence ③. Another group takes engineering approaches by making intelligent systems or intelligent machines with learning algorithms to aid human beings in many practical areas. The latter include manufacturing, financial analysis and computer aided diagnosis (CAD) and so on. The research of these two groups is inter-connected. The

---

limitation in language understanding[6]. In this book, we consider learning of machines as a mathematical induction and treat it with an engineering approach. We do not intend to go deeply into the philosophy behind human cognition and knowledge acquisition.

③ Nobel Prize laureate Francis Crick, famous for discovering the double helix structure of DNA, had devoted his later life of research centering on theoretical neurobiology and attempts to advance the scientific study of human consciousness, which is so related to human intelligence. He was skeptical about the value of using only computational models of mental function that are not based on detailed brain structure and function[20].

research presented in this book mainly belongs to the latter group. More specifically, we aim to build intelligent systems that are more accessible to human beings.

2.2.1 Searching in Hypothesis Space

We can treat machine learning as a process of searching in a large space of possible hypotheses to determine the one that best fits the observed data by giving some prior knowledge for the learner. In other words, the learning algorithm is trying to find the hypothesis that is most consistent with the available training examples [4]. According to Mitchell[21] there are three main issues related to learning:

(1) Some class of tasks T;
(2) Performance measurement P;
(3) Experience E.

If a system can be described as the ability to "learn", then its performance improves with E, with respect to T and P. Formally, for a set of noise free data x_i for $i = 1, \cdots, N$, there is a target concept function denoted as $f(x_i)$, $y_i = f(x_i)$, where y_i is the class or label of x_i. We aim to find a hypothesis h in the hypotheses space H (i.e., $h \in H$), for which $h(x_i) = f(x_i)$ for $i = 1, 2, \cdots, N$ in the instance space X, where N is the number of training examples.

Besides the hypotheses and instance space, another important "space" is called version space which is the subset of hypotheses from H consistent with training examples seen so far. In other words, version space V is the plausible space of H given x. For a particular concept target we only need to search through the version space instead of the whole hypotheses space. Fig. 2.1 gives an example of "rectangle" hypothesis space and the version space based on given positive (pluses) and negative examples (circles). The "theories" in this example are to find rectangles that cover the positive examples only. The thick outer rectangle is the maximally general positive hypothesis boundary, and the inner thick rectangle is the maximally specific positive hypothesis boundary. The intermediate (thin) rectangles represent the hypotheses in the version space bounded by these two boundaries.

---

④ In logic, we often refer to the two broad methods of reasoning as the deductive and inductive approaches, respectively. Machine learning is usually regarded as an inductive reasoning by following the steps from (A) observations; (B) pattern; (C) hypothesis to (D) theory. However, if we consider the learning a search in the hypothesis space, we are first given a paradigm with pre-assuming models (e.g., some parametric models like Gaussian mixtures). By offering the observations, we hope to find the best hypothesis to explain these data. This process is a deductive approach of reasoning: (A) theory; (B) hypothesis; (C) observations and (D) confirmation. Based on this example, we can understand that some philosophers deny the existence of pure induction in human reasoning based on the limitation of our cognitive abilities.

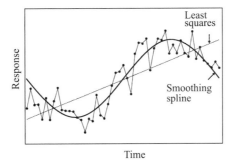

Least
squares

Response

Smoothing
spline

Time

Fig. 2.1 Version space for a "rectangle" hypothesis language in two dimensions. Pluses are positive examples, and circles are negative examples. This figure is modified from the version space illustration in Reference [9]

However, all the hypotheses in the version space are consistent with the given examples. How can we select the best one? According to Occam's razor [5] [23], we should always intend to find the simplest one [6].

In addition to the "learning capability" of the algorithms, the efficiency of searching is also largely dependent on the complexity of searching space. Some machine learning algorithms employ the hill climbing method in which one iteratively applies all possible operators, and compares the resulting states using an evaluation function, in order to select the best state [7]. Learning can be regarded as guided learning but not an exhaustive searching, so it is not guaranteed to find the optimal solution. The search procedures tend to be heuristic and no guarantees can be made about the optimality of the final result. This leaves plenty of room for "bias" where different search heuristics bias the search in different ways. For most cases, we are forced to work with a limited quantity of data, and increasing the dimensionality of the space rapidly leads to the point where the data is very sparse. This problem is referred to as the *curse of dimensionality* [24]. For example, 100 evenly-spaced samples in a unit interval of $[0, 1]$ have no more than 0.01 distance between points; an equivalent sampling of a 10-dimensional unit hypercube with a lattice with a spacing of 0.01 between adjacent points would require 2^{10} samples: thus, the 10-dimensional hypercube can be said to be a factor of 10^{18} "larger" than the unit interval [25].

Machine learning algorithms have different paradigms. Based on the paradigms proposed by Langley [7] and recent developments, we use the following several

---

⑤ Occam's razor principle may not be applicable to all practical problems because some real-world phenomena are related complex hidden factors, and the simplest hypothesis may not always be the best hypothesis. For example, some complex hierarchical Bayesian generative models perform very well in complex problems such as natural language understanding [10,11], question-answering [12] and content-based image retrieval [13].

⑥ In some other theories [22], the hypotheses consistent with data are assigned with a probability distribution that is referred to as *universal distribution* [23]. Hypotheses will be chosen according to this distribution but not the simplest one only.

general forms in this book: supervised learning, unsupervised learning, semi-supervised learning[26] and reinforcement learning. In supervised learning, a teacher/supervisor provides a category label or cost for each pattern in a training set, and seeks to reduce the sum of the costs for these patterns. In unsupervised learning or clustering which is a representative unsupervised problem, there is no explicit teacher/supervisor, and the system forms clusters of the input patterns based on some measure of similarity. The most typical way to train a classifier is to present an input, compute its tentative category label, and use the known target category label to improve the classifier[27]. In semi-supervised learning, only a small subset of data are provided with category labels. It can be regarded as weak supervised learning, After all, some supervised information is given for training. However, in reinforcement learning, like in unsupervised learning, no explicit category labels are given; instead, the teaching feedback is that the tentative category of being right or wrong will be given. A popular example is, when teaching a dog a new trick, if he performs correctly, some rewards (e.g., bones, foods) will be given. Otherwise, there will be penalties (e.g., no bones or foods). Gradually, the dog will learn the trick. One of the most well-known reinforcement learning methods, Q-learning, has been well used in game playing or mobile robot path planning[21]. In this book, we only focus on using the proposed framework for building supervised learning and unsupervised learning models. Semi-supervised learning and reinforcement learning will not be discussed in this book.

2.2.2 Supervised Learning

Supervised learning aims to devise a method or construct a model for assigning instances to one of a finite set of classes on the basis of a vector of variables measured on the instances. The information on which the rule is to be based is called a training set of instances with known vectors of measurements and known classification[28]. A typical supervised classification problem has a training set in the form:

$$DB = \{(\mathbf{x}_1, y_1), (\mathbf{x}_2, y_2), \ldots, (\mathbf{x}_n, y_n)\}$$

where $\mathbf{x}$ values are typically vectors of the form: $\mathbf{x} = \langle x_1, \ldots, x_n \rangle$, whose components can be discrete or real valued. These components are called the attributes (or features) of the database. In classification problems, the object is to infer the unknown functional mapping

$$f : x \rightarrow y$$

where y value is drawn from a discrete set of *classes* $\mathbb{C} = \{C_1, \ldots, C_k\}$ that characterize the given data $\mathbf{x}$. In prediction or regression problems, the values of $y \in \mathbb{R}$ are continuous but not discrete. The training examples will be used to build our learning model and are considered as the "experience" about some hidden truth we want to learn about.

For example, Fig. 2.2 illustrates the probability distributions of two sets of data which are assumed to be generated by two Gaussians:

$$P(x|C_1) \sim \mathcal{N}(2, 0.3)$$

$$P(x|C_2) \sim \mathcal{N}(3, 0.3)$$

where $\mathcal{N}(\mu, \delta)$ is a Gaussian distribution with mean μ and standard deviation δ. Given a new data x', the probability of it belonging to a particular class can be calculated based on the Bayes theorem:

$$P(C_i|x') \propto \prod_{i=1,2} P(x|C_i)P(C_i) \tag{2.1}$$

where $P(x|C_i)$ can be estimated based on the training data. More details about Bayesian learning can be found in Chapter 6.

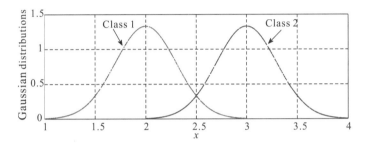

Fig. 2.2 Two classes of data characterized by two Gaussian distributions with the same standard deviation $\delta = 0.3$ but different means $\mu_1 = 2$ and $\mu_2 = 3$

The models learnt from training data are then evaluated with a different test set in order to determine if they can be generalized to new cases. Since the training data is limited and may also contain noise, then we would expect that the accuracy of the test set will be less than 100%. Usually, test data are independent and identically distributed samples are drawn from the same distribution of training examples. Why is the test set important? The following analogy [29] illustrates the importance of test sets in the learning process [30]:

Imagine yourself back in the 5th grade. The class is taking a spelling test. Suppose that, at the end of the test period, the teacher asks you to estimate your own grade in the quiz by marking the words you got wrong. You will give yourself a good grade, but your spelling will not improve. If, at the beginning of the period, you thought there should be an 'e' at the end of "tomato", nothing will have happened to change your mind when you grade your own paper. No new data has entered the system. You need a test set! Now, imagine that at the end of the test the teacher allows you to look at the papers of several neighbors before grading your own. If they all agree that "tomato" has no final 'e', you may decide to mark your own answer wrong. If the teacher gives the same quiz tomorrow, you will do better.

But how much better? If you use the papers of the very same neighbors to evaluate your performance tomorrow, you may still be fooling yourself. If they all agree that "potatoes" has no more need of an 'e' than "tomato", and you have changed your own guess to agree with theirs, then you will overestimate your actual grade in the second quiz as well. That is why the evaluation set should be different from the test set.

If the model is very complex and is trained excessively only for improving the training accuracy, we may be in danger of overfitting. Fig. 2.3 gives an illustration of overfitting the training data. Given the data in the left-hand side figure, there could be three models with different complexities. By empirical studies, we can observe the training error and test error by increasing the model complexity. The right-hand side figure shows that the best model should be the one with best test error since the training error will keep going down by overfitting the training data. All the experiments presented in the following chapters are based on separate training and test sets in order to validate the performance of the proposed algorithms.

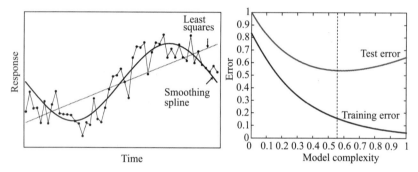

Fig. 2.3 Given the training data shown in the left-hand side figure, models with different complexities can be used, e.g., least squares (LS), smoothing spline and polynomial function. The right-hand side figure shows that the training error and test error will diverge with the increase in complexity

2.2.3 Unsupervised Learning

In contrast with supervised learning, there are no explicit target outputs in unsupervised learning. The unsupervised learner brings to bear prior biases as to what aspects of the structure of the input should be captured in the output. The only things that unsupervised learning methods have to work with are the observed input patterns x_i, which are often assumed to be independent samples forming an underlying unknown probability distribution and some explicit or implicit a priori information as to what is important. A typical problem of unsupervised learning is clustering. The basic idea behind clustering is to group similar objects together and maximize the differences between these groups. Commonly used clustering algorithms include k-means, fuzzy C-means[31], hierarchical clustering and a mixture of Gaussians. Among them, the k-means algorithm is the simplest and most widely used model for clustering. Supposing that we have N sample feature vectors $x_1, x_2, ..., x_N$, where each element is an n-dimensional real vector, the k-means algorithm aims to partition the observations into K sets $(K \leq N)$ $S = \{S_1, S_2, ..., S_K\}$ so as to minimize the within-cluster sum of dissimilarity measure J:

$$J = \arg\min_S \sum_{i=1}^{K} \sum_{x_j \in S_i} D(x_j, \mu_i) \tag{2.2}$$

where μ_i is the mean of data elements in S_i:

$$\mu_i = \frac{1}{|S_i|} \sum_{x_j \in S_i} x_j \tag{2.3}$$

and D is a distance or dissimilarity measure. Fig. 2.4 illustrates clustering 2-dimensional data (with coordinates x_1, x_2) into three clusters based on the Euclidean distance, i.e.,

$$D(x, \mathbf{y}) = \|x - \mathbf{y}\|^2 \tag{2.4}$$

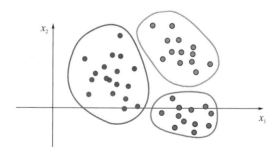

Fig. 2.4 An example of clustering in 2-dimensional space where cluster number $K = 3$

A key component of a clustering algorithm is the distance measure between data points. If the components of the data vectors are all in the same physical units then it is possible that the simple Euclidean distance metric is sufficient to successfully group similar data. For many real-world problems, how to define a sufficient distance measure that can reflect the similarity properties of data is the most important component for solving the problem but not the clustering algorithm itself. Chapter 7 in this book gives a good example by defining a distance measure between a data element to a vague concept for solving the problem of clustering mixed types of data.

To illustrate the difference between supervised and unsupervised learning, we can think of uncontaminated data as forming a fuzzy ball in a high dimensional space. Unsupervised learning puts a boundary around this ball and assigns a high suspicion score to anything outside of the boundary. Supervised learning creates a second fuzzy ball consisting of fraudulent data and assigns a high suspicion score only if the probability of being in class 2 is sufficiently higher than being in class 1. Data that are outside of the unsupervised boundary may not be in the direction of class 2. However, the supervised approach makes the assumption that future fraudulent data will have the same characteristics as past fraudulent data and further assumes that fraudulent use of the data will result in characteristics similar to those in the fraudulent use of the other account. Clustering algorithms have been used in numerous practical applications such as medical imaging, gene sequence analysis, social network analysis, grouping similar answers in information retrieval and so on[32]. A good tutorial on unsupervised learning from a statistical viewpoint can be found in Reference [33].

2.2.4 Instance-Based Learning

Besides the above paradigms based on the type of supervisions, machine learning also has other paradigms such as parametric model learning and non-parametric model learning, generative model learning and discriminative learning. Instance-based learning (IBL) or memory-based learning[34] is a non-parametric approach where learning does not take place until a query is made. Instead of performing explicit generalization, IBL compares the new instances with instances seen in training, which have been stored in the memory. We are not assuming any models that generate these data. We consider only the properties that the data exhibit.

k-nearest neighbor (k-NN) learning, one of the most popular realizations of IBL, combines the target classes (or values in prediction problems) of selected neighbors to predict the target class or estimate the function value of the given instance. Fig. 2.5 illustrates how to classify a new instance using k-NN in a 2-dimensional space with two classes of data in two scenarios where the k value is set to 3 and 7, respectively. The classification results may be different. The choice of k is data-dependent; generally, larger values of k reduce the effect of noise on the classification, but make boundaries between classes less distinct. A good k can be selected by various heuristic techniques.

k-NN can be applied to manifold learning such as locally linear embedding (LLE)[34] and locally linear reconstruction (LLR)[35]. The basic idea of these two models is about how to automatically determine two main factors of k-NN: k value and weights of neighbors by minimizing the construction error

$$E(w) = \sum_i |x_i - \sum_{j=1}^{k} w_{ij} x'_j|^2 \tag{2.5}$$

where x'_j for $j = 1, \ldots, k$ is the k-nearest neighbor of x_i and w_{ij} is the weight of x'_j respective to x_i. Based on k-nearest neighbors of x_i, the data is mapped into a

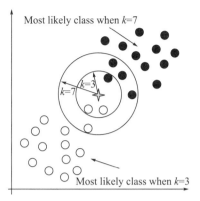

Fig. 2.5 An example of k-nearest neighbor classification in a 2-dimensional space. The selection of k may yield different classification results, e.g., the cases of $k = 3$ and $k = 7$ are illustrated

lower dimensional space through a linear transformation of w, which provides the optimal construction of each data point from its neighbors. The properties between high dimensional data instances are contained in weight matrix w. In the final stage of dimension reduction, we hope to find the lower dimensional output $\mathbf{y}_i$ of high dimensional input x_i in order to minimize the embedding cost function

$$\Phi(\mathbf{y}) = \sum_i |\mathbf{y}_i - \sum_{j=1}^{k} w_{ij}\mathbf{y}_j|^2 \tag{2.6}$$

More details are available in References [34] and [35].

2.3 Data Mining and Algorithms

Data mining, also popularly referred to as knowledge discovery in database (KDD), is a multidisciplinary field including database technology, machine learning, statistics, information retrieval, knowledge acquisition and knowledge-based systems. Specifically, it is the technology for extracting (or mining) knowledge from large amounts of data. "Data mining" has become a popular term in recent years in industry as well as in academia. Big software companies such as Google, Yahoo! and Microsoft invest heavily in data mining and machine learning technologies. In this section, we give a short introduction to this field by focusing on the following issues: What is data mining and why is it important, how do we do data mining? Brief introductions to some data mining algorithms used in this book are given in the following sections.

2.3.1 Why Do We Need Data Mining?

Generally, data mining is the process of analyzing data from different perspectives and summarizing it to provide useful information. We are overwhelmed with the unbridled growth in data across a wide range of disciplines and applications. In recent years, companies have used powerful computers to sift through volumes of supermarket scanner data and analyze market research reports. However, continuous innovations in computer processing power, disk storage and statistical software are dramatically increasing the accuracy of analysis while driving down the cost. Based on traditional statistical analysis methods and newly developed machine learning algorithms, data mining research has advanced rapidly and has become one of the most promising areas in Information Technology (IT).

Important sources of large volumes of data include scientific, engineering, financial, demographic, marketing data and World Wide Web (WWW) data. Omnipresent computers make it so easy to save things that previously we would have trashed. With the development of computer technology, collecting and storing data has become cheaper. The traditional database technology and statistical methods are not powerful enough for us to extract useful information from such large volumes of data. Classical database research was focused on how to efficiently store and query data. With the development of machine learning and data mining, some new database technology can generate new knowledge based on data reasoning to match the given queries.

Suppose you enter a library without the retrieval systems and librarians and with an endless network of rooms with bookshelves full of books, each of which has no title or author but only a content page. In such a case, it will be too hard to find the book you want. The library contains a huge amount of data but no useful information for us. This is an interesting but cruel metaphor for our growing data mining problems. We are buried by the expanding universe of data in which we are data rich but information poor. It is almost impossible for a human librarian to handle such amounts of information. We need intelligent computing systems to be a wise librarian in such a library [36]. As the volume of data increases inexorably the proportion of it that people understand decreases, alarmingly. So, we need to find useful patterns and relationships from large and potentially noisy databases.

2.3.2 How Do We do Data Mining?

According to the CRISP-DM (CRISP-Data Mining) Methodology [37], we can divide data mining into five main parts: Data Understanding, Data Preparation, Modeling, Evaluation and Deployment. In this book, we shall not attempt to give an exact solution for a data mining project. Instead, we will focus on the modelling part of data mining with the aim of providing effective and interpretable algorithms.

There are a number of different approaches toward data mining. Zhou divides data mining research into three distinct approaches: the approach from the database perspective, from the machine learning perspective and from the statistical perspective[38]. Each perspective lays strong emphasis on different aspects of data mining.

(1) Efficiency of data mining: this is emphasized by the database perspective. A database often has a huge amount of data and for some reasons of computational complexity some algorithms simply cannot be applied to such a large data set. We have to use the KDD process with high efficiency, for many industrial applications.

(2) Effectiveness of data mining: this is emphasized from the machine learning perspective. Machine learners want their algorithms to be as accurate as possible empirically. From this point of view, the accuracy of the classification and prediction is the only criterion for the evaluation of the data mining algorithm.

(3) Validity of data mining: this is emphasized from the statistical perspective. Statistics provides a solid foundation for statistical learning algorithms, so in this case we expect a mathematical justification of the process of data mining not only an empirical one.

In this book we will mainly focus on the machine learning perspective. A good data mining algorithm needs both theoretical soundness and excellent performance in experimental studies of benchmark problems, e.g., UCI Machine Learning Repository[39]. In this book, we will put our emphasis on both the effectiveness and transparency of the algorithm. In this case a good algorithm should generate models that are both interpretable and accurate. In order to make the book self-contained, we will give brief introductions to some of the data mining algorithms that will be used in later experiments.

2.3.3 Artificial Neural Networks

The learning model of Artificial Neural Networks (ANN) (or just a neural network (NN)) is an approach inspired by biological neural systems that perform extraordinarily complex computations in the real world without recourse to explicit quantitative operations. The original inspiration for the technique came from examination of bioelectrical networks in the brain formed by neurons and their synapses (see biological neural network). In a neural network model, simple nodes (called variously "neurons" or "units") are connected together to form a network of nodes hence the term "neural network".

Each node has a set of input lines which are analogous to input synapses in a biological neuron. Each node also has an "activation function" that tells the node when to fire, similar to a biological neuron. In its simplest form, this activation function can just be to generate a '1' if the summed input is greater than some value, or a '0' otherwise. Activation functions, however, do not have to be this simple. In fact to create networks that can do useful work, they almost always have to be more complex, for at least some of the nodes in the network. Typically, there are at least three layers to a feed-forward network — an input layer, a hidden layer and an output layer (see Fig. 2.6). The input layer does no processing — it is simply where the data vector is fed into the network. The input layer then feeds into the hidden layer. The hidden layer, in turn, feeds into the output layer. The actual processing in the network occurs in the nodes of the hidden layer and the output layer. Since the first model of ANN in an artificial neuron proposed by McCulloch and Pitts[40], neural network research was flourishing until Minsky and Papert's book *Perceptrons*[41] that pointed out a drawback of the linear separability problem. This drawback was overcome by Multi-layer Perceptrons (MLP) or Multi-Layer Feed-Forward Neural Network[42]. A good review of the the history of neural network research is in Reference [43].

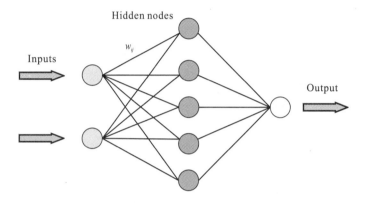

Fig. 2.6 An illustration of a two-layer neural network. The arrows represent connections with weights w_{ij} attached to them

The most commonly used algorithms for multi-layer ANN are the Back-Propagation (BP) neural networks[44]. In this book, BP-NN will be used for later comparison studies. Learning by BP algorithm for NN proceeds as follows: example inputs are presented to the network and, if the network computes an output vector that matches the target, nothing is done. If there is an error, then the weights are adjusted to reduce this error. The trick is to assess the blame for an error and divide it among the contribution weights[45] in order to minimize the error between each target output and actually computed output.

Neural networks are particularly useful for dealing with bounded real-valued data, where a real-valued output is desired; in this way neural networks will perform classification by degrees, and are capable of expressing values equivalent to "not sure". In real life applications, neural networks perform particularly well on the following common tasks:

(1) Function approximation (or regression analysis);
(2) Time series prediction;
(3) Classification;
(4) Pattern recognition.

As one of the most successful branches of artificial intelligence, ANN has a great impact in both computer science and engineering. There are many good textbooks on this topic such as References [46], [47] and [21].

2.3.4 Support Vector Machines

Support vector machines (SVM) were proposed based on Vapnik-Chervonenkis (VC) Theory, which is also referred to as statistical learning theory[47] by Vapnik and his colleagues.

Support vector machines are considered to have good generalization ability, especially in a high dimensional feature space. When used for classification, the SVM creates a hyperplane that separates the data into two classes with the maximum-margin. Given training examples labeled either "pluses" or "squares", a maximum margin hyperplane splits the positive and negative training examples, such that the distance from the closest examples (the margin) to the hyperplane is maximized (for example, see Fig. 2.7). The use of the maximum margin hyperplane is motivated by Vapnik-Chervonenkis theory, which provides a probabilistic test error bound that is minimized when the margin is maximized. However, the utility of this theoretical analysis is sometimes questioned given the large slack associated with these bounds.

The parameters of the maximum margin hyperplane are derived by solving a quadratic programming (QP) optimization problem. There exist several specialized algorithms for quickly solving the QP problem that arises from SVMs. The

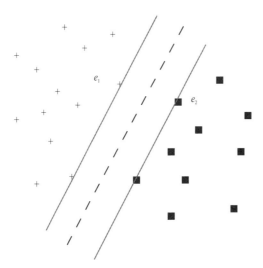

Fig. 2.7 The perpendicular distance between the separating hyperplane and a hyperplane through the closed points (the support vectors) is called margin. e_1 and e_2 are examples of support vectors of opposite class

classification problem can be restricted to consideration of the two-class problem without loss of generality. Go get a better generalization, we would expect to draw a decision boundary which maximizes the margin. Given the database:

$$DB = \left\{ (x_1, y_1), \ldots, (x_N, y_N) \right\}, \; x \in \mathbb{R}^n, y \in \{-1, 1\}$$

and let the decision function be

$$f(x) = sign(\mathbf{w} \cdot x + b) \tag{2.7}$$

If the given data is separable then the data will be correctly classified

$$\forall i, \; y^i(\mathbf{w} \cdot x + b) > 0 \tag{2.8}$$

Clearly, this relation is invariant under a positive re-scaling of the argument inside the sign function, hence we implicitly define a scale for $(\mathbf{w}, b)$ to give canonical hyperplanes such that

$$\mathbf{w} \cdot x + b = 1 \tag{2.9}$$

(denoted by H_1) on one side of the hyperplane and

$$\mathbf{w} \cdot x + b = -1 \tag{2.10}$$

which can be denoted by H_2, on the other side, since the perpendicular distance between the hyperplane

$$\mathbf{w} \cdot x + b = 0 \tag{2.11}$$

is $|b|/||\mathbf{w}||$ where $||\mathbf{w}||$ is the Euclidean norm of $\mathbf{w}$.

The distance of the hyperplane H_1 to the origin is $|b-1|/||\mathbf{w}||$ and $|b+1|/||\mathbf{w}||$. The margin, i.e., the distance between the two parallel hyperplane H_1 and H_2 is simply $2/||\mathbf{w}||$. We then can find the pair of hyperplanes which gives the maximum margin by minimizing $||\mathbf{w}||^2$. Based on the structural risk minimization (SRM) principle, which is a core theory of statistical learning[47], minimizing $||\mathbf{w}||$ is equivalent to minimizing an upper bound on the VC dimension. To maximize the margin the task therefore becomes

$$\min g(\mathbf{w}) = \frac{1}{2}||\mathbf{w}||^2 \tag{2.12}$$

subject to the constraints

$$\forall i, \; y_i(\mathbf{w} \cdot x + b) \geq 1 \tag{2.13}$$

By introducing positive Lagrange multipliers α_i, $i = 1, \ldots, l$, we can obtain the following equation,

$$\Phi(\mathbf{w}, b, \alpha) = \frac{1}{2}||\mathbf{w}||^2 - \sum_{i=1}^{l} \alpha_i \Big(y_i(x_i \cdot \mathbf{w} + b) - 1 \Big) \tag{2.14}$$

The Lagrangian has to be minimized with respect to $\mathbf{w}, b$ and maximized with respect to $\alpha_i > 0$. Classical Lagrangian duality enables the primal problem to be transformed to its dual problem, which is easier to solve.

The dual problem is given by,

$$\max_{\alpha} W(\alpha) = \max_{\alpha} \left(\min_{\mathbf{w},b} \Phi(\mathbf{w}, b, \alpha) \right) \qquad (2.15)$$

The minimum with respect to $\mathbf{w}$ and b of the Lagrangian, Φ, is given by,

$$\frac{\partial \Phi}{\partial b} = 0 \Rightarrow \sum_{i=1}^{l} \alpha_i y^i = 0 \qquad (2.16)$$

$$\frac{\partial \Phi}{\partial \mathbf{w}} = 0 \Rightarrow \mathbf{w} = \sum_{i=1}^{l} \alpha_i y^i x^i \qquad (2.17)$$

$$\forall i \ \alpha_i \geq 0 \qquad (2.18)$$

By substituting $\mathbf{w}$ into Eq. (2.14), we obtain,

$$W(\alpha) = \frac{1}{2} \mathbf{w} \cdot \mathbf{w} - \sum_{i=1}^{l} \alpha_i y^i (x^i \cdot \mathbf{w} + b) + \sum_{i=1}^{l} \alpha_i \qquad (2.19)$$

2.4 Measurement of Classifiers

Traditionally, the main criterion for evaluating the performance of a classifier is accuracy (i.e., percentage of test examples that are correctly classified) or error (i.e., percentage of misclassified examples). However, in many situations, not every misclassification has the same consequences when misclassification costs have to be taken into account. Recent studies show that the accuracy of a classifier is also influenced by the class distribution[48]. Provost *et al.* have demonstrated problems with using accuracy as a metric[49]. It can be irrelevant or misleading when misclassification costs are unequal (cost-sensitive) or classes are imbalanced. Receiver Operating Characteristics (ROC) analysis, which originated from signal detection theory, has been introduced to evaluate machine learning algorithms[48−51] and it has become increasingly popular in machine learning research. ROC analysis is not just about cost sensitive learning. It provides tools to compare classifiers across the entire range of class distributions and misclassification costs[52]. In addition to being a generally useful performance graphing method, it has properties that make it especially useful for domains with skewed class distribution and unequal classification error costs. For example, consider a classifier which has an accuracy of 80%. The accuracy doesn't make sense without knowing the class distribution: If the database consists of 90% positive and 10% negative examples. We can do better simply by classifying all the data as positive which will give 90% accuracy. Hence, ROC analysis is not just about cost-sensitive learning, it considers the relative importance of negative vs. positive examples. This relative importance can be represented by a skewed ratio taking into account both costs and class distribution[52].

Many classifiers not only give discrete predicted classes but also estimate class membership probabilities (e.g., Naive Bayes). The former are referred to as discrete classifiers and the latter as probabilistic classifiers or rankers, because the membership probabilities can be used to rank instances from most to least likely positive. By setting a threshold, a rankers can act as a discrete classifier. The area under the curve (AUC) of ROC is used to measure the quality of ranking for a probabilistic classifier[28,53]. Ling *et al.* proved that AUC is statistically consistent and more discriminating than the accuracy measure[54]. Therefore, it is fairer to use AUC rather than accuracy to evaluate a learning algorithm.

2.4.1 ROC Analysis for Classification

Traditionally, accuracy and error are widely used measures for evaluating performance of a classifier. Using accuracy as a performance measure assumes that the error costs are equal and the class distribution is balanced. However, this is not realistic if we consider problems such as medical diagnosis or fraud detection. For example, in diagnosis of a serious disease, the cost of predicting a healthy person as a virus carrier is much less than the cost of predicting a virus carrier as healthy.

We begin by considering classification problems using only two classes (i.e., binary classification problem). Let the number of positives and negatives be denoted by P and N, respectively, the predicted positives and negatives be denoted by $\hat{P}$ and $\hat{N}$. The instances are divided according to the following contingency table or confusion matrix as shown in Fig. 2.8 . And the following equations hold.

$$P = TP + FN \qquad N = FP + TN$$
$$\hat{P} = TP + FP \qquad \hat{N} = FN + TN$$

	$(\hat{P})$ Predicted Positives	$(\hat{N})$ Predicted Negatives
(P) Positive Examples	(TP) True Positives	(FN) False Negatives
(N) Negative Examples	(FP) False Positives	(TN) True Negatives

Fig. 2.8 Confusion matrix for a binary classification problem

The classification accuracy is then defined according to the confusion matrix as follows:

$$Accuracy = \frac{TP + TN}{P + N} \qquad (2.20)$$

ROC analysis decomposes performance into true and false positive rates defined as follows: the true positive rate (TPR)[7] of a classifier is:

$$TPR = \frac{TP}{P} \tag{2.21}$$

and the false positive rate (FPR) of a classifier is:

$$FPR = \frac{FP}{N} \tag{2.22}$$

2.4.2 Area Under the ROC Curve

Given a confusion matrix, if we plot FPR on the X axis and TPR on the Y axis, then a single classification is represented by a point in this 2D coordinate space referred to as ROC space. In the ROC space, the upper left point $(0, 1)$ represents the optimal classifier performance with 100% of true positive and zero false positives. This point is like the "ROC Heaven" and, correspondingly, the point $(1, 0)$ represents the worst possible classifier performance and then the "ROC Hell"[52]. The diagonal line in Fig. 2.9 represents a random classifier (dotted line) which always gives 50% of the true positive rate and 50% of the false positive rate. Each discrete classifier can be presented by a single point according to its TPR and FPR in the ROC space. Different ROC profiles will be more or less desirable under different class distributions and different error cost functions. For example, Fig. 2.9 shows 3 classifiers C_1, C_2 and C_3. If the misclassification costs are the same, and if the distribution of classes is uniform, classifier C_2 is the optimal one. If the class distribution changes to four times negatives as positives, then C_1 and C_2 will have the same accuracy. Similarly, C_2 and C_3 will have the same accuracy with four times as many positives as negatives. in the case where there are less than 20% negatives, the optimal point is where we classify all the instances as positive. More details about basic ROC space properties can be found in Reference [53].

Consider a probabilistic classifier with two classes "+" and "−". We can sort the instances according to the probabilities of belonging to class "+". Different classification results will be given according to the varying threshold T based on:

$$\forall i \quad \begin{cases} x_i \rightarrow \{+\} \text{ if} : P(+|x_i) \geq T \\ x_i \rightarrow \{-\} \text{ otherwise} \end{cases}$$

For example, Table 2.1 shows three different classification results when $T = 0.8$, $T = 0.5$ and $T = 0.3$ based on the probability values of test examples. Typically T is set to 0.5[8] when we calculate accuracy for a probability estimation model. If we vary the value of T through $[0, 1]$, it will result in a continuous curve in ROC space referred to as a ROC curve.

As discussed above, a classifier results in an ROC curve which aggregates its behavior for all possible decision thresholds. The quality of the classifier can be

---

[7] In signal detection theory, the true positive rate is called as hit rate and the false positive rate as the false alarm rate, respectively. These two concepts have been widely used in

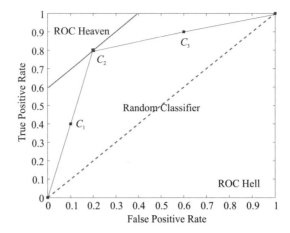

Fig. 2.9 Illustration of ROC space with three discrete classifiers C_1, C_2 and C_3

Table 2.1 Classification by a probability estimator with different thresholds

Examples	x_1	x_2	x_3	x_4	x_5	x_6	x_7	x_8	x_9	x_{10}
$Pr(+\|x_i)$	0.11	0.23	0.25	0.37	0.49	0.58	0.63	0.69	0.84	0.97
$T = 0.8$	−	−	−	−	−	−	−	−	+	+
$T = 0.5$	−	−	−	−	−	+	+	+	+	+
$T = 0.3$	−	−	−	+	+	+	+	+	+	+

measured by the area under the curve of ROC (AUC), which measures how well the classifier separates the two classes without reference to a decision threshold. In other words, AUC represents the quality of the ranking of examples by this classifier. Given k instances, there are only $k + 1$ possible thresholds. A practical method is as follows:

(1) Rank test instances in terms of decreasing membership scores.
(2) Starting at $(0, 0)$, if the next instance in the ranking list is positive then move $1/P$ up. If it is negative then move $1/N$ to the right.

where P and N are the number of positive and negative examples, respectively. Given the two classifiers C_1 and C_2 in Table 2.2 , the ROC curves drawn by the

---

decision theory. For example, Swets *et al.* wrote a good introductory article published in *Scientific American Magazine*.[55]

⑧ The optimal threshold for a probabilistic classifier depends on the class distribution and misclassification costs. The membership scores are not calibrated estimates of probabilities in most cases [56]. Therefore, assigning $T = 0.5$ (e.g., for Naive Bayes classifier) may not be the optimal choice.

above method are shown in Fig. 2.10 . The decreasing order of examples is:

$$x_{10}, x_9, \ldots, x_1$$

For C_1, the first step is moving up $1/10$ ($P = 10$ for this problem) because $x_{10} \rightarrow +$. It will keep moving up until meeting x_6 from where we move $1/10$ to the right (see Fig. 2.10). According to Hand and Till[28], the AUC value for a binary classification problem with two classes $\{+, -\}$ can be calculated by:

$$AUC = \frac{\sum_{i=1}^{P} r_i - P(P+1)/2}{PN} \tag{2.23}$$

where r_i is the rank of the ith positive example in the ranking list according to the probabilities of the class $+$. Eq. (2.23) evaluates the separability of negative and positive examples by a classifier. For example, the AUC values for classifier 1 and 2 listed in Table 2.2 are:

$$AUC_{(C_1)} = \frac{(5+7+8+9+10) - 5(5+1)/2}{5 \times 5} = \frac{24}{25}$$

$$AUC_{(C_2)} = \frac{(1+6+7+9+10) - 5(5+1)/2}{5 \times 5} = \frac{18}{25}$$

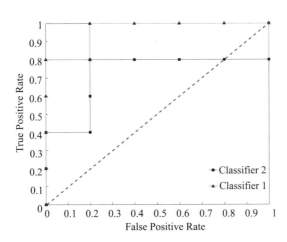

Fig. 2.10 ROC curves for the classifiers C_1 and C_2 in Table 2.2

We may notice that both classifier 1 and 2 have the same accuracy 80% (8 of 10 examples are correctly classified) and thus they can be viewed as equally good. However, intuition suggests that classifier 1 is better than classifier 2 since classifier 1 gives a better overall ranking. Consider an intuitive example, where the ranking tells us how poisonous ten different kinds of mushrooms are, so that "$-$" represents

Table 2.2 Two classifiers with the same accuracy but different AUC values. This table is inspired by a similar Table in Reference [55]

Examples	x_1	x_2	x_3	x_4	x_5	x_6	x_7	x_8	x_9	x_{10}
Classifier 1 (C_1)	−	−	−	−	+	−	+	+	+	+
r_i for Classifier 1					5		7	8	9	10
Classifier 2 (C_2)	+	−	−	−	−	+	+	−	+	+
r_i for Classifier 2	1					6	7		9	10

poisonous and "+" edible. In this case, classifier 2 will classify a very poisonous mushroom as edible. However, classifier 1 makes less serious errors by classifying a less poisonous mushroom as edible. So, classifier 1 is better for the mushrooms classification problem. This can be seen from the AUC measure but not the accuracy measure. Ling *et al.* mathematically proved that the AUC measure is consistent and more discriminating than the accuracy measure[54]. The method for calculating AUC for multi-class problems is given in [28]

2.5 Summary

Machine learning research has been developed rapidly in recent years and many new models have been proposed and have been successfully applied into many applications, such as time-series prediction[57,58], flood forecasting[59−61], fraud detection[62], medical imaging, drug design[63,64], encoding and decoding[65], gene classification[15], and so on. In this chapter we are not trying to give a full review of machine learning and data mining algorithms but a general background to this research area and some of the algorithms that will be used in subsequent chapters. Besides discussing the basics of machine learning and data mining and why they are so important. We also discussed the necessity of using intelligent methods to analysis loads of data, and measurements of classifiers.

References

[1] http://en.wikipedia.org/wiki/Plato's_Problem, accessed on March 01, (2011).
[2] Bensusan H.: Is machine learning experimental philosophy of science? ECAI Workshop on Scientific Reasoning in AI and Philosophy of Science. (2000).
[3] Nilsson N. J.: Introduction to Machine Learning, Unpublished book drafts. (1996).
[4] http://en.wikipedia.org/wiki/Herbert_Simon, accessed on March 23, 2011.
[5] Penrose R.: The Emperor's New Mind: Concerning Computers, Minds, and the Laws of Physics, Oxford Univ. Press. (1989).

[6] Searle J.: Minds, brains and programs, Behavioral and Brain Sciences, 3(3): pp. 417-517. (1980).

[7] Langley P.: Element of Machine Learning, Morgan Kaufmann Pub. Inc. (1996).

[8] Mjolsness E., DeCoste D.: Machine learning for science: state of the art and future prospects, Science, 293: pp. 2051-2055. (2001).

[9] http://en.wikipedia.org/wiki/Version_space, accessed on April 11, (2011).

[10] Blei D., Ng A., Jordan M.: Latent Dirichlet allocation. Journal of Machine Learning Research 3: pp. 993-1022. (2003).

[11] Griffiths T., Steyvers M.: Finding scientific topics, Proceedings of the National Academy of Sciences, 101 (Suppl. 1): pp. 5228-5235. (2004).

[12] Qin Z., Thint M., Huang Z.: Ranking answers by hierarchical topic models, Proceedings of The 22nd International Conference on Industrial, Engineering & Other Applications of Applied Intelligent Systems (IEA/AIE), LNAI 5579, pp. 103-112, Springer. (2009).

[13] Rasiwasia N., Pereira J. C., Coviello E., Doyle G., Lanckriet G. R. G., Levy R., Vasconcelos N.: A new approach to cross-modal multimedia retrieval, ACM-Multimedia. 2010.

[14] Wan T., Qin Z.: An application of compressive sensing for image fusion. Proceedings of the 9th ACM International Conference on Image and Video Retrieval (CIVR 2010), pp. 3-9. (2010).

[15] Rogers S., Girolami M., Campbell C., Breitling R.: he latent process decomposition of cDNA microarray data sets, ACM Trans. on Computational Biology and Bioinformatics, 2(2), April-June. (2005).

[16] Turnbull O., Richards A., Lawry J., Lowenburg M.: Fuzzy decision tree cloning of flight trajectory optimisation for rapid path planning. Proceedings of 45th IEEE Conference on Decision and Control, pp. 6361-6366. (2006).

[17] Liao R., Wang X., Li L., Qin Z.: A novel serial crime prediction model based on Bayesian learning theory. International Conference on Machine Learning and Cybernetics (ICMLC 2010), pp. 1757-1762. 2010.

[18] Dietterich T. G.: Machine-learning research: four current directions. AI Magazine, AAAI, Winter. (1997).

[19] Ma Y., Li G., Dong Y., Qin Z.: Minority game data mining for stock market predictions, Agents and Data Mining Interaction, 6th International Workshop on Agents and Data Mining Interaction (ADMI 2010), LNCS 5980, pp. 178-189. (2010).

[20] http://en.wikipedia.org/wiki/Francis_Crick, accessed on March 16, (2011).

[21] Mitchell T.: Machine Learning, McGraw-Hill, New York. (1997).

[22] http://en.wikipedia.org/wiki/Ray_Solomonoff, accessed on April 11, (2011).

[23] Kirchherr W., Li M., Vitányi P.: The miraculous universal distribution, Mathematical Intelligencer, 19(4), pp. 7-15. (1997).

[24] Bishop C. M.: Neural Networks for Pattern Recognition. Oxford Uni. Press. (1995).

[25] http://en.wikipedia.org/wiki/Curse_of_dimensionality, accessed on Feb 08, (2011).

[26] Zhu X., Goldberg A. B.: Introduction to semi-supervised learning, Synthesis Lectures on Artificial Intelligence and Machine Learning 3:1, 1-130, Morgan & Claypool Publishers. (2009).

[27] Duda R., Hart P. E., Stork D. G.: Pattern Classification, Second Edition. John Wiley & Sons. (2001).

[28] Hand D., Till R. J.: A simple generalization of the area under the ROC curve for multiple class classification problems, Machine Learning, 45, pp. 171-186. (2001).

[29] Berry M. J. A., Linoff G.: Data Mining Techniques for Marketing, Sales, and Customer Support, John Wiley & Sons. (1997).

[30] Flach P. A.: On the state of the art in machine learning, Artificial Intelligence, 131: pp. 199-222. (2001).

[31] Bezdek J. C., Keller J. M., Krishnapuram R., and Pal N.: Fuzzy models and algorithms for pattern recognition and image processing. The Handbooks on Fuzzy Sets, Netherlands, (1999).

[32] http://en.wikipedia.org/wiki/Data_clustering, accessed on March 30, 2011.

[33] Ghahramani Z.: Unsupervised leanring, Bousquet O., Raetsch G., and von Luxburg U.(Eds.), Advanced Lectures on Machine Learning, LNAI3176, Springer. (2004).

[34] Roweis S. T., Saul L. K.: Nonlinear dimensionality reduction by locally linear embedding,Science, 290: pp. 2323-2326. (2000).

[35] Kang P., Cho S.: Locally linear for reconstruction for instance-based learning, Pattern Recognition, 41: pp. 3507-3518. (2008).

[36] Adriaans P., Zantinge D.: Data Mining, UK Addison Wesley Longman. (1996).

[37] CRISP-DM 1.0: step-by-step data mining guide. SPSS Inc, (1999), (2000).

[38] Zhou Z. H.: Three perspectives of data mining, Artificial Intelligence, 143, 1: 139-146. (2003).

[39] Blake C., Merz C. J.: UCI machine learning repository.

[40] McCulloch W. S., Pitts W.: A logical calculus of the ideas immanent in nervous activity. Bulletin of Mathematical Biophysics 5: pp. 115-133. (1943).

[41] Minsky M., Papert S.: Perceptrons, MIT Press, Cambridge, MA. (1969).

[42] Berthold M., Hand D. J. , Ed. , Intelligent Data Analysis, Springer. Berlin Heidelberg. (1999).

[43] Pollack J. B.: Connectionism: past, present and future, Artificial Intelligence Review, 3: pp. 3-20. (1989).

[44] Rumelhart D. E., McClelland J. L.: Parallel Distributed Processing: Exploration in the Microstructure of Cognition, MIT Press, Cambridge, MA. (1987).

[45] Russell S. J., Norvig P.: Artificial Intelligence-a morden approach, Prentice-Hall, Inc., A Simon & Schuster Company, New Jersey. (1995).

[46] Hertz J., Krogh A., Palmer R. G.: Introduction to The Theory of Neural Computation, Addison-Wesley. (1992).

[47] Vapnik V.: Statistical Learning Theory, New York: Wiley, (1998).

[48] Provost F., Fawcett T.: Robust classification for imprecise environments. Machine Learning. 42, pp. 203-231. (2001).

[49] Provost F., Fawcett T., Kohavi R.: The case against accuracy estimation for comparing induction algorithms, In J. Shavlik, editor, Prced. of ICML98, pp. 445-453. (1998).

[50] Fawcett T.: ROC graphs: notes and practical considerations for data mining researchers, HP Technical Report HPL-2003-4, HP Laboratories. (2003).

[51] Flach P. A.: The geometry of ROC space: understanding machine learning metrics through ROC isometrics, Proceedings of the ICML-04. (2004).

[52] Flach P. A.: The many faces of ROC analysis in machine learning, http://www.cs.bris.ac.uk/~flach/ICML04tutorial/index.html.

[53] Provost F., Domingos P.: Tree induction for probability-based ranking, Machine Learning, 52, pp. 199-215. (2003).

[54] Ling C. X., Huang J., Zhang H.: AUC: a statistically consistent and more discriminating measure than accuracy, Proceedings of IJCAI. (2003).

[55] Swets J. A., Dawes R. M., Monahan J.: Better decisions through science. Scientific American, 283: pp. 82-87, October. (2000).

[56] Zadrozny B., Elkan C.: Obtaining calibrated probability estimates from decision trees and naive Bayesian classifiers, Proceedings of ICML-01. (2001).

[57] Keogh E., Smyth P.: A probabilistic approach to fast pattern matching in time series databases, Proceedings of the 3rd International Conference of Knowledge Discovery and Data Mining, pp. 24-20. (1997).

[58] Keogh E.: Mining and indexing time series data, Tutorial of (2001) IEEE International Conference on Data Mining, San Jose, California. (2001).

[59] Lawry J., Han D., Cluckie I.D.: Fuzzy rule generation in hydrological modelling, Soft Methodology and Random Information Systems-Proceedings of the 2nd International Conference on Soft Methods in Probability and Statistics (SMPS'2004), Springer. (2004).

[60] Qin Z., Lawry J.: Prediction trees using linguistic modelling, to appear in the Proceedings of International Fuzzy Association World Congress-05, September 2005, Beijing, China. (2005).

[61] Randon N. J.: Fuzzy and Random Set Based Induction Algorithms, PhD Thesis, Department of Engineering Mathematics, University of Bristol. (2004).

[62] Bolton R. J., Hand D. J.: Statistical fraud detection: A review. Statistical Science, 17(3), pp. 235-255. (2002).

[63] Borgelt C., Berthold M. R., Patterson D. E.: Molecular fragment mining for drug discovery, Lluis Godo (Ed.) Symbolic and Quantitative Approaches to Reasoning with Uncertainty, 8th European Conference, ECSQARU 2005, LNAI 3571, pp. 1002-1013. (2005).

[64] Morent D., Patterson D. E., Berthold M.: Towards context-aware similarity metrics, Proceedings of the International Conference on Machine Learning and Cybernetics-2005. (2005).

[65] Mackay D. J. C.: Information Theory, Inference, and Learning Algorithms, Cambridge University Press. (2003).

3

Label Semantics Theory

When one admits that nothing is certain one must, I think, also admit that some things are much more nearly certain than others.

– Bertrand Russell (1872-1970), "Am I an atheist or an agnostic?"

3.1 Uncertainty Modeling with Labels

As we have discussed in Chapter 1, modeling real world problems typically involves processing two distinct types of uncertainty. These are, firstly, uncertainty arising from a lack of knowledge relating to concepts which, in the sense of classical logic, may be well defined and, secondly, uncertainty due to inherent vagueness in concepts themselves. Traditionally, these two types of uncertainties are modeled in terms of probability theory and fuzzy set theory, respectively, though, Zadeh recently pointed out that all the approaches for uncertainty modeling can be unified into a general theory of uncertainty (GTU)[1]. The first type of uncertainty has been a focus of Bayesian probabilistic models[2]. The most recent advancement in machine learning has been about using using hierarchical Bayesian generative models to describe data.

Furthermore, there are many situations where we have insufficient information regarding vague or fuzzy concepts. That is where both types of uncertainty are present. Fuzzy logic is an extension of traditional Boolean logic. In a wider sense, which is in predominant use today, fuzzy logic is almost synonymous with the theory of fuzzy sets; a theory which relates to classes of objects with blurred boundaries in which membership is a matter of degree. In this chapter, we will introduce an alternate approach for modeling uncertainties by using randoms set and probability theory.

3.1.1 Fuzzy Logic

The world is not fuzzy in some sense. We can look out and see precisely a leaf falling from an old oak tree whose shadow lies on a green grassland. There are five people playing and laughing on the grassland. Not far away, there are two cars parked on the side of the road, one is blue and the other is red. Which of them is fuzzy? But this precision which we can see with our eyes if we wish is often unwanted detail when it comes to categorizing and classifying and clustering the real world into groups which we can label. We give labels to such objects as people, cars, grassland, trees and leaves, so that we can talk about these objects in terms of their common properties within their group. Plato said: *Ordinary objects are classified together if they "participate" in the same abstract form.* Based on this intuition, set theory has become the foundation of mathematics before Kurt Godel overthrew the edifice. Another intuition is that sometimes we cannot really tell if an object belongs to a particular set, sometimes, maybe partially. That is why we need a new mathematics.

Fuzzy Logic was first proposed by Zadeh in the 1960s as an extension of traditional Boolean logic [3]. It is basically a multi-valued logic that allows more human-like interpretation in machine reasoning by resolving intermediate categories between notations such as true and false, black and white, etc. used in Boolean logic that originated from ancient Greek philosophy ①. The mathematics built on fuzzy logic was developed into fuzzy set theory and fuzzy mathematics. In contrast to a classical set, which has a crisp boundary, the boundary of a fuzzy set is blurry. This smooth transition is characterized by membership functions which give fuzzy sets flexibility in modeling linguistic expressions. For example, in dice rolling games, we can define a fuzzy set *small* to describe dice scores by:

$$small = 1/1 + 2/0.8 + 3/0.2$$

where $1, 0.8$ and 0.2 are the associated mass for the dice score $1, 2$ and 3, respectively. It means that the truth value of 1 being small is 1, 2 being small is 0.8 and 3 being small is 0.2.

In the case of a continuous variable, membership functions could be in various forms. Fig. 3.1 shows a few commonly used membership functions generated by Matlab Fuzzy Logic Toolbox Demo^{TM}. Each membership function has its own special property for modeling uncertainties in different scenarios. In this book, we will mainly use trapezoidal (trapmf) and trianglar shape (trimf) membership functions.

Fig. 3.2 gives another example with a set of membership functions defined on human height: *short, medium* and *tall*. As same as the prior probability in Bayesian statistics, the pre-assumptions of fuzzy membership have been the weakest link of the theory since there are always disagreeable points of views in the definition of an imprecise concept. In fuzzy reasoning, we always say "suppose we are given the expert knowledge or the fuzzy memberships ..." the effectiveness of fuzzy reasoning

---

① Although the fact that bi-valued logic has been regarded as the basic rule in ancient Greek philosophy. Actually, Greek philosopher Parminedes proposed the "the way of truth" around 400 B.C. and stated amidst controversy that statements could be both true and not true at the same time [4]. The "grey" area of the black and white has always been well-accepted in Eastern philosophy such as Taoism that states the inter-correlations and transitions between two states such as true/false, black/white, good/bad, right/wrong, etc.

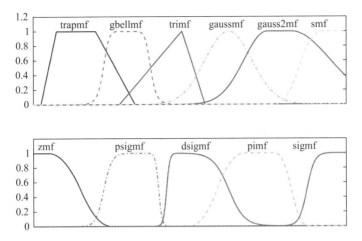

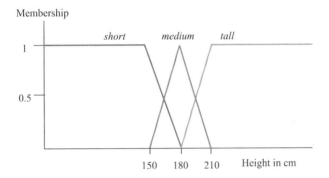

Fig. 3.1 Different forms of continuous membership functions generated using Matlab Fuzzy Toolbox[TM]

Fig. 3.2 Membership functions defined on human height

or fuzzy calculation is based on the correctness of the given assumptions. It is a universally true for other theories as well in the philosophy of science. It should not be treated as a defect of fuzzy theory. More details of fuzzy set theory, fuzzy logic and fuzzy applications are available in several classical text books[5,6].

3.1.2 Computing with Words

In early research, fuzzy logic was successfully applied in expert systems where the linguistic interpretation fuzzy sets allow for an interface between the human user and a computer system. Because our language is full of uncertainty and impreciseness, one word has many different meanings. To describe one meaning, we could use many different words. Therefore, it can be a good way of trying to use fuzzy sets to model human natural language. This idea provides a good method for bridging the gap between human users and computing machines, and this also motivates research into Computing with Words[7].

Zadeh suggests a form of precisiated natural language (PNL) based on the theory of generalized constraints and linguistic variables[8]. A linguistic variable is a quintuple $\langle L, T(L), S, \Omega, M \rangle$ in which L is the name of the variable, Ω is a universe of discourse, $T(L)$ is a term set of words to describe elements of Ω, S is a set of syntactic rules for generating new elements of $T(L)$ from existing words and M is a set of semantic rules which identify a fuzzy subset of Ω for each word in $T(L)$, corresponding to its fuzzy extension.

The term set can be generated recursively from the initial set of labels by using logical operators such as "$\wedge$, $\vee$ and $\neg$" and linguistic hedges such as *quite, very*, etc. The semantic rule M is based on the standard truth-functional fuzzy calculus: e.g., $\forall \theta_1, \theta_2 \in T(L)$:

$$M(\neg \theta_1) = 1 - M(\theta_1)$$

$$M(\theta_1 \wedge \theta_2) = \min(M(\theta_1, \theta_2))$$

$$M(\theta_1 \vee \theta_2) = \max(M(\theta_1, \theta_2))$$

Zadeh also defines semantic rules for a linguistic hedge that is practically computable.

$$M(very\theta) = M(\theta)^2$$

$$M(very^n \theta) = M(\theta)^{2n}$$

where $very^n$ denotes n occurrences of the hedge *very*. However, this definition is very arbitrary and hardly to be used in dealing with practical natural language problems. Qin *et al.* first used this CW framework for designing a question-answering system in specified domains[9]. Though it can tackle some challenging natural language problems, it has serious limitations that so few natural language sentences can match the prototypes of computing[10].

Almost all the labels we give to groups of objects are fuzzy. For example, friends, pretty faces, tall trees, etc. An object may belong to the set of objects with a certain label with a certain membership value. In traditional set theory, this membership value only has two possible values, 1 and 0, which represent the case where the object belongs to, or does not belong to, the set, respectively. We use a fuzzy term such as "big" to label a particular group, because it shares the property of objects within this group (i.e., they are big). The objects within this group will have different membership values varying from 0 to 1 qualifying the degree to which they satisfy the concept. An object with a membership of 0.8 is more likely to be described as "big" than an object with a membership of 0.4.

3.1.3 Mass Assignment Theory

Mass assignment theory allows inference under fuzzy and probabilistic reasoning. The theory includes an algebra, a conditioning process for inference under uncertainty[11]. A mass assignment over a set S is a probability distribution over the power set of S, in which the probabilities associated with the subsets are called masses. If a fuzzy set was defined in a discrete universe S, then mass assignments provide a way of interpreting fuzzy sets as a probability distributions on subsets of S. Mass assignment theory gives us a new way of understanding fuzzy sets from a probabilistic prospective. Based on this theory, Baldwin *et al.* developed a fuzzy logic based inductive logic programming language *FRIL*② by incorporating fuzzy reasoning to Prolog styled A.I. programming[11].

We will use a simple example to introduce mass assignment theory: Suppose we have a fair dice and we the use linguistic labels, *small, medium* and *large* to describe the values the dice can show, i.e., {1 2 3 4 5 6}[12]. These labels are fuzzy, and not everyone would identify the same subset of the values as satisfying a given label. How we can interpret these linguistic values is a key problem for us.

Consider the dice problem, for a particular value of dice. Suppose we have a set of people who are asked to accept or reject the value as satisfying a linguistic expression. We may need two assumptions in the voting model: the first one is the constant threshold constraint.

Definition 3.1 (*Constant threshold constraint*) *A voter who accepts a given value will also accept the values with a greater membership value, it is called the constant threshold constraint.*

It simply means, if a person accepts 2 as small, it has the implication that 1 is small too. That makes the mass assignment consonant (or nested) when we decide the mass for each subset. For example, we may ask 10 people that if they accept 1 as small, will they accept that by saying "Yes" or refute to saying "No". We then get the survey where all 10 people accept that 1 is small, and 8 people accept 2 is small and 2 people accept 3 as small (Table 3.1). So the membership value of 1 being small is 1, 2 is 0.8 and 3 is 0.2. From this voting model, we can get the fuzzy set of small in normal fuzzy notation as,

$$small = 1/1 + 2/0.8 + 3/0.2$$

Table 3.1 The voting table for each voter from V_1 to V_{10}

Voter	V_1	V_2	V_3	V_4	V_5	V_6	V_7	V_8	V_9	V_{10}
Accept 1 as *small*	Yes	Yes	Yes	Yes	Yes	Yes	Yes	Yes	Yes	Yes
Accept 2 as *small*	Yes	No	Yes	Yes	No	Yes	Yes	Yes	Yes	Yes
Accept 3 as *small*	No	No	No	No	No	No	Yes	No	Yes	No
Accept 4 as *small*	No	No	No	No	No	No	No	No	No	No

Among voters, 100% of people accept 1 as small, 80% of people accept that 2 is small, but only 20% accept 3 as small. So, the proportion of people who accept that only 1 (but not others) is small is 100% − 80% = 20%. We can say the distribution of the set {1} over all dice numbers given the fuzzy set small, is 20%. We also can see from Table 3.2 that there are only two voters of ten accept {1} is the only set

② The name FRIL was originally an acronym for Fuzzy Relational Inference Language.

of being small. Based on the constant threshold constraint assumption, we can get the probability of set {1, 2} is the proportion of those who agree with 2 is small, which is 0.8, minus the proportion of who agree 3 as small 0.2. The result 0.6 is the proportion who agree that both 1 and 2 are small only. Finally, 20% of people accept that 1,2 and 3 are all small. This equals the proportion of voters who accept 3 as small, since if a voter accepts 3 as small and he must accept the fact that 1, 2 and 3 are all small according to the constant threshold constraint.

Example 3.1 *Given the voting Table* 3.1 *, how can we generate the mass assignments of small?*

From the voting Table 3.1 *, we can obtain the Table* 3.2 *of voting statistics, and the fuzzy set of small as follows:*

$$small = 1/1 + 2/0.8 + 3/0.2$$

Then the mass assignment over small is:

$$m_{small} = \{1\} : 0.2, \{1,2\} : 0.6, \{1,2,3\} : 0.2$$

We need to notice that, unlike fuzzy memberships, mass assignment is a probability distribution. To be precise it is a probability distribution on a set of possible values.

Table 3.2 The voting statistics: we re-order the voters in Table 3.1 to get this nested structure

The Number of Voters	1	2	3	4	5	6	7	8	9	10
The number accepted as small	1	1	1	1	1	1	1	1	1	1
The number accepted as small	2	2	2	2	2	2	2	2		
The number accepted as small	3	3								

3.2 Label Semantics

In contrast to fuzzy sets and linguistic variables, label semantics proposed by Lawry encodes the meaning of linguistic labels according to how they are used by a population of communicating agents to convey information[13]. Label semantics is an epistemic theory of uncertainty for vague concepts based on appropriateness measures and mass functions. Most current approaches to modeling vague or imprecise concepts are based on the explicit definition of the extension of that concept, corresponding to the fuzzy description of objects for which the concept holds. For example, in a recent analysis of models of vagueness, Dubois *et al.* categorize different semantics for fuzzy sets on the basis of the nature of the division between the extension of a vague concept and its negation[14]. However human reasoning with imprecise concepts is based on the explicit use of their extensions irrespective of whether they are fuzzy or crisp.

The focus of label semantics is on the crisp decision problems associated with the use of labels and the underlying uncertainty associated with these decisions. It means that it is somewhat related to a number of alternative theories of vague concepts proposed in the literature. In some sense, label semantics is very close to the epistemic view of vagueness as expounded by Williamson, who assumes that for the extension of a vague concept there is a precise but unknown dividing boundary between it and the extension of the negation of that concept[15]. For example, consider the set of weights which are classified as being "fat". Then there is, according to the epistemic view, a precise but unknown weight for which all values less than this weight are not fat while all those greater than it are fat. From this viewpoint, Sorites problems are resolved by denying the assumption that practically indistinguishable elements satisfy the same vague predicates. Hence, for a finite sequence of increasing weights x_i: $i = 1, \ldots, k$, where x_1 is not "fat", x_k is fat and $x_{i+1} \leq \varepsilon$. For some very small positive number ε, it holds that: $\exists i$ for which 'x_i is not fat' and 'x_{i+1} is fat'. Although the exact value of i will be virtually impossible for anyone to identify precisely[16].

3.2.1 Epistemic View of Label Semantics

First, the epistemic view assumes the existence of some objectively correct, but unknown, set of criteria for determining whether or not a given instance satisfies a vague concept, while label semantics argues that individuals when faced with decision problems regarding assertions find it useful as part of a decision making strategy to assume that there is a clear dividing line between those labels which are and those which are not appropriate to describe a given instance.

Lawry argues that in practice, these rules underling the appropriate use of labels would not be imposed by some outside authority, even not exist at all in a formal sense[17]. Rather, they are represented as a distributed body of knowledge concerning the assertability of predicates in various cases, shared across a population of agents, and emerging as the result of interactions and communications between individual agents all adopting the epistemic stance. The idea is that the learning processes of individual agents, all sharing the fundamental aim of understanding how words can be appropriately used to communicate information, will eventually converge to some degree on a set of shared conventions. To summarize, both the epistemic theory and label semantics identify vagueness as being a type of ignorance. And in both cases, the association of vagueness with ignorance strongly contrasts with the fuzzy logic approach in which the applicability of concept labels is viewed as being a matter of degree.

For the characteristics of label semantics discussed above, it has some advantages when applied in data mining and knowledge engineering. In many data mining and knowledge engineering applications information is available both in the form of high-level qualitative background knowledge as provided by domain experts and low-level numerical data from experimental studies. It is necessary to combine or fuse these two different sources of information to obtain optimal models.

In Bayesian statistical machine learning, the expert knowledge is the bias towards choosing prior distribution and the model fuses the prior information and observable evidence by posterior calculation.

This is particularly true in cases where the data provided is sparse due to the expense or difficulty of experimental trials. The type of fusion method appropriate to a particular problem will be dependent on a number of factors. In classical analysis the representation of the form of the available background knowledge is restricted to one of a few mathematical forms. However, for many applications the expert knowledge is more naturally represented as "rules of thumb" expressed as natural language statements. Such statements are likely to be both imprecise and uncertain making their translation into mathematical forms difficult and often inappropriate. Instead, label semantics represent the background knowledge in a logical framework which is as close to natural language as possible and also incorporates vagueness, imprecision and uncertainty. That makes the fusion of data much easier and more understandable. In the next chapters several kinds of data mining algorithms based on label semantics will be introduced.

The modeling of concept vagueness in artificial intelligence has been dominated by ideas from fuzzy set theory. It does not in the narrowest manifestations adopt an epistemic view of vagueness. It is possible to build bridges between probability and fuzzy sets where the latter are viewed as possibility distributions. In particular, we shall interpret possibility measures in the framework of random sets and belief function theory and we shall consider the problem of transforming a possibility distribution into a probability distribution and vice versa.

3.2.2 Random Set Framework

Vague or imprecise concepts are fundamental to natural language. Human beings use imprecise language to communicate with each other. We usually say "John is tall and strong" but not "John is exactly 1.85 meters in height and he can lift 100 kg weights". We will focus on developing an understanding of how an intelligent agent can use vague concepts to convey information and meaning as part of a general strategy for practical reasoning and decision making. Such an agent could be an artificial intelligence program or a human, but the implicit assumption is that their use of vague concepts is governed by some underlying internally consistent strategy or algorithm. We may notice that labels are used in natural language to describe what we see, hear and feel. Such labels may have different vagueness (i.e., when we say Mary is young and she is female, the label young has more vagueness than the label female because most people have many more differing opinions on being young than being female. For a particular concept, there could be more than one label that is appropriate for describing this concept. Some labels could be more appropriate than others. Here, we will use a random set framework to interpret these facts. Label semantics, first proposed by Lawry, is a framework for modeling with linguistic expressions, or labels such as small, medium and large[18]. Such labels are defined by overlapping fuzzy sets which are used to cover the universe of continuous variables.

The underlying question posed by label semantics is how to use linguistic expressions to label vague concepts. For a variable x within a domain of discourse Ω we identify a finite set of linguistic labels $\mathbb{L} = \{L_1, \ldots, L_n\}$ with which to label the values of x. Then, for a specific value $x \in \Omega$ an individual I identifies a subset of $\mathbb{L}$, denoted $\mathscr{D}_x^I$ to stand for the description of x given by I, as the set of labels with which it is appropriate to label x. If we allow I to vary across a population V with prior distribution P_V, then $\mathscr{D}_x^I$ will also vary and generate a random set denoted $\mathscr{D}_x$ into the power set of $\mathbb{L}$ denoted by $\mathbb{S}$. We can view the random set $\mathscr{D}_x$ as a description of the variable x in terms of the labels in $\mathbb{L}$. The frequency of occurrence of a particular label, say S, for $\mathscr{D}_x$ across the population then gives a distribution on $\mathscr{D}_x$ referred to as a mass assignment of labels[3].

Definition 3.2 (Label description) *For $x \in \Omega$ the label description of x is a random set from V into the power set of $\mathbb{L}$, denoted $\mathscr{D}_x$, with associated distribution m_x, which is referred to as mass assignment:*

$$\forall S \subseteq \mathbb{L}, \quad m_x(S) = P_V(\{I \in V | \mathscr{D}_x^I = S\}) \tag{3.1}$$

where $m_x(S)$ is called the mass associated with a set of labels S and

$$\sum_{S \subseteq \mathbb{L}} m_x(S) = 1 \tag{3.2}$$

Intuitively mass assignment is a probability distribution on appropriate label sets and $m_x(S)$ quantifies the evidence that S is the set of appropriate labels for x. Based on the data distribution $p(x)$, we can calculate the prior distribution of labels by summing up the mass assignment across the database as follows:

$$pm(S) = p(S) = \frac{\int_\Omega m_x(S)p(x)\mathrm{d}x}{\sum_{S \subseteq \mathbb{L}} \int_\Omega m_x(S)p(x)\mathrm{d}x} \tag{3.3}$$

However, the dominator equals to 1 according to the definition of mass assignment and Eq. (3.2), so that:

$$pm(S) = \int_\Omega m_x(S)p(x)\mathrm{d}x \tag{3.4}$$

and in a discreet case:

$$pm(S) = \sum_{x \in \Omega} m_x(S)P(x) \tag{3.5}$$

If in expectation form:

$$pm(S) = E_x[m(S)|x] = E_x[m_x(S)] \tag{3.6}$$

For example, an expression such as "the score on a dice is small", as asserted by individual I, is interpreted to mean $\mathscr{D}_{SCORE}^I = \{small\}$, where $SCORE$ denotes

---

[3] Given the power set of $\mathbb{L}$, $\mathbb{S}$, the element $S \in \mathbb{S}$ can be written as $S \subseteq \mathbb{L}$. This representation will be used throughout this book. For example, given $\mathbb{L} = \{L_1, L_2\}$, the powerset $\mathbb{S} = \{\emptyset, \{L_1\}, \{L_2\}, \{L_1, L_2\}\}$. For every element in $\mathbb{S}$: $S \in \mathbb{S}$, the relation $S \subseteq \mathbb{L}$ will hold.

the value of the score given by a single throw of a particular dice. When I varies across a population V, different sets of labels could be given to describe the variable $SCORE$, so that we obtain the random set of $\mathcal{D}_{SCORE}$ into the power set of $\mathbb{L}$. The above definitions and equations can be illustrated by the following example:

Example 3.2 *Suppose the variable SCORE with universe $\{1,2,3,4,5,6\}$ gives the outcome of a single throw of a particular dice. Let $\mathbb{L} = \{small, medium, large\}$ and $V = \{I_1, I_2, I_3\}$ then a possible definition of $\mathcal{D}_{SCORE}$ is given as follows:*

$$\mathcal{D}_1^{I_1} = \mathcal{D}_1^{I_2} = \mathcal{D}_1^{I_3} = \{small\}, \mathcal{D}_2^{I_1} = \{small, medium\}, \mathcal{D}_2^{I_2} = \mathcal{D}_2^{I_3} = \{small\}$$

$$\mathcal{D}_3^{I_1} = \mathcal{D}_3^{I_2} = \{medium\}, \mathcal{D}_3^{I_3} = \{small, medium\},$$

$$\mathcal{D}_4^{I_1} = \{medium, large\}, \mathcal{D}_4^{I_2} = \mathcal{D}_4^{I_3} = \{medium\}, \mathcal{D}_5^{I_2} = \{large\}$$

$$\mathcal{D}_5^{I_1} = \mathcal{D}_5^{I_3} = \{medium, large\}, \mathcal{D}_6^{I_1} = \mathcal{D}_6^{I_2} = \mathcal{D}_6^{I_3} = \{large\}$$

Assuming a uniform prior distribution on V, so that $P_V = 1/|V|$, then the mass assignment of $\mathcal{D}_x$ can be represented according to Definition 3.2 as follows[4]:

$$\forall S \subseteq \mathbb{L}, \quad m_x(S) = \frac{|\{I \in V | \mathcal{D}_x^I = S\}|}{|V|} \tag{3.7}$$

We can determine mass assignments on $\mathcal{D}_{SCORE}$ according to Eq. (3.7). For example, if $SCORE = 4$ we have

$$m_4(\{medium, large\}) = \frac{|\{I \in V | D_4^I = \{medium, large\}\}|}{|V|} = \frac{|\{I_1\}|}{|V|} = \frac{1}{3}$$

$$m_4(\{medium\}) = \frac{|\{I \in V | D_4^I = \{medium\}\}|}{|V|} = \frac{|\{I_2, I_3\}|}{|V|} = \frac{2}{3}$$

We then have the mass assignment for $SCORE = 4$ as follows,

$$m_4 = \{medium, large\} : \frac{1}{3}, \{medium\} : \frac{2}{3}$$

In the sequel 1/3 and 2/3 are also referred to as the associated mass for {medium, large} and {medium}, respectively. Similarly, we can obtain the mass assignment on 1, 2, 3 and 5 as follows:

$$m_1 = \{small\} : 1, m_2 = \{small\} : \frac{2}{3}, \{small, medium\} : \frac{1}{3}$$

$$m_3 = \{small, medium\} : \frac{1}{3}, \{medium\} : \frac{2}{3}$$

---

[4] $|A|$ represents the absolute value of A when A is a number or the cardinality of A when A is a set.

$$m_5 = \{medium, large\} : \frac{2}{3}, \{large\} : \frac{1}{3}, m_6 = \{large\} : 1$$

Now, let us consider the calculation of label distribution. In order to obtain the label distribution, we need to know the distribution on the universe {1, ..., 6}. Suppose a biased distribution is given on SCORE as follows (see the left-hand side figure of Fig. 3.3):

$$P(1) = \frac{1}{10}, P(2) = \frac{1}{10}, P(3) = \frac{1}{10}, P(4) = \frac{1}{5}, P(5) = \frac{1}{5}, P(6) = \frac{3}{10}$$

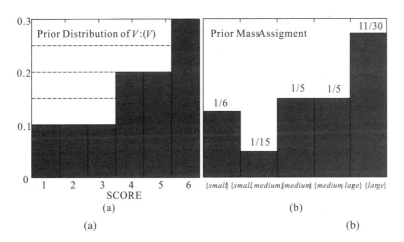

Fig. 3.3 (a): the prior distribution $P(V)$ (or P_V) on variable *SCORE* and its prior mass assignment (*pm*) on 5 focal elements (b)

The probability (associated mass) of {medium, large} can be calculated according to Eq. (3.5):

$$m(\{medium, large\}) = \sum_{x=1}^{6} m_x(\{medium, large\})P(x) \tag{3.8}$$

$$= \sum_{x=4,5} m_x(\{medium, large\})P(x) \tag{3.9}$$

$$= \frac{1}{3} \times \frac{1}{5} + \frac{2}{3} \times \frac{1}{5} = \frac{1}{5} \tag{3.10}$$

Similarly, we can calculate the prior mass assignment on other label sets as follows:

$$m(\{small\}) = \sum_{x=1}^{6} m_x(\{small\})P(x) \tag{3.11}$$

$$= \sum_{x=1,2} m_x(\{small\})P(x) \tag{3.12}$$

$$= 1 \times \frac{1}{10} + \frac{2}{3} \times \frac{1}{10} = \frac{1}{6} \tag{3.13}$$

$$m(\{small, medium\}) = \sum_{x=1}^{6} m_x(\{small, medium\})P(x) \tag{3.14}$$

$$= \sum_{x=2,3} m_x(\{small, medium\})P(x) \tag{3.15}$$

$$= \frac{1}{3} \times \frac{1}{10} + \frac{1}{3} \times \frac{1}{10} = \frac{1}{15} \tag{3.16}$$

$$m(\{medium\}) = \sum_{x=1}^{6} m_x(\{medium\})P(x) \tag{3.17}$$

$$= \sum_{x=3,4} m_x(\{medium\})P(x) \tag{3.18}$$

$$= \frac{2}{3} \times \frac{1}{10} + \frac{2}{3} \times \frac{1}{5} = \frac{1}{5} \tag{3.19}$$

$$m(\{large\}) = \sum_{x=1}^{6} m_x(\{large\})P(x) \tag{3.20}$$

$$= \sum_{x=5,6} m_x(\{large\})P(x) \tag{3.21}$$

$$= \frac{1}{3} \times \frac{1}{5} + 1 \times \frac{3}{10} = \frac{11}{30} \tag{3.22}$$

The prior assignment on these 5 focal elements is shown on Fig. 3.3 (b).

3.2.3 Appropriateness Degrees

In this framework, appropriateness degrees are used to evaluate how appropriate a label is for describing a particular value of variable x. Simply, given a particular value α of variable x, the appropriateness degree for labeling this value with the label L, which is defined by fuzzy set F, is the membership value of α in F. The reason we use the new term "appropriateness degrees" is partly because it more accurately reflects the underlying semantics and partly to highlight the quite distinct calculus based on this framework[18]. This definition provides a relationship between mass assignments and appropriateness degrees.

Definition 3.3 (Appropriateness degrees)

$$\forall x \in \Omega, \ \forall L \in \mathbb{L} \quad \mu_L(x) = \sum_{S \subseteq \mathbb{L}: L \in S} m_x(S)$$

Example 3.3 *Let us consider Example* 3.2 *again. According to Definition* 3.3:

$$\mu_{small}(1) = \sum_{S \subseteq \mathbb{L}: small \in S} m_1(S) = m_1(\{small\}) = 1$$

$$\mu_{small}(2) = \sum_{S \subseteq \mathbb{L}: small \in S} m_2(S) = m_2(\{small\}) + m_2(\{small, medium\}) = 1$$

Hence, the overall the non-zero appropriateness degrees for each fuzzy label are given by:

$$\mu_{small}(1) = 1, \mu_{small}(2) = 1, \mu_{small}(3) = \frac{1}{3}$$

$$\mu_{medium}(2) = \frac{1}{3}, \mu_{medium}(3) = 1, \mu_{medium}(4) = 1, \mu_{medium}(5) = \frac{1}{3}$$

$$\mu_{large}(4) = \frac{1}{3}, \mu_{large}(5) = 1, \mu_{large}(6) = 1$$

As we can see from the above example, given mass assignment on labels, we can obtain the fuzzy sets by which these labels are defined. For example, the label small is defined by fuzzy set:

$$small = 1/1 + 2/1 + 3/ \left(\frac{1}{3} \right)$$

There is a unique mapping from mass assignments to fuzzy sets. Does it hold for the inverse process? We will discuss it in the subsequent section.

It is certainly true that a mass assignment on $\mathscr{D}_x$ determines a unique appropriateness degree for any functions of μ_L but generally the converse does not hold. If we know the appropriateness degrees of the labels, we may not be able to infer a unique underlying mass assignment. For example, given $\mu_{L_1} = 0.3$ and $\mu_{L_2} = 1$, we may obtain the sets of appropriate labels with associated masses as:

$$\{L_2\} : 0.7, \{L_1, L_2\} : 0.3$$
$$\{L_1\} : 0.1, \{L_2\} : 0.8, \{L_1, L_2\} : 0.2$$
$$\{L_1\} : 0.2, \{L_2\} : 0.9, \{L_1, L_2\} : 0.1$$
$$\cdots \quad \cdots \quad \cdots \quad \cdots \quad \cdots$$

There are infinite number of possible representations. This fact is schematically illustrated by Fig. 3.4 . To overcome this problem, we will introduce some assumptions. The first one is the consonance assumption, according to which we can determine the mass assignment uniquely from the appropriateness degrees as follows.

3.2.4 Assumptions for Data Analysis

Definition 3.4 (*Consonant mass assignments on labels*)
Let $\{\beta_1, \ldots, \beta_k\} = \{\mu_L(x) | L \in \mathbb{L}, \mu_L(x) > 0\}$ *ordered such that* $\beta_t > \beta_{t+1}$ *for* $t = 1, 2, \ldots, k-1$ *then:*

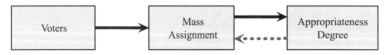

Fig. 3.4 The mapping from voters via mass assignments to appropriateness degrees of labels is unique while the mapping from appropriateness degrees to mass assignments are not

$$m_x = M_t : \beta_t - \beta_{t-1}, \text{ for } t = 1, 2, \ldots, k-1,$$

$$M_k : \beta_k, \quad M_0 : 1 - \beta_1$$

where $M_0 = \emptyset$ and $M_t = \{L \in \mathbb{L} | \mu_L(x) \geq \beta_t\}$ for $t = 1, 2 \ldots, k$.

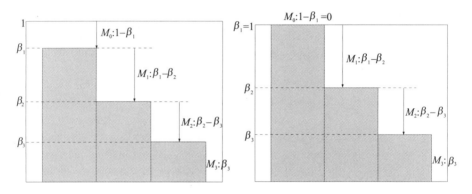

Fig. 3.5 Calculating mass assignments given the consonance assumption. The right-hand figure is with a full fuzzy covering while the left-hand figure is not

For the previous example, given $\mu_{L_1}(x) = 0.3$ and $\mu_{L_2}(x) = 1$, we can calculate the consonant mass assignments as follows: The appropriateness degrees are ordered as $\{\beta_1, \beta_2\} = \{1, 0.3\}$ and $M_1 = \{L_2\}$, $M_2 = \{L_1, L_2\}$. We then can obtain

$$m_x = \{L_2\} : \beta_1 - \beta_2, \{L_1, L_2\} : \beta_2 = \{L_2\} : 0.7, \{L_1, L_2\} : 0.3$$

Because the appropriateness degrees are sorted in Definition 3.4, the resulting mass assignments are "nested" (see Fig. 3.5). Clearly then, there is a unique consonant mapping to mass assignments for a given set of appropriateness degree values. The justification of the consonance assumption can be found in Reference [11] and [19]. Notice that in some cases we may have a non-zero mass associated with the empty set (left-hand diagram of Fig. 3.5). This means that some voters believe that x cannot be described by any labels in $\mathbb{L}$. This property would add to the complexity of our learning algorithms and hence we avoid it by introducing a full linguistic covering defined as follows:

Definition 3.5 (*Full linguistic covering*) *Given a continuous discourse Ω, the labels $\mathbb{L}$ form a full linguistic (fuzzy) covering of Ω if for every value $x \in \Omega$ there exists a label such that its appropriateness degree as a descriptor of x is 1:*

$$\forall x \in \Omega, \, \exists L \in \mathbb{L} \qquad \mu_L(x) = 1$$

Additionally, if only two labels can overlap at a time, the covering is said to be "pairwise overlapping", that is, for every value x in the universe there exist at most two labels with non-zero appropriateness degrees:

$$\forall x \in \Omega, \, \exists i, j \in \{1, \ldots, m\} : \{L \in \mathbb{L} : \mu_L(x) \neq 0\} = \{L_i, L_j\}$$

In another words, the full fuzzy covering assumes that, for any element, there always exists a particular label which all the voters agree is appropriate to describe this data, though the voters may have different opinions on other labels. Unless otherwise stated, we will use N_F fuzzy sets[5] with 50% overlap to cover a continuous universe (see Fig. 3.8), so that the appropriateness degrees satisfy: $\forall x \in \Omega, \, \exists i \in \{1, \ldots, N_F - 1\}$ such that

$$\mu_{L_i}(x) = \alpha, \, \mu_{L_{i+1}}(x) = \beta$$

and

$$\mu_{L_j}(x) = 0 \quad for : j < i \, or \, j > i+1$$

and where $\max(\alpha, \beta) = 1$. In the case that $\alpha = 1$ according to the full fuzzy covering assumption, then m_x has the following form.

$$m_x = \{L_i\} : 1 - \beta, \{L_i, L_{i+1}\} : \beta \tag{3.23}$$

It is also important to note that, given definitions for the appropriateness degrees on labels, we can isolate a set of subsets of $\mathbb{L}$ with non-zero masses. These are referred to as focal sets and the appropriate labels with non-zero masses as focal elements.

Definition 3.6 (*Focal set*) *The focal set of $\mathbb{L}$ is a set of label sets that satisfy the following condition:*

$$\mathbb{F} = \{S \subseteq \mathbb{L} | \exists x \in \Omega, m_x(S) > 0\}$$

where label sets with non-zero masses S are referred to as focal elements.

Consider the Example 3.2, the focal set decided by voters is:

$$\mathbb{F} = \{\{small\}, \{small, medium\}, \{medium\}, \{medium, large\}, \{large\}\}$$

There are a number of label sets that are not focal elements such as $\{small, large\}$ and $\{small, medium, large\}$ because both of them have zero associated mass. If *small*, *medium* and *large* are defined by trapezoidal membership functions, the membership functions for the focal elements are triangular. The corresponding relations in the general case are shown in Fig. 3.6 .

If the labels are defined by differently shaped fuzzy membership functions (e.g., bell-shape or Gaussian), the corresponding focal elements will also be different as well. More details are available in Lawry's book on label semantics theory[16].

---

[5] Because a fuzzy label is usually defined by a trapezoidal fuzzy set in this book, we use both terms to indicate a label in different scenarios.

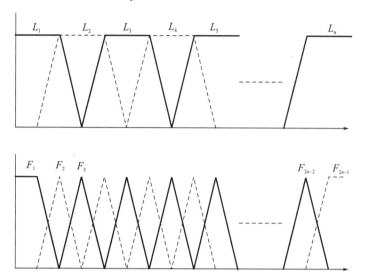

Fig. 3.6 Given linguistic labels $L_1, \ldots L_n$ are defined by trapezoidal membership functions, the corresponding focal elements $F_1, \ldots, F_{2n-1}$ in triangular shapes are shown under these linguistic labels

3.2.5 Linguistic Translation

Based on the above assumptions (consonant, full linguistic covering with 50% overlap) defined on a particular continuous universe, we can then always find the unique and consistent translation from a given data element to a mass assignment on focal elements, specified by the function $\mu_L : L \in \mathbb{L}$. Fig. 3.7 illustrates the mapping relations among numerical universe, mass assignments and fuzzy memberships (appropriateness degrees).

For example, Fig. 3.8 shows the universes of two variables x_1 and x_2 which are fully covered by 3 fuzzy sets with 50% overlap, respectively. For x_1, the following focal elements occur: $\{small_1\}$, $\{small_1, medium_1\}$, $\{medium_1\}$, $\{medium_1, large_1\}$ and $\{large_1\}$. Since $small_1$ and $large_1$ do not overlap, the set $\{small_1, large_1\}$ cannot occur as a focal element according to Definition 3.6. We can always find a unique translation from a given data point to a mass assignment on focal elements, as specified by the function μ_L. This is referred to as linguistic translation (LT) and is defined as follows:

Definition 3.7 (Linguistic translation) *Suppose we are given a numerical data set* $DB = \{\langle x_1(i), \ldots, x_n(i) \rangle | i = 1, \ldots, N\}$ *and focal set on attribute* j: $\mathbb{F}_j = \{F_j^1, \ldots, F_j^{h_j} | j = 1, \ldots, n\}$, *we can obtain the following new data base LD by applying linguistic translation to DB:*

$$LD = \{A_1(i), \ldots, A_n(i) | i = 1, \ldots N\}$$

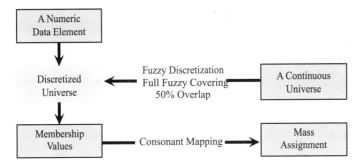

Fig. 3.7 A schematic illustration of the process of linguistic translation. We used a few assumptions to generate mass assignment of labels such as the consonant mass assignment assumption, full linguistic covering and 50% overlap on labels. These assumptions will guarantee a unique mapping from numerical data to mass assignment on given linguistic labels

$$A_j(i) = \{\langle m_{x_j(i)}(F_j^1), \ldots, m_{x_j(i)}(F_j^{h_j})\rangle\}$$

where $m_{x_j(i)}(F_j^r)$ is the associated mass of focal element F_j^r as appropriate labels for data element $x_j(i)$ where $r = 1, \ldots, h_j$ and $j = 1, \ldots, n$.

For a particular attribute with an associated focal set, linguistic translation is a process of replacing its data elements with the focal element masses of these data elements. For a variable x, it defines a unique mapping from data element $x(i)$ to a vector of associated masses $\langle m_{x(i)}(F^1), \ldots, m_{x(i)}(F^h)\rangle$.

Example 3.4 *Fig. 3.8 shows the universes of two variables x_1 and x_2 which are fully covered by 3 fuzzy sets with 50% overlap, respectively. For x_1, the following focal elements occur: $\{small_1\}$, $\{small_1, medium_1\}$, $\{medium_1\}$, $\{medium_1, large_1\}$ and $\{large_1\}$. Since $small_1$ and $large_1$ do not overlap, the set $\{small_1, large_1\}$ cannot occur as a focal element according to Definition 3.6. We can always find a unique translation from a given data point to a mass assignment on focal elements, as specified by the function μ_L according to the linguistic translation.*

$$\mu_{small_1}(x_1(1) = 0.27) = 1 \quad \mu_{medium_1}(0.27) = 0.6 \quad \mu_{large_1}(0.27) = 0$$

They are simply the memberships read from the fuzzy sets. We then can obtain the mass assignment of this data element according to Definition 3.3 under consonance assumption[20]:

$$m_{0.27}(small_1) = 0.4, \quad m_{0.27}(small_1, medium_1) = 0.6$$

Similarly, the linguistic translations for two data

$$x_1 = \langle x_1(1) = 0.27\rangle, \langle x_2(1) = 158\rangle$$

$$x_2 = \langle x_1(2) = 0.7\rangle, \langle x_2(2) = 80\rangle$$

are illustrated on each attribute independently as follows:

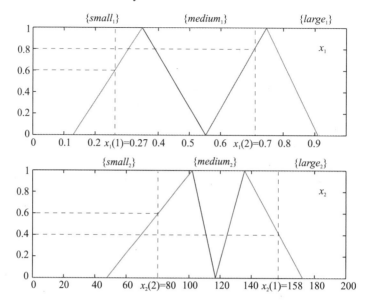

Fig. 3.8 A full fuzzy covering (discretization) with three fuzzy sets with 50% overlap on two attributes x_1 and x_2, respectively

$$\begin{bmatrix} x_1 \\ \hline x_1(1) = 0.27 \\ x_1(2) = 0.7 \end{bmatrix} \xrightarrow{LT} \begin{bmatrix} m_x(\{s_1\}) & m_x(\{s_1,m_1\}) & m_x(\{m_1\}) & m_x(\{m_1,l_1\}) & m_x(\{l_1\}) \\ 0.4 & 0.6 & 0 & 0 & 0 \\ 0 & 0 & 0.2 & 0.8 & 0 \end{bmatrix}$$

$$\begin{bmatrix} x_2 \\ \hline x_2(1) = 158 \\ x_2(2) = 80 \end{bmatrix} \xrightarrow{LT} \begin{bmatrix} m_x(\{s_2\}) & m_x(\{s_2,m_2\}) & m_x(\{m_2\}) & m_x(\{m_2,l_2\}) & m_x(\{l_2\}) \\ 0 & 0 & 0 & 0.4 & 0.6 \\ 0.4 & 0.6 & 0 & 0 & 0 \end{bmatrix}$$

Therefore, we can obtain:

$$x_1 \rightarrow \langle \{s_1\} : 0.4, \{s_1,m_1\} : 0.6 \rangle, \langle \{m_2,l_2\} : 0.4, \{l_2\} : 0.6 \rangle$$

$$x_2 \rightarrow \langle \{m_1\} : 0.2, \{m_1,l_1\} : 0.8 \rangle, \langle \{s_2\} : 0.4, \{s_2,m_2\} : 0.6 \rangle$$

The pseudo-code of the linguistic translation is shown in Algorithm 1. We need to notice that the linguistic translation is related to the given fuzzy labels. It may result in different linguistic data based on a different setting of fuzzy labels. We assume that the predefined fuzzy labels are involved with some expert knowledge. It is the prior information we need before conducting the linguistic translation.

As we may notice, the linguistic translation heavily depends on the predefined fuzzy labels. The linguistic data is not unique by giving variant ways of discretization methods. In the next section, we will discuss a few discretization methods with details.

Algorithm 1: Linguistic translation

---

input : Given a database $DB = \{\langle x_1(i), \ldots, x_n(i)\rangle | i = 1, \ldots, |DB|\}$
output: Linguistic dataset LD

for $j \leftarrow 1$ **to** n **do**
  foreach x_j **do** : Cover the universe of x_j with N_F fuzzy sets with 50% overlap ;
  for $i \leftarrow 1$ **to** $|DB|$ **do**
    foreach $x_j(i) \in DB_j$ **do** ;
    Read appropriateness degrees for $x_j(i)$ from the corresponding fuzzy set ;
    Calculating the mass assignments: $LD_{i,j} = \langle m_{x(i)}(F_j^1), \ldots, m_{x(i)}(F_j^{h_j})\rangle$ on focal elements from appropriateness degrees based on Eq. (3.23) ;

Save dataset $LD \leftarrow \{LD_{i,j} | i = 1, \ldots, |DB|, j = 1, \ldots, n\}$

3.3 Fuzzy Discretization

Basically, fuzzy discretization provides an interpretation between numerical data and linguistic data based on label semantics. The effectiveness of fuzzy discretization depends much on the algorithm's performance based on the linguistic data. The simplest approach is to use uniformly distributed fuzzy sets for discretization. In uniform discretization, labels are drawn uniformly on the continuous universe of the variable. For example, Fig. 3.9 shows a uniform discretization of one of the eight attributes, Clump Thickness in millimeters (or triceps skin fold thickness), of the Pima Indian Diabetics Problem[21]. We can also see the relation between trapezoidal fuzzy sets and triangular focal elements.

However, in some real-world applications, background knowledge about attributes may be available and can be used directly for discretization rather than an automatic discretization technique. For example, a feature ranging from 1 to 99 to describe human age can be uniformly discretized into 3 intervals: $[1, 33)$, $[34, 66)$ and $[67, 99]$. Our background knowledge (experience) suggests that the partition $[1, 30)$, $[30, 50)$ and $[50, 99]$ could be more reasonable. However, if no relevant background knowledge is available, the question remains as to whether we can improve on uniform discretization.

In label descriptions, focal elements are used in data modeling but not the fuzzy labels. In fact, there is a unique mapping from trapezoidal fuzzy sets to focal elements which can be represented by triangular functions[6]. Formally, these functions correspond to the $m_x(F)$ as x varies, for each focal element F. In order to improve the performance of our algorithm, we need to generate focal elements that are as discriminative as possible and the associated fuzzy sets can then be obtained according to Definitions 3.3 and 3.6. The following two discretization methods are introduced and will be used to generate fuzzy labels in further experimental studies.

---

[6] The focal elements at the two extreme sides are still trapezoidal but not triangular, for examples see Figs. 3.9 , 3.11 and 3.13 .

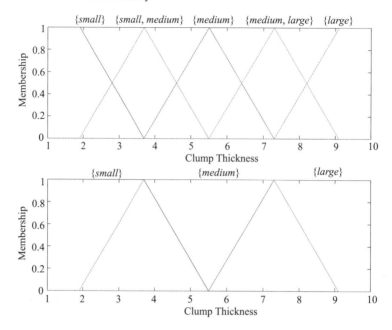

Fig. 3.9 Relationships between fuzzy labels and the corresponding focal elements based on uniform fuzzy discretization

3.3.1 Percentile-Based Discretization

In this approach discretization is based on data distribution, so that the attribute universe is partitioned into intervals which each contain approximately the same number of data elements. It is a very intuitive way of generating fuzzy labels based on the data distribution. For example, consider the same data from the Pima Indian Diabetics problem[21]. The data distribution shown in Fig. 3.10 . Fig. 3.11 shows the

continuous attribute universe is labeled by 3 fuzzy sets: *small*, *medium* and *large* ($N_F = 3$). According to the assumptions we made in Section 3.2, there are 5 focal elements. We then need 4 cut points that partition the universe into 5 intervals each containing approximately the same number of examples. The functions of focal elements $m_x(F)$ as x varies are drawn in the upper sub-figure and the fuzzy sets obtained are shown in the lower sub-figure. However, if the data is uniformly distributed, percentile-based discretization has the same affect as uniform discretization.

3.3.2 Entropy-Based Discretization

In this approach, the discretization is based on the expected entropy of the resulting partition. In fact we aim to obtain the partition maximizing the information gain[22].

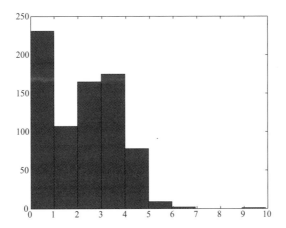

Fig. 3.10 Data distribution on the *Clump Thickness* in the Pima Indian Diabetics data[21]

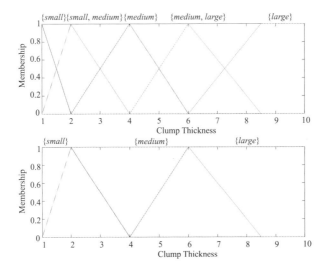

Fig. 3.11 Relationships between fuzzy labels and the corresponding focal elements based on percentile-based fuzzy discretization

For a particular attribute, suppose we have a set of data values $S = \{x_1, \ldots, x_N\}$ according to which we want to define q focal elements, then initially we need to find $q - 1$ cut points forming a partition of the universe. These boundary points are identified so as to maximize information gain in the following way. Every pair of adjacent data points suggests a potential boundary point,

$$\gamma_i = \frac{(x_i + x_{i+1})}{2}, \quad i = 1, \ldots, N - 1 \tag{3.24}$$

Fayyad has proved that only the class boundary points can be the boundary points if we are to obtain the maximum information in classification, which implies that γ_i cannot lead to a partition that has maximum information gain if x_i and x_{i+1} belong to the same class[23]. Therefore, we should generate a candidate set, which contains all class boundary points, from which we then need to find $q - 1$ points with which we can maximize the information gain defined by Eq. (3.25)[22].

$$Gain(S, \Phi) = Entropy(S) - \sum_{v=1,\dots,q} \frac{|S_v|}{|S|} Entropy(S_v) \tag{3.25}$$

where Φ is subset of the candidate set containing the $q - 1$ cut points that partition the original universe S into q intervals: $S_1, \dots, S_q$. The entropy is defined in Eq. (3.26), where m is the number of classes and p_i is the percentage of instances belonging to a particular class within S.

$$Entropy(S) = \sum_{i=1}^{m} -p_i \log_2 p_i \tag{3.26}$$

$$p_i = \frac{|S_i|}{|S|} \text{ where} : S_i = \sum_{x_j \in S} x_j \rightarrow C_i \tag{3.27}$$

Fig. 3.12 shows the conditional distribution of lump Thickness given two classes of the Pima Indian Diabetics Problem[21]. Fig. 3.13 shows the entropy-based discretization of the same attribute.

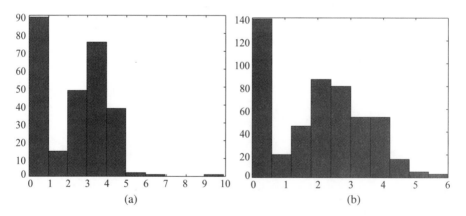

(a)   (b)

Fig. 3.12 Data distribution of Clump Thickness given class 1 (a) and class 2 (b)

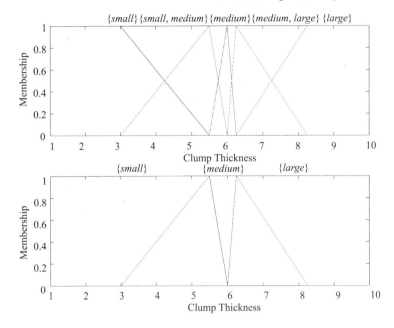

Fig. 3.13 Relationships between fuzzy labels and the corresponding focal elements based on entropy-based discretization

3.4 Reasoning with Fuzzy Labels

So far we have introduced how to use the label semantics framework for data modeling. In this section, we will go for more details in label semantics theory especially in linguistic reasoning and other theoretical aspects.

3.4.1 Conditional Distribution Given Mass Assignments

As we have introduced in the previous section, mass assignment can be used to describe vague concepts. How to convey and use the information in reasoning is a key problem. We will start by defining the conditional probability given a vague concept in mass assignment representation.

Definition 3.8 (*Conditional distribution given a mass assignment*) *Given a mass assignment on labels* $m : 2^{\mathbb{L}} \to [0, 1]$ *then for* Ω *finite:*

$$\forall x \in \Omega \quad P(x|m) = P(x) \sum_{S \subseteq \mathbb{L}} m_x(S) \frac{m(S)}{pm(S)} \tag{3.28}$$

and for infinite Ω *the conditional density is given by:*

$$\forall x \in \Omega \quad f(x|m) = f(x) \sum_{S \subseteq \mathbb{L}} m_x(S) \frac{m(S)}{pm(S)} \tag{3.29}$$

where pm(S) is the prior mass assignment (see Eq. (3.4))

This definition can be justified in terms of the theorem of total probability as follows: Suppose that instead of a mass assignment, you knew that the set of appropriate labels for value y selected at random from Ω was certain to be S, i.e., that $D_y = S$ (Definition 3.2). In this case, you could apply Bayes' theorem to obtain a conditional distribution on Ω as follows:

$$\forall x \in \Omega \quad P(y = x | D_y = S) = \frac{P(y = x)P(D_y = T | y = x)}{P(D_y = T)} = \frac{P(x)m_x(S)}{pm(S)} \tag{3.30}$$

However, you do not know the exact value of D_y for a randomly selected value y but rather you only know a distribution for the values of D_y corresponding to mass assignment m. Hence, in this case you can apply the theorem of total probability to obtain a conditional distribution according to:

$$\forall x \in \Omega \quad P(x|m) = \sum_{S \subseteq \mathbb{L}} P(y = x | D_y = S)m(S) = \sum_{S \subseteq \mathbb{L}} \frac{P(x)m_x(S)}{pm(S)}$$

$$= P(x) \sum_{S \subseteq \mathbb{L}} m_x(S) \frac{m(S)}{pm(S)}$$

This will be used to evaluate conditional probabilities for label semantics based Bayesian classifiers (see Chapter 6).

3.4.2 Logical Expressions of Fuzzy Labels

Given a universe of discourse Ω containing a set of objects or instances to be described, it is assumed that all relevant expression can be generated recursively from a finite set of basic labels $\mathbb{L} = \{L_1, \ldots, L_n\}$. Operators for combining expressions are restricted to the standard logical connectives of negation "$\neg$", conjunction "$\wedge$", disjunction "$\vee$" and implication "$\rightarrow$". Hence, the set of logical expressions of labels can be formally defined as follows.

Definition 3.9 (*Logical expressions of labels*) *The set of logical expressions, LE, is defined recursively as follows:*

(i) $L_i \in LE$ for $i = 1, \ldots, n$.
(ii) If $\theta, \varphi \in LE$ then $\neg\theta, \theta \wedge \varphi, \theta \vee \varphi, \theta \rightarrow \varphi \in LE$

Basically, we interpret the main logical connectives as follows: $\neg L$ means that L is not an appropriate label, $L_1 \wedge L_2$ means that both L_1 and L_2 are appropriate labels, $L_1 \vee L_2$ means that either L_1 or L_2 are appropriate labels, and $L_1 \rightarrow L_2$ means that

L_2 is an appropriate label whenever L_1 is. The reason we use such logical forms is because linguistic expressions such as not small and not large, or medium and high etc., are more intuitively describable for human cognition compared to the mass assignment on label sets.

We have developed a mechanism for measuring the appropriateness of using a linguistic label to describe an object. We are also interested in evaluating the appropriateness degrees of a complex logical expression $\theta \in LE$. Consider the set of logical expressions LE obtained by recursive application of the standard logical connectives in $\mathbb{L}$. In order to evaluate the appropriateness degrees of such expressions we must identify what information they provide regarding the appropriateness of labels. In general, for any label expression θ we should be able to identify a maximal set of label sets, $\lambda(\theta)$ that are consistent with θ so that the meaning of θ can be interpreted as the constraint $\mathscr{D}_x \in \lambda(\theta)$.

Definition 3.10 (λ-function) *Let θ and φ be expressions generated by recursive application of the connectives $\neg, \vee, \wedge$ and $\rightarrow$ to the elements of $\mathbb{L}$ (i.e. $\theta, \varphi \in LE$). Then the set of possible label sets defined by a linguistic expression can be determined recursively as follows.*

(i) $\lambda(L_i(x)) = \{S \subseteq \mathbb{F} | \{L_i\} \subseteq S\}$
(ii) $\lambda(\neg\theta) = \overline{\lambda(\theta)}$
(iii) $\lambda(\theta \wedge \varphi) = \lambda(\theta) \cap \lambda(\varphi)$
(iv) $\lambda(\theta \vee \varphi) = \lambda(\theta) \cup \lambda(\varphi)$
(v) $\lambda(\theta \rightarrow \varphi) = \overline{\lambda(\theta)} \cup \lambda(\varphi)$

It should also be noted that the λ-function provides us with a notion of logical equivalence for label expressions,

$$\theta \equiv_L \varphi \Longleftrightarrow \lambda(\theta) = \lambda(\varphi)$$

Basically, λ-function provides a way of transferring logical expressions of labels (or linguistic rules) to random set descriptions of labels (i.e., focal elements). $\lambda(\theta)$ corresponds to those subsets of $\mathbb{F}$ identified as being possible values of $\mathscr{D}_x$ by expression θ. In this sense the imprecise linguistic restriction 'x is θ' on x corresponds to the strict constraint $\mathscr{D}_x \in \lambda(\theta)$ on $\mathscr{D}_x$. Hence, we can view label descriptions as an alternative to linguistic variables as a means of encoding linguistic constraints[24]. Reasoning with linguistic constraints will be introduced in Chapters 4 and 5, respectively.

Based on Definition 3.10, we can evaluate that the appropriateness degree of $\theta \in LE$ is to aggregate the values of m_x across $\lambda(\theta)$. This motivates the following general definition of appropriateness measures.

Definition 3.11 (Appropriateness measures) *$\forall \theta \in LE, \forall x \in \Omega$ the measure of appropriateness degrees of θ as a description of x is given by*

$$\mu_\theta(x) = \sum_{S \in \lambda(\theta)} m_x(S)$$

Appropriateness degrees (Definition 3.3) introduced at the beginning of this chapter can be regarded as a special case of appropriateness measures. Note that in label semantics there is no requirement for the mass associated with the empty set to be zero. Instead, $m_x(\emptyset)$ quantifies the agent's belief that none of the labels are appropriate to describe x. Given the Definition 3.11 it can be shown that the appropriateness measures have the following properties [16].

Theorem 3.1 *General properties of appropriateness measures $\forall \theta, \varphi \in LE$ then the following properties hold:*

(i) *If $\theta \models \varphi$ then $\forall x \in \Omega \; \mu_\theta(x) \leq \mu_\varphi(x)$*
(ii) *if $\theta \equiv_L \varphi$ then $\forall x \in \Omega \; \mu_\theta(x) = \mu_\varphi(x)$*
(iii) *θ is a tautology then $\forall x \in \Omega \; \mu_\theta(x) = 1$*
(iv) *θ is a contradiction then $\forall x \in \Omega \; \mu_\theta(x) = 0$*
(v) *$\forall x \in \Omega \; \mu_{\neg\theta}(x) = 1 - \mu_\theta(x)$*
(vi) *Let $LE^{\wedge,\vee} \subseteq LE$ denote those expressions generated recursively from $\mathbb{L}$ using only the connectives $\wedge$ and $\vee$. $\forall x \in \Omega$ it holds that:*

$$\mu_{\theta \wedge \varphi}(x) = \min(\mu_\theta(x), \mu_\varphi(x)) \tag{3.31}$$

$$\mu_{\theta \vee \varphi}(x) = \max(\mu_\theta(x), \mu_\varphi(x)) \tag{3.32}$$

Note that by implication $\mu_{\theta \to \varphi}(x)$ quantifies that agent's belief that if θ is appropriate to describe a given x then so is φ.

Example 3.5 *Given a continuous variable x: $\mathbb{L}_x = \{small, medium, large\}$, $\mathbb{F}_x = \{\{small\}, \{small, medium\}, \{medium\}, \{medium, large\}, \{large\}\}$. Suppose we are told that "x is not large but it is small or medium". This constraint can be interpreted as the logical expression*

$$\theta_x = \neg large \wedge (small \vee medium)$$

According to Definition 3.10, the possible label sets of the given logical expression θ_x are calculated as follows:

$$\lambda(\neg large) = \{\{small\}, \{small, medium\}, \{medium\}\}$$

$$\lambda(small) = \{\{small\}, \{small, medium\}\}$$

$$\lambda(medium) = \{\{small, medium\}, \{medium\}, \{medium, large\}\}$$

so that we can obtain,

$\lambda(\theta_x) = \lambda(\neg large \wedge (small \vee medium)) = \{\{small\}, \{small, medium\}, \{medium\}\}$ $\wedge$ ($\{\{small\}, \{small, medium\}\} \vee \{\{small, medium\}, \{medium\}, \{medium, large\}\}$) $= \{\{small\}, \{small, medium\}, \{medium\}\}$

If a prior distribution on focal elements of variable x are given as follows:

$$p(x) = \{\{small\} : 0.1, \{small, medium\} : 0.3,$$

$$\{medium\} : 0.1, \{medium, large\} : 0.5, \{large\} : 0.0\}$$

The appropriateness measure for $\theta_x = \neg large \land (small \lor medium)$ *is,*

$$\mu_\theta(x) = \sum_{S \in \lambda(\theta)} m_x(S)$$
$$= m_x(\{small\}) + m_x(\{small, medium\}) + m_x(\{medium\})$$
$$= 0.1 + 0.3 + 0.1 = 0.5$$

3.4.3 Linguistic Interpretation of Appropriate Labels

Based on the inverse of the λ-function (Definition 3.10), a set of logical label expressions (linguistic rules) can be obtained from a given set of possible label sets. For example, suppose we are given the possible label sets $\{\{small\}, \{small, medium\}, \{medium\}\}$, which does not have an immediately obvious interpretation. However by using the α-function, we can convert this set into a corresponding linguistic expression $(small \lor medium) \land \neg large$ or its logical equivalence.

Definition 3.12 (α-function)

$$\forall F \in \mathbb{F} \quad let \quad \mathbb{N}(F) = \left(\bigcup_{F' \in \mathbb{F}: F' \supseteq F} F' \right) - F \tag{3.33}$$

$$then \quad \alpha_F = \left(\bigwedge_{L \in F} L \right) \land \left(\bigwedge_{L \in \mathbb{N}(F)} \neg L \right) \tag{3.34}$$

Then map a set of focal sets to label expressions based on the α-function as follows:

$$\forall R \in \mathbb{F} \quad \theta_R = \bigvee_{F \in R} \alpha_F \quad where \quad \lambda(\theta_R) = R \tag{3.35}$$

The motivation of this mapping is as follows. Given a focal set $\{small, medium\}$ this states that the labels appropriate to describe the attribute are exactly *small* and *medium*. Hence, they include *small* and *medium* and exclude all other labels that occur in focal sets that are supersets of $\{small, medium\}$. Given a set of focal sets $\{\{small, medium\}, \{medium\}\}$ this provides the information that the set of labels is either $\{small, medium\}$ or $\{medium\}$ and hence the sentence providing the same information should be the disjunction of the α sentences for both focal sets. The following example gives the calculation of the α-function.

Example 3.6 *Let* $\mathbb{L} = \{very \ small \ (vs), \ small \ (s), \ medium \ (m), \ large(l), \ very \ large \ (vl)\}$ *and* $\mathbb{F} = \{\{vs, s\}, \{s\}, \{s, m\}, \{m\}, \{m, l\}, \{l\}, \{l, vl\}\}$. *For calculating* $\alpha_{\{l\}}$, *we obtain,*

$$F' \in \mathbb{F} : F' \supseteq \{l\} = \{\{m, l\}, \{l\}, \{l, vl\}\} = \{m, l, vl\}$$

$$\mathbb{N}(\{l\}) = \left(\bigcup_{F' \in \mathbb{F}: F' \supseteq \{l\}} F' \right) - \{l\} = \{l, vl, m\} - \{l\} = \{vl, m\}$$

$$\alpha_{\{l\}} = \left(\bigwedge_{L \in F} L \right) \wedge \left(\bigwedge_{L \in \mathbb{N}(F)} \neg L \right) = (l) \wedge (\neg m \wedge \neg vl) = \neg m \wedge l \wedge \neg vl$$

Also we can obtain,

$$\alpha_{\{m,l\}} = m \wedge l \quad \alpha_{\{l,vl\}} = l \wedge vl$$

Hence, a set of label sets $\{\{m,l\}, \{l\}, \{l,vl\}\}$ can be represented by a linguistic expression as follows:

$$\theta_{\{\{m,l\},\{l\},\{l,vl\}\}} = \alpha_{\{m,l\}} \vee \alpha_{\{l\}} \vee \alpha_{\{l,vl\}} =$$

$$(m \wedge l) \vee (\neg m \wedge l \neg vl) \vee (l \wedge vl) \equiv_L large$$

where '$\equiv_L$' represents logical equivalence (Definition 3.10).

Basically, α-function provides a way of obtaining logical expressions from a random set description of labels. It is an inverse process of λ-function.

3.4.4 Evidence Theory and Mass Assignment

Evidence theory, also known as Dempster-Shafer (D-S) theory[25], is based on two dual non-additive measures: belief measures, denoted by *Bel*, and plausibility measures, denoted by *Pl*. Let us suppose that we have a finite universe Ω. Then, for each subset, S in the power set of Ω, 2^Ω, we can interpret $Bel(S)$ as the degree of belief that a given element of Ω belongs to the set S. We may also view the subsets of Ω as answers to a particular question or alternative hypothesis explaining the state of the world. We assume that some of the answers are correct, but we do not know with full certainty which ones they are.

Definition 3.13 (Belief measure) *Given a finite universal set Ω, a belief measure is a function:*

$$Bel : 2^\Omega \rightarrow [0, 1]$$

such that,

$$Bel(\emptyset) = 0, \ Bel(\Omega) = 1$$

and for all possible families of subsets: $S_1, \ldots, S_n$ of Ω:

$$Bel(S_1 \cup \ldots \cup S_n) \geq \sum_{i=1}^{n} Bel(S_i) - \sum_{i>j}^{n} Bel(S_i \cap S_j) +, \ldots, +$$

$$(-1)^{n+1} Bel(S_1 \cap \ldots \cap S_n) \tag{3.36}$$

Belief can be defined as a measure of total evidence in favor. When the sets $S_1, \ldots, S_n$ are pair-wise disjoint, the inequality requires that the degree of belief associated with union of the set, which is not smaller than the sum of the degree of belief associated with the union of the sets is not smaller than the sum of the degrees of belief pertaining to the individual sets. This basic property of belief measures is thus a weaker version of the additivity property of probability measures. This implies that probability measures are special cases of belief measures of which (Eq. (3.36)) becomes an equality.

Belief measures have the following properties:

$$\forall S, T \in 2^\Omega : S \subseteq T, Bel(S) \le Bel(T) \tag{3.37}$$

$$\forall S \in 2^\Omega : Bel(S) + Bel(\bar{S}) \le 1 \tag{3.38}$$

where $\bar{S}$ denotes the complement of S in Ω.

The first property in Eq. (3.37) means that $Bel(\cdot)$ is a monotonic function. The second property in Eq. (3.38) means that lack of belief in $x \in S$ does not imply a strong belief in $x \in \bar{S}$. Associated with each belief measure is a *plausibility measure* defined by:

$$\forall S \in 2^\Omega, \ Pl(S) = 1 - Bel(\bar{S}) \tag{3.39}$$

Similarly, we have that,

$$\forall S \in 2^\Omega, \ Bel(S) = 1 - Pl(\bar{S}) \tag{3.40}$$

Definition 3.14 (*Plausibility measure*) *Given a finite universal set Ω, a plausibility measure is a function:*

$$Pl : 2^\Omega \to [0,1] \tag{3.41}$$

such that,

$$Pl(\emptyset) = 0, \ Pl(\Omega) = 1 \tag{3.42}$$

In other words, plausibility is a measure of total evidence not against while belief measure is total evidence in favor.

Mass assignment can be regarded as an extension of Shafer-Dempster's evidence theory. Shafer-Dempster belief functions are defined by a probability distribution on the power set Ω. Belief is defined as

$$Bel(A) = \sum_{B \subseteq A} m(B) \tag{3.43}$$

and plausibility as

$$Pl(A) = \sum_{B:B \cap A \ne \emptyset} \tag{3.44}$$

Based on mass assignment, $Bel()$ and $Pl()$ can be defined as Belief:

$$Bel(S) = \sum_{T \subseteq S} m(T)$$

Plausibility,

$$Pl(S) = \sum_{T:T \cap S \neq \emptyset} m(T)$$

Additivity is weakened in evidence theory:

$$Bel(A \cup B) \geq Bel(A) + Bel(B) - Bel(A \cap B)$$

$$Pl(A \cup B) \leq Pl(A) + Pl(B) - Pl(A \cap B)$$

While for probability measure:

$$P(A \cup B) = P(A) + P(B) - P(A \cap B)$$

Example 3.7 *It is known that a patient is either healthy (H) or has one of two diseases D_1 or D_2, (see Fig. 3.14). What should be our belief that the patient is suffering from either diseases D_1 or D_2 (i.e., that he is not healthy)?*

$$Bel(\{D_1, D_2\}) = m(\{D_1\}) + m(\{D_2\}) + m(\{D_1, D_2\}) \tag{3.45}$$

It is the sum of evidence that supports the patient not being healthy. However, the plausibility of this hypothesis is

$$Pl(\{D_1, D_2\}) = m(\{D_1\}) + m(\{D_2\}) + m(\{D_1, D_2\}) \tag{3.46}$$

$$+ m(\{H, D_1\}) + m(\{H, D_2\}) + m(\{H, D_1, D_2\})$$

Although label semantics is based on random set theory and is quite different from evidence theory, there are overlaps between these two theories. There is a clear link between the appropriateness measures of disjunctions and conjunction of basic labels and plausibility and commonality measures in D-S theory. Given m_x as conditional mass assignment on $2^{\mathbb{L}}$ given a random variable x. In this case, for any labels $L_i \in \mathbb{L}$ for $i = 1, \ldots, n$. The appropriateness measure of the disjunction $L_1 \vee L_2 \ldots \vee L_n$ is given by:

$$\mu_{L_1 \vee \ldots \vee L_n}(x) = \sum_{S:\{L_1,\ldots,L_k\} \cap S \neq \emptyset} m_x(S) = Pl(\{L_1, \ldots, L_k\}|x) \tag{3.47}$$

Similarly, the appropriateness measure of the conjunction $L_1 \wedge \ldots \wedge L_n$ as a description of x is given by:

$$\mu_{L_1 \wedge L_n}(x) = \sum_{S:\{L_1,\ldots,L_n\} \subseteq S} m_x(S) = Bel(\{L_1, \ldots, L_n\}|x) \tag{3.48}$$

Despite this relationship, we should not treat the appropriateness measures as a specical case of D-S theory. The general method of evaluating appropriateness measures by summing over λ-sets has no equivalency in D-S theory [26].

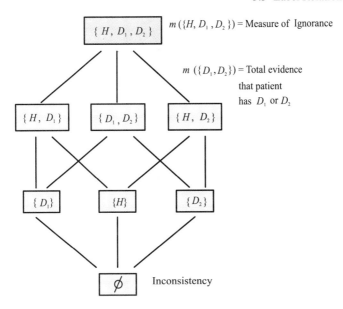

Fig. 3.14 An example of evidence based on mass assignment. A patient is either healthy (H) or has one of two diseases D_1 or D_2

3.5 Label Relations

In this section, we will consider how to use one set of fuzzy labels to describe another fuzzy labels. Here, using the term high level labels does not mean a hierarchical structure. We will actually consider two set of fuzzy labels which are independently defined on the same universe. If the cardinality of a set of labels $\mathbb{L}$ is denoted by $|\mathbb{L}|$, we then can say $\mathbb{L}_1$ higher level labels of $\mathbb{L}_2$ if $|\mathbb{L}_1| \leq |\mathbb{L}_2|$. We will actually consider the methodology of using one set of fuzzy labels to represent the other set of fuzzy labels. Generally, we want to use a set of fuzzy labels with a smaller cardinality (which are relatively more vague) to represent a set of labels with bigger cardinality (which are less vague).

For example, a fuzzy concept *about_m* is defined by an interval on $[a,b]$ (see Fig. 3.15), so that the appropriateness degree of using fuzzy label *small* to label *about_m* is:

$$\mu_{small}(about\_m) = \frac{1}{b-a} \int_a^b \mu_{small}(u)\mathrm{d}u \qquad (3.49)$$

If the vagueness of the concept *about_m* depends on the interval denoted by δ where the length of the interval $|\delta| = b - a$, we then can obtain

$$\mu_{small}(about\_m) = \frac{1}{|\delta|} \int_{u \in \delta} \mu_{small}(u)\mathrm{d}u \qquad (3.50)$$

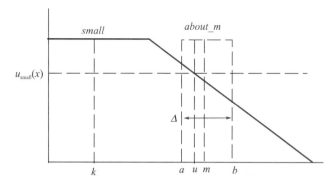

Fig. 3.15 The appropriateness degree of using *small* to label a vague concept *about_m* is defined by the ratio of the area covered by both labels to the area covered by *about_m* only. This is the case where *about_m* is defined by an interval

If *about_m* is defined by other fuzzy labels rather than an interval, for example, a triangular fuzzy set (e.g., Fig. 3.16), how can we define the appropriateness degrees?

We begin by considering a data element $x \in [a,b]$, the function $\mu_{about\_m}(x)$ represents the degree of x belonging to the fuzzy label F. Function $\mu_{small}(x)$ defines the appropriateness degrees of using the label *small* to describe x [7]. We essentially hope to obtain the appropriateness degrees of using *small* to label *about_m*. We then consider each of the elements belonging to *about_m*. If $\mu_{about\_m}(x) = 1$, which means x is absolutely belongs to *about_m*, then the appropriateness degree is just $\mu_{small}(x)$. However, if $\mu_{about\_m} < \mu_{small}(x)$, we can only say it is belonging to *about_m* in certain degrees. Logically, fuzzy operation AND is used, and in practical calculation the $\min(\cdot)$ function is employed. The appropriateness is then defined by

$$\mu_{small}(about\_m) = \frac{\int_{u \in \delta} \min(\mu_{small}(u), \mu_{about\_m}(u)) \mathrm{d}u}{\int_{u' \in \delta} \mu_{about\_m}(u') \mathrm{d}u'} \tag{3.51}$$

where function $\min(x,y)$ returns the minimum value between x and y. Eq. (3.50) is a special case of Eq. (3.51) where the following equations always hold:

$$\mu_{small}(u) = \min(\mu_{small}(u), \mu_{about\_m}(u))$$

$$|\delta| = \int_{u \in \delta} \mu_{about\_m}(u) \mathrm{d}u$$

Definition 3.15 *Given a vague concept (or a fuzzy label) F and a set of labels* $\mathbb{L} = \{L_1, \ldots, L_m\}$ *defined on a continuous universe* Ω*, the appropriateness degrees of using label L (L $\in \mathbb{L}$) to describe F are:*

---

[7] Here we interpret $\mu(\cdot)$ in different manners: membership function and appropriateness degrees, though they are mathematically the same.

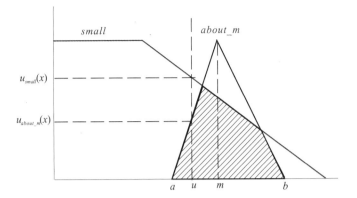

Fig. 3.16 The appropriateness degree of using *small* to label a vague concept *about_m* is defined by the ratio of the area covered by both labels to the area covered by *about_m* only. This is the case where *about_m* is defined by a triangular membership function

$$\mu_L(F) = \frac{\int_{u\in\delta} \min(\mu_L(u), \mu_F(u)) du}{\int_{u'\in\delta} \mu_F(u') du'} \tag{3.52}$$

where δ is the universe covered by fuzzy label F.

Given appropriateness degrees, the mass assignment can be obtained from the appropriateness degrees by the consonance assumption. Eq. (3.51) is a general form for all kinds of fuzzy sets which are not limited to an interval or a triangular fuzzy sets.

Example 3.8 *Fig. 3.17 gives a set of isosceles triangular fuzzy labels $F_1,\ldots,F_8$, and two high level fuzzy labels, small and large, defined on the same universe. The membership functions (the non-zero part) for F_5, F_6 and small are defined as follows:*

$$PS \rightarrow y = \frac{5}{2}x - 3, \ \ PT \rightarrow y = -\frac{5}{2}x + 5$$

$$QR \rightarrow y = \frac{5}{2}(x - 0.4) - 3, \ \ QU \rightarrow y = -\frac{5}{2}(x - 0.4) + 5$$

$$OU \rightarrow y = -\frac{5}{6}x + 2$$

As we can see from Fig. 3.17 : $\mu_{F_5}(x) = 0.75$ and $\mu_{F_6}(x) = 0.25$ given $x = 1.7$. According to Definition 3.15 we can obtain

$$\mu_{small}(F_5) = 0.8, \ \mu_{large}(F_5) = 1$$

$$\mu_{small}(F_6) = 0.5, \ \mu_{large}(F_6) = 1$$

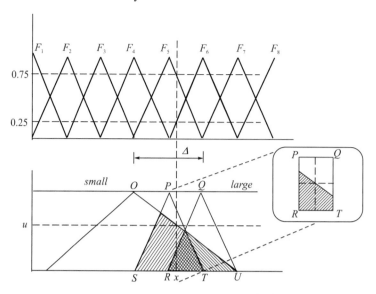

Fig. 3.17 The relations between fuzzy labels

So that the corresponding consonant mass assignments (see Definition 3.4) are

$$m_{F_5} = \{small, large\} : 0.8, \{large\} : 0.2$$

$$m_{F_6} = \{small, large\} : 0.5, \{large\} : 0.5$$

High level labels small and large can be used to describe $x = 1.7$ by the following steps:

$$m_x = \{F_5, F_6\} : 0.25, \{F_5\} : 0.5, \emptyset : 0.25$$

F_5 and F_6 can be represented by the mass assignments of high level fuzzy labels, small and large. Considering the term $\{F_5, F_6\}$, it means that both two labels F_5 and F_6 are appropriate for labeling x with a certain degree. It defines a area covered both by F_5 and F_6 which is an interval between R and T. Therefore, according to Definition 3.15 we can obtain the mass assignment for $\{F_5, F_6\}$:

$$m_{\{F_5, F_6\}} = \{small, large\} : 0.5, \{large\} : 0.5$$

Finally, we obtain

$$
\begin{aligned}
m_x = & (\{small, large\} : 0.5, \{large\} : 0.5) : 0.25, \\
& (\{small, large\} : 0.8, \{large\} : 0.2) : 0.5, \emptyset : 0.25 \\
= & \{small, large\} : 0.525, \{large\} : 0.225, \emptyset : 0.25
\end{aligned}
$$

From example 3.8, if we use *small* and *large* to describe x directly. By the function of *small* we can obtain $u = \frac{7}{12}$, so that the mass assignments are

$$m_x = \{small, large\} : \frac{7}{12}, \{large\} : \frac{5}{12}$$

which is different from the result presented in Example 3.1. It is because precision is lost by using two level of fuzzy labels. In our example, x is firstly repressed by F_5 and F_6 which are precise. However, the description of x by *small* and *large* through F_5 and F_6 is not precise any more, because F_5 and F_6 are not exact representation of x by involving uncertainties decided by δ. As we can see from the Figs. 3.18 and 3.19 : the appropriateness degrees of using high level labels to describe low level concepts are dependent on the uncertainty parameter δ. For example, given a data element m:

$$|\mu_{small}(F(\delta_1)) - \mu_{small}(m)| < |\mu_{small}(F(\delta_2)) - \mu_{small}(m)| < |\mu_{small}(F(\delta_3)) - \mu_{small}(m)|$$

So that,

$$\mu_{small}(m) = \lim_{\delta \to 0} \mu_{samll}(F(\delta))$$

where F is the function of the fuzzy label (a function of δ–either an interval, triangular fuzzy set or other type of fuzzy set) centered on m.

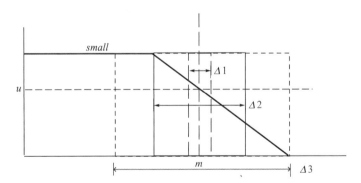

Fig. 3.18 The appropriateness degrees of *small* depend on the width of the vague concept of *about_m*, where *about_m* is a uniform interval

3.6 Summary

Reasoning with uncertainty is an important area in artificial intelligence. In this chapter, a random set based framework for modeling uncertainty is introduced. In this framework the appropriateness of describing a concept with a particular

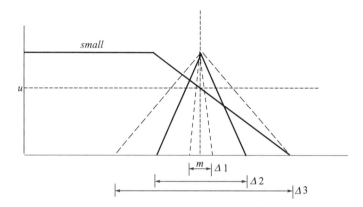

Fig. 3.19 The appropriateness degrees of *small* depend on the width of the vague concept of *about_m*, where *about_m* is a triangular fuzzy set

fuzzy label is used for modeling. The basic semantics is presented with examples. The method for using it for data analysis is also discussed and that will be used for designing new machine learning and data mining algorithms in the subsequent chapters.

Generally, a human being posses a mechanism for deciding whether or not to make assertions or to agree to a classification. Further, this underling decision process is fundamentally crisp although the concepts concerned are vague. In this sense, label semantics provides a new perspective on vague concepts by focusing on the decision process you must go through in order to identify which labels or expressions can actually be used to describe an object or instance. The foundation of this theory is based on quantifying your subjective belief that a label is appropriate to describe an object. Such belief evaluation would be made on the basis of your previous experience of the use of labels and label expressions by other agents to describe other similar instances.

References

[1] Zadeh L. A.: Toward a generalized theory of uncertainty (GTU)- an outline, Information Sciences, 172/1-2, pp. 1-40. (2005).
[2] Jaynes E. T.: Probability Theory: The Logic of Science. Cambridge University Press, (2003).
[3] Zadeh L. A.: Fuzzy sets, Information and Control, 8: pp. 338-353. (1965).
[4] http://en.wikipedia.org/wiki/Parmenides, accessed on January 19, (2011).
[5] Klir G. J., Yuan B.: Fuzzy Sets and Fuzzy Logic, Prentice Hall. (1995).
[6] Jang J. S. R., Sun C. T., Mizutani E.: Neuro-Fuzzy and Soft Computing, Prentice-Hall, Inc. Simon & Schuster. (1997).

[7] Zadeh L. A.: Fuzzy logic = computing with words, IEEE Transaction on Fuzzy Systems. 4(2): pp. 103-111. (1996).

[8] Zadeh L. A.: Precisiated natural language (PNL), AI Magazine, 25(3), pp. 74-91. (2004).

[9] Qin Z., Thint M., Beg M. M. S.: Deduction engine designs for PNL-based question answering systems, Foundations of Fuzzy Logic and Soft Computing, Lecture Notes in Artificial Intelligence 4529, pp. 253-262, Springer. (2007).

[10] Beg M. M. S., Thint M., Qin Z.: PNL-enhanced restricted domain question answering system, the Proceedings of IEEE-FUZZ, pp. 1277-1283, London, IEEE Press. (2007).

[11] Baldwin J. F., Martin T. P., Pilsworth B. W.: Fril-Fuzzy and Evidential Reasoning in Artificial Intelligence, John Wiley & Sons Inc. (1995).

[12] Baldwin J. F.: Lecture Notes in Computational Intelligence. Department of Engineering Mathematics, University of Bristol. (2001)-(2002).

[13] Lawry J.: A framework for linguistic modelling, Artificial Intelligence, 155: pp. 1-39. (2004).

[14] Dubois D., Prade H., Yager R.R.: Information engineering and fuzzy logic. Proceedings of 5th IEEE International Conference on Fuzzy Systems, pp. 1525-1531. (1996).

[15] Williamson T.: Vagueness, Routledge. (1994).

[16] Lawry J.: Modelling and Reasoning with Vague Concepts, Springer. (2006).

[17] Lawry J.: Appropriateness measures: an uncertainty model for vague concepts. Synthese, 161:2, pp. 255-269. (2008).

[18] Lawry J.: Label semantics: A formal framework for modelling with words. Symbolic and Quantitative Approaches to Reasoning with Uncertainty, LNAI 2143: pp. 374-384, Springer-Verlag. (2001).

[19] Lawry J.: A voting mechanism for fuzzy logic, International Journal of Approximate Reasoning 19, pp. 315-333. (1998).

[20] Qin Z., Lawry J.: Decision tree learning with fuzzy labels, Information Sciences, 172/1-2: pp. 91-129. (2005).

[21] Blake C., Merz C. J.: UCI machine learning repository.

[22] Mitchell T.: Machine Learning, McGraw-Hill, New York. (1997).

[23] Fayyad U. M., Irani K. B.:Multi-interval discretization of continuous-valued attributes for classification learning, Proceedings of the Thirteenth International Joint Conference on Artificial Intelligence, 2, Chambery, France. (1993).

[24] Lawry J., Hall J. W., Bovey R.: Fusion of expert and learnt knowledge in a framework of fuzzy labels, Journal of Approximate Reasoning, 36: pp. 151-198. (2004).

[25] Shafer G.: A Mathematical Theory of Evidence, Princeton University Press. (1976).

[26] Lawry J., He H.: Linguistic attribute hierarchies for multiple-attribute decision making, Proceedings of IEEE-FUZZ, (2007).

4

Linguistic Decision Trees for Classification

Science is the systematic classification of experience.

— *George Henry Lewes (1817-1878)*

4.1 Introduction

In this chapter, label semantics theory is applied to designing transparent data mining models. A label semantics based decision tree model is proposed where nodes are linguistic descriptions of variables and leaves are sets of appropriate labels. For each branch, instead of labeling it with a certain class, the probability of a particular class given this branch can be computed based on the given training dataset. This new model is referred to as a linguistic decision tree (LDT).

A new algorithm for building such a tree model guided by information based heuristics is proposed by modifying the classical ID3 algorithms in accordance with label semantics theory. By empirical experiments on real-world datasets it is verified that LDTs have better or equivalent classification accuracy compared to three well-known machine learning algorithms: C4.5, Naive Bayes (NB) and Back Propagation (BP) Neural Networks. Each LDT can be interpreted as a set of linguistic rules that give this model a good transparency compared to other black-box data mining models. By applying a new proposed forward branch merging algorithm, the complexity of the tree can be greatly reduced without significant loss of accuracy. Finally, a method for linguistic query evaluation is discussed and supported with an example at the end of this chapter. This methodology can be extended to learning from fuzzy data.

4.2 Tree Induction

Tree induction learning models have received a great deal of attention over recent years in the fields of machine learning and data mining because of their simplicity

and effectiveness. Among them, the Iterative Dichotomiser 3 (ID3)[1] algorithm
for decision trees induction has proved to be an effective and popular algorithm
for building decision trees from discrete valued data sets. The C4.5[2] algorithm
was proposed as a successor to ID3 in which an entropy based approach to crisp
partitioning of continuous universes was adopted.

Decision tree induction is one of the simplest and yet most successful learning
algorithms. A decision tree (*DT*) consists of internal and external nodes and the
interconnections between nodes are called branches of the tree. An internal node
is a decision-making unit to decide which child nodes to visit next depending on
different possible values of associated variables. In contrast, an external node, also
known as leaf node, is the terminated node of a branch. It has no child nodes and is
associated with a class label that describes the given data. A decision tree is a set of
rules in a tree structure. Each branch can be interpreted as a decision rule associated
with nodes visited along this branch. For example, Fig. 4.2 is a decision tree which
is generated from the "play-tennis" problem[3]. The database for this problem is
shown in Fig. 4.1 .

Day	Outlook	Temperature	Humidity	Wind	Play-tennis
D1	Sunny	Hot	High	Weak	No
D2	Sunny	Hot	High	Strong	No
D3	Overcast	Hot	High	Weak	Yes
D4	Rain	Mild	High	Weak	Yes
D5	Rain	Cool	Normal	Weak	Yes
D6	Rain	Cool	Normal	Strong	No
D7	Overcast	Cool	Normal	Strong	Yes
D8	Sunny	Mild	High	Weak	No
D9	Sunny	Cool	Normal	Weak	Yes
D10	Rain	Mild	Normal	Weak	Yes
D11	Sunny	Mild	Normal	Strong	Yes
D12	Overcast	Mild	High	Weak	Yes
D13	Overcast	Hot	Normal	Weak	Yes
D14	Rain	Mild	High	Strong	No

Fig. 4.1 Database for the "play-tennis" problem[3]. Each instance is with 4 attributes and
one class label of either Yes or No, all attributes are with discrete values

Decision trees classify instances by sorting instances down the tree from root to
leaf nodes. This tree-structured classifier partitions the input space of the data set
recursively into mutually exclusive spaces. Following this structure, each training
data is identified as belonging to a certain subspace, which is assigned a label, a
value, or an action to characterize its data points. The decision tree mechanism
has good transparency in that we can follow a tree structure easily in order to
explain how a decision is made. Thus interpretability is enhanced when we clarify
the conditional rules characterizing the tree.

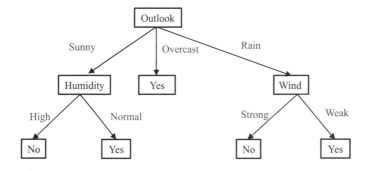

Fig. 4.2 A decision tree built from the play-tennis problem[3]

4.2.1 Entropy

Entropy of a random variable is the average amount of information generated by observing its value. Consider the random experiment of tossing a coin with probability of heads equal to 0.9, i.e., a random variable x with

$$P(x = Head) = 0.9 \quad P(x = Tail) = 0.1$$

The amount of information generated by observing a head is less than the information generated by observing a tail. Intuitively, one can appreciated the observing the outcome "heads" provides little information, since the probability of heads is 0.9, i.e., heads is almost certain to come up. Observing "tails" on the other hand provides much information, since its probability is low[4]. In statistical physics, entropy is used to evaluate the randomness of a state, a large entropy value indicates that there is more randomness involved. If an event x happens with probability $P(x)$, the function for measuring information content $H(x)$ should be inversely proportional to $P(x)$. It should satisfy

$$H(x) = \frac{1}{P(x)} \tag{4.1}$$

If both events x_1 and x_2 happen, where the probability of these two events happen is $P(x_1)P(x_2)$. However, the information content should satisfy

$$H(x_1, x_2) = H(x_1) + H(x_2) \tag{4.2}$$

If we use a logarithm function

$$H(x) = \log \frac{1}{P(x)} \tag{4.3}$$

both the above two conditions can be satisfied. Given a random variable x with probability $P(x)$, the entropy is the expectation of the information content function $H(x)$:

$$E(x) = \sum_x P(x)H(x) = \sum_x P(x) \left(\log \frac{1}{P(x)} \right) = -\sum_x \log P(x)P(x) \qquad (4.4)$$

Because we basically use binary code for computing and communications. For convenience, we choose the base 2. Therefore, the entropy can be formally defined by

$$Entropy(x) = -\sum_i p_i \log_2 p_i \qquad (4.5)$$

We have introduced DT and how DTs make decisions. The hardest problem is how to build a DT based on training data? The most popular decision tree induction algorithm is called ID3 and was introduced by Quinlan in 1986[1]. It has proved to be an effective and popular algorithm for building decision trees from discrete valued data sets. The decision tree is guided heuristically according to the information content of each attribute. In classification problems, we can also say that entropy is a measurement of the impurity in a collection of training examples: the larger the entropy is, the more random is the data. If the entropy equals 1, this means that the data is distributed uniformly across the classes. Fig. 4.3 shows the entropy function when the proportion of positive examples varies from 0 to 1 in a binary classification problem.

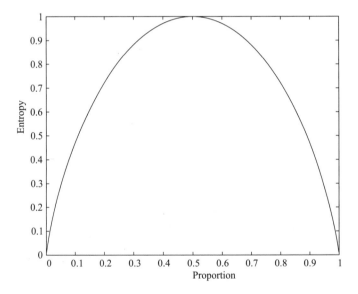

Fig. 4.3 The entropy for binary classification problems

Based on entropy, Information Gain (*IG*) is used to measure the effectiveness of an attribute as a means of discriminating between classes.

$$IG(S,A) = Entropy(S) - \sum_{v \in Values(A)} \frac{|S_v|}{|S|} Entropy(S_v) \qquad (4.6)$$

It is simply the expected reduction of entropy caused by partitioning the examples according to this attribute. More details regarding the ID3 algorithm are given in [3]. The ID3 algorithm is a hill-climbing algorithm, which is guided by information gain in the hypotheses space. This gives us the following approximation of its inductive bias: Shorter trees are preferred over longer trees. Trees that place high information gain attributes close to the root are preferred over those that do not. The pseudo-code is given in Algorithm 2.

Algorithm 2: ID3 algorithm for decision tree learning

ID3 (Examples, Target_Attribute, Attributes)

- Create a root node for the tree.
- If all examples are positive, Return the single-node tree Root, with label $= +$.
- If all examples are negative, Return the single-node tree Root, with label $= -$.
- If number of predicting attributes is empty, then Return the single node tree Root, with label = most common value of the target attribute in the examples.
- Otherwise Begin:
    - A = The Attribute that best classifies examples.
    - Decision Tree attribute for Root = A.
    - For each possible value, v_i, of A:
        · Add a new tree branch below Root, corresponding to the test $A = v_i$.
        · Let Examples(v_i), be the subset of examples that have the value v_i for A
        · If Examples(v_i) is empty:
            · Then below this new branch add a leaf node with label = most common target value in the examples.
        · Else below this new branch add the subtree ID3 (Examples(v_i), Target_Attribute, Attributes $\notin A$).
- End
- Return Root

Also, it is important to realize that the ID3 algorithm is not suitable for all learning and classification problems. Typically, problems that have the following main characteristics can be modeled as a decision tree.

(1) Instances are represented by attribute-value pairs.
(2) The target function has discrete values.

In dealing with the first problem, techniques of "learning from structured data" have been developed as a part of Inductive Logic Programming (ILP). For the second problem, much real-world data, including scientific and engineering data, medical data and financial data, are continuous. In order to learn from continuous data, we need to partition the continuous universe using some type of discretization algorithms, as will be discussed in the following chapters.

4.2.2 Soft Decision Trees

One inherent disadvantage of crisp partitioning is that it tends to make the induced decision trees sensitive to noise. This noise is not only due to the lack of precision or errors in measured features but is often present in the model itself, since the available features may not be sufficient to provide a complete model of the system. For each attribute, disjoint classes are separated with clearly defined boundaries. These boundaries are "critical" since a small change close to these points will probably cause a complete change in classification.

Due to the existence of uncertainty and imprecise information in real-world problems, the class boundaries may not be defined clearly. In this case, decision trees may produce high misclassification rates in testing, even if they perform well in training [3,5].

This fact can be illustrated as follows: Fig. 4.4 shows a decision tree in a two-class problem, in which there are two continuous attributes x and y. Using crisp discretization, the decision space is partitioned into a set of non-overlapping sub-regions A_1, A_2 and A_3, which have clear boundaries with each other. The object for classification will definitely fall into one of these areas. For example, the given object $(x = 13.5, y = 46.0)$ will be classified as A_3, However, if this object is distorted due to noise so that $(x = 12.9, y = 46.2)$, then the object will be misclassified as A_1 (see Fig. 4.4 (a)). In contrast, consider the use of fuzzy discretization (Fig. 4.4 (b)), where the continuous universe is partitioned by overlapped trapezoidal fuzzy sets $\{x_1, x_2\}$ and $\{y_1, y_2\}$. As shown in the right-hand figures of Fig. 4.4 , A_1, A_2 and A_3 generated from fuzzy discretization appear as overlapping subregions with blurred boundaries. The possibility degree of an object belonging to each region will be given by the membership of pre-defined fuzzy sets. The object may fall in the overlapping area. These results can then aid the human users to make their final decisions or suggest further investigation.

Many fuzzy approaches for decision tree learning have been proposed to overcome the weaknesses described above [5–8]. In particular, gives a comprehensive overview of the fuzzy decision tree literature [8]. The algorithm we will present can be also considered as a soft decision. It is based on the label semantics theory (see Chapter 3) and provides a good interpretation of decision rules by using linguistic labels.

4.3 Linguistic Decision for Classification

In order to avoid being confusing about the complicated notations used in label semantics and the LDT model, we highlight a few most important notations and list them in Table 4.1 . Generally, a tree is considered as a set of branches and each branch is a set of non-zero focal elements with a probability distribution on classes.

Consider a database $DB = \{x_1, \ldots, x_{|DB|}\}$ where each instance has n attributes (i.e., $x_i = \langle x_1(i), \ldots, x_n(i) \rangle$) and each instance is categorized as belonging to one of the classes: $\mathbb{C} = \{C_1, \ldots, C_{|\mathbb{C}|}\}$. Unless otherwise stated, we use uniformly

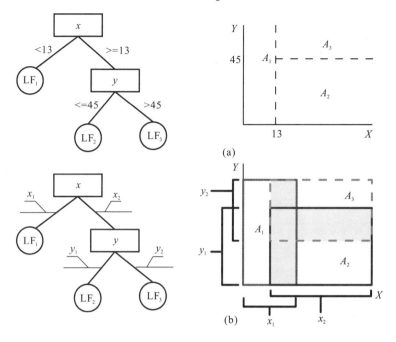

Fig. 4.4 Comparisons of crisp discretization and fuzzy discretization for decision tree models. The decision tree in (a) has crisp boundaries that divide the data into 3 non-overlapping areas A_1, A_2 and A_3. In (b), x_1, x_2, y_1 and y_2 are defined by fuzzy functions that embed more robustness with blurred boundaries

Table 4.1 Important notations for the linguistic decision tree model

DB	a database with the size of $|DB|$: $\{x_1, \ldots, x_{|DB|}\}$
x_i	a n-dimensional instance that: $x_i \in DB$ for $i = 1, \ldots, |DB|$
$\mathbb{L}_j$	a set of linguistic labels defined on the attribute j : $j = 1, \ldots, n$
$\mathbb{F}_j$	the focal set on attribute j given $\mathbb{L}_j$ for $j = 1, \ldots, n$
	$|\mathbb{F}_j| = 2|\mathbb{L}_j| - 1$ if $L_k \in \mathbb{L}_j$ $(k = 1, \ldots, |\mathbb{L}_j|)$ are with 50% overlapping
$\mathbb{C}$	a set of classes with the size of $|\mathbb{C}|$: $\{C_1, \ldots, C_{|\mathbb{C}|}\}$
T	a linguistic decision tree that contains $|T|$ branches: $\{B_1, \ldots, B_{|T|}\}$
$\mathbb{B}$	a set of branches: $\mathbb{B} = \{B_1, \ldots, B_M\}$, $T \equiv \mathbb{B}$ iif: $M = |T|$
B	a branch of LDT, it has $|B|$ focal elements: $B = \{F_1, \ldots, F_{|B|}\}$
	focal elements $F_i, F_j \in B$ are defined on different attributes

distributed fuzzy sets with 50% overlap to discretize each continuous attribute universe and obtain a corresponding linguistic data set by applying linguistic translation (Definition 3.7). A linguistic decision tree is a decision tree where the nodes are the random set label descriptions and the branches correspond to particular focal elements based on *DB*.

Definition 4.1 (*Linguistic decision tree*) *A linguistic decision tree is a set of branches with associated class probabilities in the following form:*

$$T = \{\langle B_1, P(C_1|B_1), \dots, P(C_{|\mathbb{C}|}|B_1)\rangle, \dots, \\ \langle B_{|T|}, P(C_1|B_{|T|}), \dots, P(C_{|\mathbb{C}|}|B_{|T|})\rangle\}$$

where $|T|$ *is the number of branches of the linguistic decision tree* T.

A branch B is defined as a set of focal elements

$$B = \langle F_1, \dots, F_{|B|}\rangle$$

where $F_j \in \mathbb{F}_j$. $\mathbb{F}_j$ is the focal set for attribute j (Definition 3.6). $|B|$ is the length of a branch, corresponding to the number of component nodes (attributes), is less than or equal to n, the number of attributes.

   Within an LDT (see Fig. 4.5) each node is an attributes that can be split into branches according to the focal elements of this node (attribute). One attribute is not allowed to appear more than once in a branch, and an attribute which is not currently part of a branch is referred to as a free attribute.

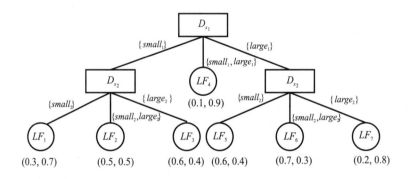

Fig. 4.5 An example of a linguistic decision tree in a binary classification problem, where each attribute is discretized by two fuzzy labels: small and large. The tree has 7 branches and each leaf from LF_1 to LF_7 is labeled with a class distribution

Definition 4.2 (*Free attributes*) *The set of attributes free to use for expanding a given branch B is defined by*

$$ATT_B = \{x_j | \forall F \in \mathbb{F}_j; F \notin B\}$$

In an LDT, the length of the longest branch $Dep(T)$ is called the *depth of the LDT*, which is also less than or equal to n:

$$Dep(T) \leq n \tag{4.7}$$

Each branch has an associated probability distribution on the classes. For example, an LDT shown in Fig. 4.5 might be obtained from training where the branch LF_6:

$$\langle \langle \{large_1\}, \{small_2, large_2\} \rangle, 0.7, 0.3 \rangle$$

means the probability of class C_1 is 0.3 and C_2 is 0.7 given attribute 1 that can be only described as *large* and attribute 2 that can be described as small and large. We need to be aware that the linguistic expressions such as small, medium or large for each attribute are not necessarily the same, since they are defined independently on each attribute. E.g. $large_2$ means the fuzzy label *large* defined on attribute 2.

4.3.1 Branch Probability

According to the definition of LDT (Definition 4.1), given a branch of an LDT in the form of $B = \langle F_1, \ldots, F_{|B|} \rangle$, the probability of class C_t $(t = 1, \ldots, |\mathbb{C}|)$ given B can then be evaluated from a training set DB. First, we consider the probability of a branch B given a particular example $x \in DB$, where $x = \langle x_1, \ldots, x_n \rangle \in \Omega_1 \times, \ldots, \times \Omega_n$. This probability is evaluated by:

$$P(B|x) = \prod_{r=1}^{|B|} m_{x_r}(F_r) \tag{4.8}$$

where $m_{x_r}(F_r)$ are the associated masses of data element x_r for $r = 1, \ldots, |B|$. Basically, the above equation can be justified as follows:

$$P(B|x) = P(D_{x_1} = F_1, \ldots, D_{x_{|B|}} = F_{|B|} | \langle x_1, \ldots, x_n \rangle) \tag{4.9}$$

where $D_{x_1} = F_1, \ldots, D_{x_{|B|}} = F_{|B|}$ are conditionally independent, so that we can obtain

$$P(D_{x_1} = F_1, \ldots, D_{x_{|B|}} = F_{|B|} | \langle x_1, \ldots, x_n \rangle) = \prod_{r=1}^{|B|} P(D_{x_r} = F_r | x_r) \tag{4.10}$$

$$= \prod_{r=1}^{|B|} m_{x_r}(F_r) \tag{4.11}$$

Based on Eq. (4.8), the probability of class C_t given B can then be evaluated by

$$P(C_t|B) = \frac{\sum_{i \in DB_t} P(B|x_i)}{\sum_{i \in DB} P(B|x_i)} \tag{4.12}$$

where DB_t is the subset consisting of instances which belong to class C_t.

$$DB_t = \{x_i | x_i \rightarrow C_t\} : \ i = 1, \ldots, |DB|.$$

In the case where the dominator equals zero (i.e., $\sum_{i \in DB} P(B|x_i) = 0$), which can occur when the training database for the LDT is small so that there is no non-zero linguistic data covered by the branch. In this case, we obtain no information from the database so that equal probabilities are assigned to each class.

$$P(C_t|B) = \frac{1}{|\mathbb{C}|} \qquad \text{for} \quad t = 1, \ldots, |\mathbb{C}| \qquad (4.13)$$

In the process of building a linguistic decision tree, if one of the class probabilities reaches a certain threshold at a particular depth, for example 0.9, then we might take the view that this branch is sufficiently discriminating and that further expansion may lead to overfitting. In this case terminating the tree expansion at the current depth will probably help maintain accuracy on the test set. To this end, we employ a threshold probability to determine whether or not a particular branch should terminate.

Definition 4.3 (*Threshold probability of a LDT*) *In the process of building a linguistic decision tree, if the maximum class probability, given a particular branch, is greater than, or equal to a given threshold probability T, then the branch will be terminated at the current depth.*

Obviously, when using this probability-based thresholding, the branches of a tree may have different lengths. For example, see Fig. 4.5 , where the threshold probability $T = 0.9$, so that the 4th branch $\langle \{small_1, large_1\} \rangle$ is terminated at the depth 1 while the other branches expand to the next depth.

In the above discussions we have been concerned about continuous (or numerical) attributes, but can we learn with discrete (or nominal) attributes? One problem is that the values of discrete attributes may not have a natural ordering like continuous ones. For example, values for a person's age can be sorted in an increasing manner so that the labels young, middle-aged and old can be meaningfully defined by fuzzy sets. However, if we consider the gender of a person, there are only two possible values male or female, which are unordered. Hence, partitioning discrete attribute domains using fuzzy labels is problematic. Instead, we do not attempt to group discrete values but treat discrete values as distinct labels which do not overlap with each other. Hence, the following focal elements for the attribute "gender" are $\{male\}$ and $\{female\}$. In this representation the associated masses for each focal element will be binary, i.e. either zero or one. For instance,

$$m_{\text{gender}}(\{male\}) = \begin{cases} 1 & \text{if gender= male} \\ 0 & \text{otherwise} \end{cases}$$

Missing values can be handled simply by assigning the equal masses of corresponding focal elements. For example, given the database shown in Table 4.2 , the 4th instance has a missing value in Attribute 1. Instead of using some ad-hoc pre-processing[①] techniques, we simply assign equal probabilities to the focal elements of this missing value.

Table 4.2 An example of a small-scale artificial dataset after linguistic translation. Each attribute has 2 independently defined fuzzy labels: *small* (*s*) and *large* (*l*)

# Instance	Attribute 1 (x_1)			Attribute 2 (x_2)			Class
	$\{s_1\}$	$\{s_1, l_1\}$	$\{l_1\}$	$\{s_2\}$	$\{s_2, l_2\}$	$\{l_2\}$	
1	0	0.4	0.6	0	0.7	0.3	+
2	0.2	0.8	0	0.5	0.5	0	−
3	0	0.9	0.1	1	0	0	−
4	0.333	0.333	0.333	0	1	0	+
5	0	1	0	0.3	0.7	0	+

Example 4.1 *Consider a two-class problem with 2 attributes, where* $\mathbb{L}_1 = \{small_1$ *(s_1), $large_1$ (l_1)\} and* $\mathbb{L}_2 = \{small_2 (s_2), large_2 (l_2)\}$. *We assume the focal set* $\mathbb{F}_1 = \{\{s_1\}, \{s_1, l_1\}, \{l_1\}\}$ *and* $\mathbb{F}_2 = \{\{s_2\}, \{s_2, l_2\}, \{l_2\}\}$. *Suppose that the database generated from the linguistic translation from the original training database is given in Table 4.2, and it has two target classes, positive* $(+)$ *and negative* $(-)$ *where*

$$DB_+ = \{x_1, x_4, x_5\}, \ DB_- = \{x_2, x_3\}$$

Now suppose we are given two branches of the form:

$$B_1 = \langle\langle\{small_1\}, \{small_2\}\rangle, P(+|B_1), P(-|B_1)\rangle$$
$$B_2 = \langle\langle\{small_1, large_1\}, \{small_2, large_2\}\rangle, P(+|B_2), P(-|B_2)\rangle$$

These two branches are evaluated according to Eqs. (4.8) and (4.12) (or Eq. (4.13)):

$$P(+, B_1) = \frac{\sum_{i=1,4,5} P(B_1|x_i)}{\sum_{i=1}^{5} P(B_1|x_i)} = \frac{\sum_{i=1,4,5} m_{x_1(i)}(\{s_1\}) \times m_{x_2(i)}(\{s_2\})}{\sum_{i=1}^{5} m_{x_1(i)}(\{s_1\}) \times m_{x_2(i)}(\{s_2\})}$$

$$= \frac{0 \times 0 + 0.333 \times 0 + 0 \times 0.3}{0 \times 0 + 0.2 \times 0.5 + 0 \times 1 + 0.333 \times 0 + 0 \times 0.3} = 0$$

---

① Some pre-processing techniques treat the missing values as a new value of "missing" for nominal attributes[13].

$$P(-,B_1) = \frac{\sum_{i=2,3} P(B_1|x_i)}{\sum_{i=1}^5 P(B_1|x_i)} = \frac{\sum_{i=2,3} m_{x_1(i)}(\{s_1\}) \times m_{x_2(i)}(\{s_2\})}{\sum_{i=1}^5 m_{x_1(i)}(\{s_1\}) \times m_{x_2(i)}(\{s_2\})}$$

$$= \frac{0.2 \times 0.5 + 0 \times 1}{0 \times 0 + 0.2 \times 0.5 + 0 \times 1 + 0.333 \times 0 + 0 \times 0.3} = \frac{0.1}{0.1} = 1$$

$$P(+,B_2) = \frac{\sum_{i=1,4,5} P(B_2|x_i)}{\sum_{i=1}^5 P(B_2|x_i)} = \frac{\sum_{i=1,4,5} m_{x_1(i)}(\{s_1,l_1\}) \times m_{x_2(i)}(\{s_2,l_2\})}{\sum_{i=1}^5 m_{x_1(i)}(\{s_1,l_1\}) \times m_{x_2(i)}(\{s_2,l_2\})}$$

$$= \frac{0.4 \times 0.7 + 0.333 \times 1 + 1 \times 0.7}{0.4 \times 0.7 + 0.8 \times 0.5 + 0.9 \times 0 + 0.333 \times 1 + 1 \times 0.7} = 0.767$$

$$P(-,B_2) = \frac{\sum_{i=2,3} P(B_2|x_i)}{\sum_{i=1}^5 P(B_2|x_i)} = \frac{\sum_{i=2,3} m_{x_1(i)}(\{s_1,l_1\}) \times m_{x_2(i)}(\{s_2,l_2\})}{\sum_{i=1}^5 m_{x_1(i)}(\{s_1,l_1\}) \times m_{x_2(i)}(\{s_2,l_2\})}$$

$$= \frac{0.8 \times 0.5 + 0.9 \times 0}{0.4 \times 0.7 + 0.8 \times 0.5 + 0.9 \times 0 + 0.333 \times 1 + 1 \times 0.7} = 0.233$$

4.3.2 Classification by LDT

Now consider classifying an unlabeled instance in the form of $x = \langle x_1, \ldots, x_n \rangle$ which may not be contained in the training data set DB. We apply a linguistic translation to x based on the fuzzy covering of the training data DB. In the case that a data element appears beyond the range of the training data set $[R_{min}, R_{max}]$ for a particular attribute, we assign the appropriateness degrees of R_{min} or R_{max} to the element depending on which side of the range it appears.

$$\mu_{F_i}(x) = \mu_{F_i}(R_{min}) \quad \text{if} \quad x < R_{min}$$
$$\mu_{F_i}(x) = \mu_{F_i}(R_{max}) \quad \text{if} \quad x > R_{max}$$

where $i = 1, \ldots, |\mathbb{F}|$. Jeffrey's rule:

$$P(a) = P(a|b)P(b) + P(a|\neg b)P(\neg b) \tag{4.14}$$

is used for classifying a new data element, where $P(b)$ and $P(\neg b)$ are considered as the beliefs in b and not b, respectively[11]. This can be generalized when given a new condition c②:

$$P(a|c) = P(a|b)P(b|c) + r(a|\neg b)P(\neg b|c) \tag{4.15}$$

Hence, we can evaluate the probabilities of class C_t based on a given LDT, T, by using Jeffrey's rule as follows:

$$P(C_t|x) = \sum_{v=1}^{|T|} P(C_t|B_v)P(B_v|x) \tag{4.16}$$

---

② There is an implicit assumption that a is conditionally independent of c given b.

where $P(B_v|x)$ and $P(C_t|B_v)$ are evaluated according to Eqs. (4.8) and (4.12) (or Eq. (4.13)), respectively. In classical decision trees, classification is made according to the class label of the branch in which the data falls. In our approach, the data for classification partially satisfies the constraints represented by a number of branches and the probability estimates across the whole decision tree are then used to obtain an overall classification.

Example 4.2 *Suppose we are given the linguistic decision tree shown in Fig. 4.5 for a two-class problem with* $\mathbb{F}_1 = \{\{small_1\},\{small_1,large_1\},\{large_1\}\}$, $\mathbb{F}_2 = \{\{small_2\},\{small_2,large_2\},\{large_2\}\}$. *A data element* $\mathbf{y} = \langle y_1, y_2 \rangle$ *for classification is given such that* $\mu_{small_1}(y_1) = 1$, $\mu_{large_1}(y_1) = 0.4$ *and* $\mu_{small_2}(y_2) = 0.2$, $\mu_{large_2}(y_2) = 1$.

The LDT given in Fig. 4.5 can be written as

$LDT = \{B_1, B_2, B_3, B_4, B_5, B_6, B_7\} = \{$
$\langle\langle\{small_1\},\{small_2\}\rangle, 0.3, 0.7\rangle,$
$\langle\langle\{small_1\},\{small_2,large_2\}\rangle, 0.5, 0.5\rangle,$
$\langle\langle\{small_1\},\{large_2\}\rangle, 0.6, 0.4\rangle,$
$\langle\langle\{small_1,large_1\}\rangle, 0.1, 0.9\rangle,$
$\langle\langle\{large_1\},\{small_2\}\rangle, 0.6, 0.4\rangle$
$\langle\langle\{large_1\},\{small_2,large_2\}\rangle, 0.7, 0.3\rangle$
$\langle\langle\{large_1\},\{large_2\}\rangle, 0.2, 0.8\rangle \}$

The mass assignments on $\mathbf{y}$ *are*

$$m_{y_1} = \{small_1, large_1\} : 0.4, \{small_1\} : 0.6$$

$$m_{y_2} = \{small_2, large_2\} : 0.2, \{large_2\} : 0.8$$

According to Eq. (4.8), we obtain

$$P(B_1|\mathbf{y}) = P(B_5|\mathbf{y}) = P(B_6|\mathbf{y}) = P(B_7|\mathbf{y}) = 0$$

$$P(B_2|\mathbf{y}) = m_{y_1}(\{small_1\}) \times m_{y_2}(\{small_2, large_2\}) = 0.6 \times 0.2 = 0.12$$

$$P(B_3|\mathbf{y}) = m_{y_1}(\{small_1\}) \times m_{y_2}(\{large_2\}) = 0.6 \times 0.8 = 0.48$$

$$P(B_4|\mathbf{y}) = m_{y_1}(\{small_1, large_1\}) = 0.4$$

Hence, based on Jeffrey's rule (Eq.(4.16)), we can obtain

$$P(C_1|\mathbf{y}) = \sum_{v=1}^{7} P(C_1|B_v)P(B_v|\mathbf{y}) = \sum_{v=2,3,4} P(C_1|B_v)P(B_v|\mathbf{y})$$
$$= 0.12 \times 0.5 + 0.48 \times 0.6 + 0.4 \times 0.1 = 0.388$$

$$P(C_2|\mathbf{y}) = \sum_{v=1}^{7} P(C_2|B_v)P(B_v|\mathbf{y}) = \sum_{v=2,3,4} P(C_2|B_v)P(B_v|\mathbf{y})$$
$$= 0.12 \times 0.5 + 0.48 \times 0.4 + 0.4 \times 0.9 = 0.612$$

Usually, the decision threshold for a probabilistic classifier is 0.5 without assuming any other prior information. Therefore, in this example, $\mathbf{y}$ is classified as C_2 because $P(C_2|\mathbf{y}) > 0.5$. However, in cost-sensitive learning, the decision threshold is not necessarily 0.5 when considering the misclassification cost and prior class distribution.

From the above examples we have known how to calculate the class probabilities and how to use them in classification. In the next section, we will introduce the algorithm for building a linguistic decision tree.

4.3.3 Linguistic ID3 Algorithm

Linguistic ID3 (LID3) is the learning algorithm we propose for building the linguistic decision tree based on a given linguistic database. Similar to the ID3 algorithm[1], search is guided by an information based heuristic, but the information measurements of an LDT are modified in accordance with label semantics. The measure of information defined for a branch B can be viewed as an extension of the entropy measure used in ID3.

Definition 4.4 (*Branch entropy*) *The entropy of branch B given a set of classes $\mathbb{C} = \{C_1, \ldots, C_{|\mathbb{C}|}\}$ is*

$$E(B) = -\sum_{t=1}^{|\mathbb{C}|} P(C_t|B) \log_2 P(C_t|B) \tag{4.17}$$

Now, given a particular branch B, suppose we want to expand it with the attribute x_j. The evaluation of this attribute will be given based on the expected entropy defined as follows:

Definition 4.5 (*Expected entropy*)

$$EE(B, x_j) = \sum_{F_j \in \mathbb{F}_j} E(B \cup F_j) \cdot P(F_j|B) \tag{4.18}$$

where $B \cup F_j$ represents the new branch obtained by appending the focal element F_j to the end of branch B. The probability of F_j given B can be calculated as follows:

$$P(F_j|B) = \frac{\sum_{i \in DB} P(B \cup F_j|x_i)}{\sum_{i \in DB} P(B|x_i)} \tag{4.19}$$

We can now define the Information Gain (IG) obtained by expanding branch B with attribute x_j as:

$$IG(B, x_j) = E(B) - EE(B, x_j) \tag{4.20}$$

The goal of tree-structured learning models is to make subregions partitioned by branches be less "impure" in terms of the mixture of class labels than the unpartitioned dataset. For a particular branch, the most suitable free attribute for further expanding (or partitioning), is the one by which the "pureness" is maximally increased with expandsion. That corresponds to selecting the attribute with maximum information gain. As with ID3 learning, the most informative attribute will form the root of a linguistic decision tree, and the tree will expand into branches associated with all possible focal elements of this attribute. For each branch, the free attribute with maximum information gain will be the next node, from level to level, until the tree reaches the maximum specified depth or the maximum class probability reaches the given threshold probability.

Algorithm 3: Linguistic decision tree learning

---

   input : LD: Linguistic dataset obtained from Algorithm 1.
   output: T: Linguistic Decision Tree

Set a maximum depth M_{dep} and a threshold probability T.;
for $l \leftarrow 0$ **to** M_{dep} **do**
    $\mathbb{B} \leftarrow \emptyset$ when $l = 0$;
    The set of branches of LDT at depth l is $\mathbb{B}_l = \{B_1, \ldots, B_{|\mathbb{B}_l|}\}$;
    for $v \leftarrow 1$ **to** $|\mathbb{B}|$ **do**
        foreach B_v **do** : ;
        for $t \leftarrow 1$ **to** $|\mathbb{C}|$ **do**
            foreach t **do** Calculating conditional probabilities:
            $P(C_t|B_v) = \sum_{i \in DB_t} P(B_v|x_i) / \sum_{i \in DB} P(B_v|x_i)$;
            if $P(C_t|B_v) \geq T$ **then**
                break (step out the loop)

        if $\exists x_j$: x_j is free attribute **then**
            foreach x_j **do** : Calculate: $IG(B_v, x_j) = E(B_v) - EE(B_v, x_j)$;
            $IG_{\max}(B_v) = \max_{x_j}[IG(B_v, x_j)]$;
            Expanding B_v with $x_{\max}$ where $x_{\max}$ is the free attribute we can obtain
            the maximum IG value $IG_{\max}$. ;
            $\mathbb{B}'_v \leftarrow \bigcup_{F_j \in \mathbb{F}_j} \{B_v \cup F_j\}$.
        else
            exit;
    $\mathbb{B}_{l+1} \leftarrow \bigcup_{r=1}^{s} \mathbb{B}'_r$.
$T \leftarrow \mathbb{B}$

---

(1) Linguistic Translation: to translate real valued data into linguistic form data (see Definition 3.7). We first discretize the continuous universe of each attribute with fuzzy sets uniformly or non-uniformly (see Section 3.3). For each data element, find appropriateness degrees which will be used in subsequent calculations of mass assignments. This is because a new database is saved for use in the second step.

(2) Decision Tree Learning: A linguistic decision tree will be developed level by level according to the information heuristics. At each level, we will examine each branch for calculating class probabilities and compare it with the given threshold probability to determine if it should be terminated or not, until the maximum depth has been reached or all branches are terminated. The pseudo-code of the tree learning process is shown in Algorithm 3.

(3) Classification: Given an LDT, we classify a data element according to class probabilities, given branches of the tree according to Eq. (4.16).

4.4 Experimental Studies

We evaluated the LID3 algorithm by using 14 datasets taken from the UCI Machine Learning repository[9]. These datasets have representative properties of real-world data, such as missing values, multi-classes, mixed-type data (numerical, nominal) and unbalanced class distributions, etc. Table 4.3 shows the dataset, the number of classes, the number of instances, the number of numerical (Num.) and nominal (Nom.) attributes and whether or not the database contains missing values.

Table 4.3 Descriptions of datasets from UCI machine learning repository. Other details about these data sets are available in Reference [9]

#	Dataset	Number of Classes	Data Size	Missing Values	Attributes Number Num.	Nom.
1	Balance	3	625	no	4	0
2	Breast-Cancer*	2	286	yes	3	6
3	Breast-w	2	699	no	9	0
4	Ecoli	8	336	no	7	1
5	Glass	6	214	no	9	0
6	Heart-c	2	303	yes	6	7
7	Heart-Statlog	2	270	no	7	6
8	Heptitis	2	155	yes	6	13
9	Ionosphere	2	351	no	34	0
10	Iris	3	150	no	4	0
11	Liver	2	345	no	6	0
12	Pima	2	768	no	8	0
13	Sonar	2	208	no	60	0
14	Wine	3	178	no	14	0

In the following experiments, unless otherwise stated, attributes are discretized by 2 trapezoidal fuzzy sets with 50% overlap, and classes are evenly split into two sub-datasets, one half for training and the other half for testing. This is referred to as a 50-50 split experiment. The maximal depth is set manually and the results show the best performance of LID3 across a range of depth settings. We also test the LID3 algorithm with different threshold probabilities T ranging from 0.6 to 1.0 in steps of 0.1 and for the different fuzzy discretization methods: uniform, entropy-based and percentile-based (see Section 3.3). For each dataset, we ran 50-50 random split experiment 10 times. The average test accuracy with standard deviation is shown on the right-hand side of Table 4.5 and the probability and the depth at which we obtain this accuracy are listed in Table 4.4 .

Table 4.4 Summary of the threshold probabilities and depths for obtaining the best accuracy with different discretization methods in the given datasets

#	LID3-Uniform		LID3-Entropy		LID3-Percentile	
	Threshold	Best Depth	Threshold	Best Depth	Threshold	Best Depth
1	1.0	4	1.0	4	1.0	4
2	0.7	2	0.7	2	0.7	2
3	1.0	4	1.0	3	1.0	3
4	1.0	7	1.0	7	1.0	7
5	0.9	9	0.8	9	0.8	8
6	0.9	3	0.9	4	0.9	3
7	0.9	3	0.9	3	0.9	4
8	0.9	4	0.9	4	0.9	3
9	0.9	6	0.9	6	0.9	6
10	1.0	3	1.0	3	1.0	3
11	0.9	5	1.0	5	1.0	5
12	0.9	5	0.9	4	0.9	3
13	1.0	8	1.0	8	1.0	8
14	1.0	4	1.0	5	1.0	5

4.4.1 Influence of the Threshold

As can be seen from the results, the best accuracy is usually obtained with high threshold probabilities $T = 0.9$ or $T = 1.0$, especially for datasets with only numerical attributes (such as breast-w, iris, balance, wine) or where numerical attributes play important roles in learning (ecoli, heptitis). Recent work on PETs

Table 4.5 Accuracy (with standard deviation) of LID3 based on different discretization methods and three other well-known machine learning algorithms

#	C4.5	Naive Bayes	Neural Network	LID3-Uniform	LID3-Entropy	LID3-Percentile
1	79.20±1.53	89.46±2.09	90.38±1.18	83.80±1.19	83.07±3.22	86.23±0.97
2	69.16±4.14	71.26±2.96	66.50±3.48	73.06±3.05	73.47±2.66	73.06±3.05
3	94.38±1.42	96.28±0.73	94.96±0.80	96.43±0.70	96.11±0.78	96.11±0.89
4	78.99±2.23	85.36±2.42	82.62±3.18	85.41±1.94	86.53±1.28	85.59±2.19
5	64.77±5.10	45.99±7.00	64.30±3.38	65.96±2.31	65.60±2.57	65.87±2.32
6	75.50±3.79	84.24±2.09	79.93±3.99	76.71±3.81	78.09±3.58	77.96±2.88
7	75.78±3.16	84.00±1.68	78.89±3.05	76.52±3.63	78.07±3.63	79.04±2.94
8	76.75±4.68	83.25±3.99	81.69±2.48	82.95±2.42	83.08±2.82	83.08±1.32
9	89.60±2.13	82.97±2.51	87.77±2.88	88.98±2.23	89.11±2.30	88.01±1.83
10	93.47±3.23	94.53±2.63	95.87±2.70	96.00±1.26	96.13±1.60	96.40±1.89
11	65.23±3.86	55.41±5.39	66.74±4.89	58.73±1.99	64.62±2.80	69.25±2.84
12	72.16±2.80	75.05±2.37	74.64±1.41	76.22±1.81	76.22±1.85	76.54±1.34
13	70.48±0.00	70.19±0.00	81.05±0.00	86.54±0.00	87.50±0.00	89.42±0.00
14	88.09±4.14	96.29±2.12	96.85±1.57	95.33±1.80	95.78±1.80	95.89±1.96

(Probability Estimation Trees)[12] also suggests that the full expanded estimation trees give better performance than pruned trees[3].

The reason for this is that the heuristics used to generate small and compact trees by pruning tend to reduce the quality of the probability estimates[12]. In this context linguistic decision trees can be thought of as a type of probability estimation tree but where the branches correspond to linguistic descriptions of objects. Strictly speaking, our linguistic decision tree model is a probability estimation tree though we employ the name of "linguistic decision tree". The key difference between these two types of trees is that PETs give probability estimation according to which we can rank the examples given a target class[12]. We may have different classification results based on a different given threshold which are related to class distribution or cost matrix in cost-sensitive problems, while the decision trees only give the crisp classification of examples. The difference in accuracy resulting from varying the threshold probability T is quite data dependent. Figs. 4.6 to 4.8 show the results of the datasets given in Table 4.3 . We will consider the results for 4 typical datasets: *Breast-w*, *Heart-statlog*, *Glass* and *Breast-Cancer*. In *Breast-w*, the accuracy curves are nested relative to increasing values of T. The models with high T values outperform those with lower T values at all depths. Dataset *Iris*, *Balance*, *Sonar*,

---

[3] In classical decision tree learning such as ID3 and C4.5, pruning can reduce overfitting so that the pruned trees have better generalization and perform better then unpruned trees. However, this is not the case for probability estimation trees[12].

Vine, *Ecoli* also behave in this way. On the other hand, for datasets *Heart-Statlog*, *Pima*, *Liver*, *Heart-C* and *Heptitis*, the accuracy curve of $T = 0.9$ is better than all other T values at certain depths. In addition, datasets *Glass* and *Ecoli* have accuracy curves which are very close to each other and are even identical on some trials. For the *Breast-Cancer* dataset the accuracy actually decreases with increasing T. All of the datasets we tested have almost the same trends.

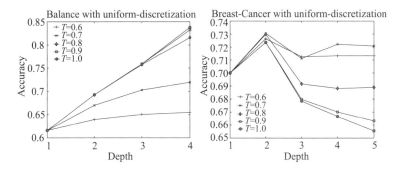

Fig. 4.6 Comparisons of accuracy at different depths with threshold probability ranges from 0.6 to 1.0 on data set # 1 and # 2 in Table 4.3

4.4.2 Overlapping Between Fuzzy Labels

As we can see from Chapter 3, we usually use the trapezoidal fuzzy sets with 50% overlapping in linguistic translation. In this section, we will investigate the influences of overlapping degrees on the accuracy by some empirical studies.

First, we introduce a new parameter PT by which to measure the degree of overlapping of fuzzy labels. $PT = 0.5$ represents 50% of overlapping between each two neighboring fuzzy labels (e.g., see Fig. 4.9 (a)). $PT = 0$ represents no overlapping at all (see Fig. 4.9 (c)). The relation between different overlapping and PT values is schematically shown in Fig. 4.9 . Given fuzzy labels F and G, m is the distance between the center of a fuzzy label to the meeting point of these two fuzzy labels. a is actually the length of the overlapping area. PT is then defined as follows:

$$PT = a/2m \tag{4.21}$$

Suppose there is a 50% overlapping between two neighboring fuzzy labels, a equals m so that $PT = 0.5$. If there is no overlapping at all, $a = 0$ so that $PT = 0$. Fig. 4.10 shows an example of fuzzy discretiztion with different PT values on a continuous universe.

We tested 10 datasets taken from UCI[9] repository and the average results with standard deviation based on 10 runs of 50-50 split experiments are shown in Fig. 4.11 and 4.12 . As we can see from these figures, accuracy generally increase with

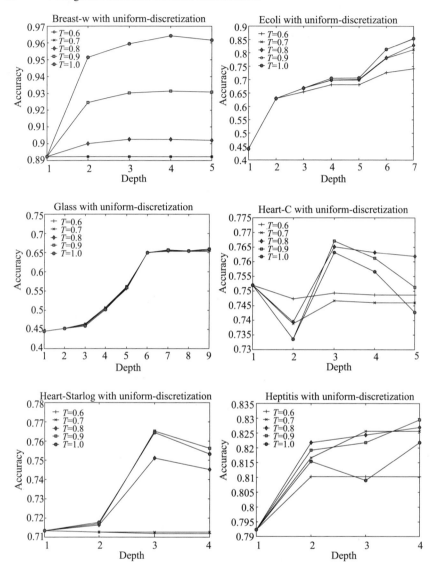

Fig. 4.7 Comparisons of accuracy at different depths with threshold probability ranges from 0.6 to 1.0 on data set #3 to #8 in Table 4.3

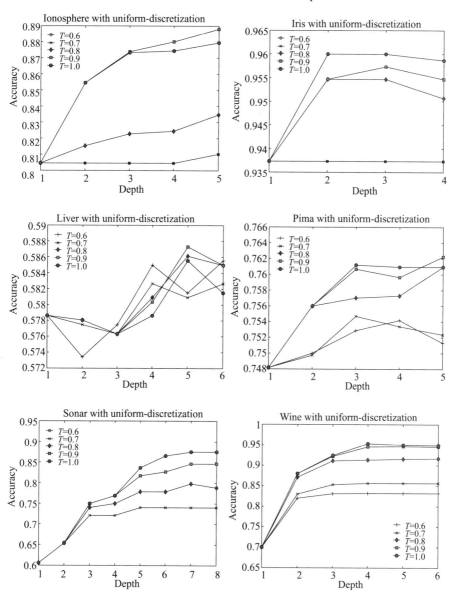

Fig. 4.8 Comparisons of accuracy at different depths with threshold probability ranges from 0.6 to 1.0 on data set from #9 to #14 in Table 4.3

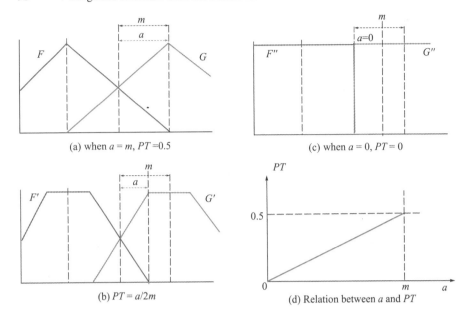

(a) when $a = m$, $PT = 0.5$

(b) $PT = a/2m$

(c) when $a = 0$, $PT = 0$

(d) Relation between a and PT

Fig. 4.9 A schematic illustration of calculating the overlap parameter PT given different degrees of overlaps

the increases in the PT values. Only the data *Ionosphere* is an exception. In order to simplifying the label semantics, it is not necessary to use fuzzy labels with more than 50% overlapping. Hence, we will use the fuzzy labels with 50% overlapping for discretization in the following experiments.

4.5 Comparison Studies

From the Table 4.4 , we also see that the optimal values of T and depth are relatively invariant across the discretization techniques. Overall the entropy-based and percentile-based discretization methods performed better than the uniform discretization although no statistically significant difference was found between the three methods. In order to conduct the comparison studies, we first start by introducing the neural networks.

We now compare LID3 with different discretization with C4.5, Naive Bayes Learning and Neural Networks [④] using 10 50-50 splits on each dataset and the average accuracy and standard deviation for each test are shown in Table 4.5 . The reason for choosing these three particular learning algorithms is as follows: C4.5 is the most well-known tree induction algorithm, Naive Bayes is a simple

④ WEKA is used to generate the results of J48 (C4.5 in WEKA) unpruned tree, Naive Bayes and Neural Networks with default parameter settings. [13]

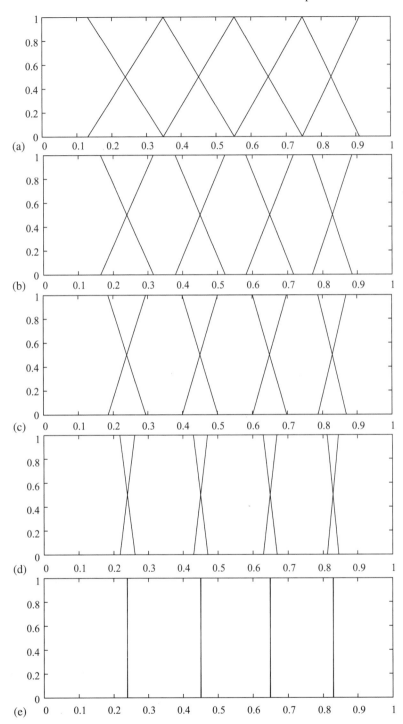

Fig. 4.10 Fuzzy discretization with focal elements with different overlapping degrees. The degrees of overlapping are $PT = 0.0, 0.3, 0.5, 0.8, 1.0$ from subfigure (a) to (e)

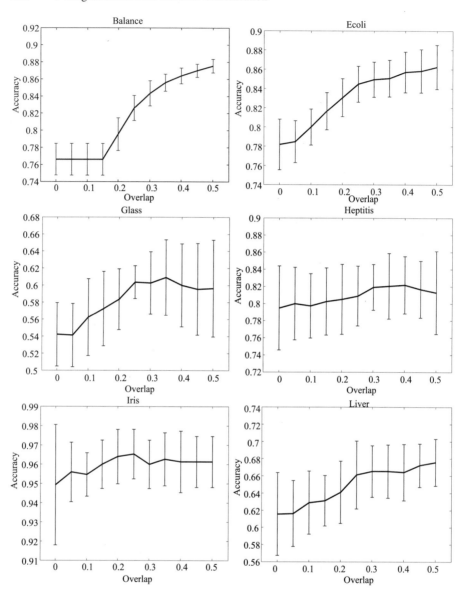

Fig. 4.11 Average accuracy with standard deviation with different *PT* values

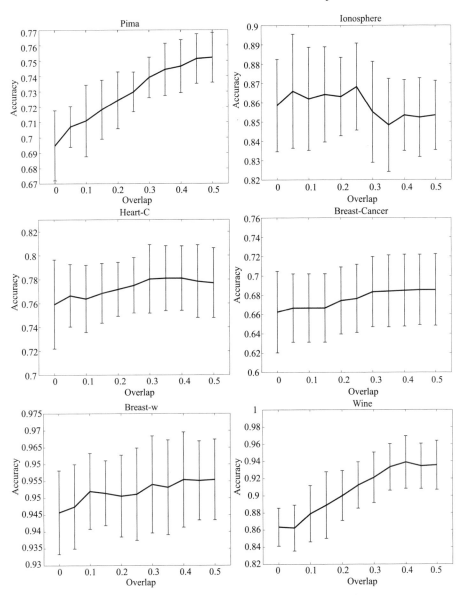

Fig. 4.12 Average accuracy with standard deviation with different *PT* values

but effective probability estimation method and neural networks are a black-box model well known for its high predictive accuracy. We then carried out paired t-tests with confidence level of 90% to compare LID3-Uniform, LID3-Entropy and LID3-Percentile with each of the three algorithms[3]. A summary of the results is shown in Table 4.6 .

Table 4.6 Summary of comparisons of LID3 based on different discretization methods with three other well-known machine learning algorithms

	LID3-Uniform	LID3-Entropy	LID3-Percentile
Decision Tree (C4.5) vs.	9 wins-4 ties-1 losses	9 wins-5 ties-0 losses	10 wins-4 ties-0 losses
Naive Bayes vs.	3 wins-8 ties-3 losses	7 wins-4 ties-3 losses	7 wins-4 ties-3 losses
Neural Network vs.	5 wins-6 ties-3 losses	5 wins-8 ties-1 losses	5 wins-8 ties-1 losses

Across the data sets, all LID3 algorithms (with different discretization techniques) outperform C4.5, with LID3-Percentile achieving the best results with 10 wins, 4 ties and no losses. The performance of the Naive Bayes algorithm and LID3-Uniform is roughly equivalent although LID3-Entropy and LID3-Percentile outperform Naive Bayes. From Table 4.5 , we can see that the datasets on which Naive Bayes outperforms LID3 are those with a mixture of continuous and discrete attributes, namely *Heart-C*, *Heart-Statlog* and *Heptitis*. Most of the comparisons with the Neural Network result in ties rather than wins or losses, especially for LID3-Entropy and LID3-Percentile. Due to the limited number and type of datasets we used for evaluation, we may not draw the strong conclusion that LID3 outperforms all the other 3 algorithms. However we can at least conclude that based on our experiments, the LID3 outperforms C4.5 and has equivalent performance to Naive Bayes and the Neural Networks. For the datasets with only numerical values, LID3 outperforms both C4.5 and Naive Bayes. Between different discretization methods, percentile-based and entropy-based approaches achieve better results than uniform discretization.

4.6 Merging of Branches

In the previous section, we showed that LID3 performs at least as well as and often better than, three well-known classification algorithms across a range of datasets. However, even with only 2 fuzzy sets for discretization, the number of branches increases exponentially with the depth of the tree. Unfortunately, the transparency of the LDT decreases with the increasing number of branches. To help to maintain transparency by generating more compact trees, a forward merging algorithm based on the LDT model is introduced in this section and experimental results are given to support the validity of our approach.

4.6.1 Forward Merging Algorithm

See Fig. 4.13 for instance, with the first round of merging, the adjacent branches L_2 and L_3, L_5 and L_6 are merged into two new branches. If any of two adjacent branches have sufficiently similar class probabilities according to some criteria, these two branches give similar classification results and therefore can then be merged into one branch in order to obtain a more compact tree. We employ a *merging threshold* to determine whether or not two adjacent branches can be merged.

Definition 4.6 (*Merging threshold*) *In a linguistic decision tree, if the maximum difference between class probabilities of two adjacent branches B_1 and B_2 is less than or equal to a given merging threshold T_m, then the two branches can be merged into one branch. Formally, if*

$$T_m \geq \max_{c \in \mathbb{C}} |P(c|B_1) - P(c|B_2)| \tag{4.22}$$

where $\mathbb{C} = \{C_1, \ldots, C_{|\mathbb{C}|}\}$ is the set of classes, then B_1 and B_2 can be merged into one branch MB. A merged linguistic decision tree MT can be represented by a set of merged branches MB, or formally

$$MT = \{MB_1, \ldots, MB_{|MT|}\}$$

where each merged MB_j has a class distribution

$$P(C_1|MB_j), \ldots, P(C_{|\mathbb{C}|}|MB_j)$$

Definition 4.7 (*Merged branch*) *A merged branch MB nodes is defined as*

$$MB = \langle \mathbf{M}_{j_1}, \ldots, \mathbf{M}_{j_{|MB|}} \rangle$$

$|MB|$ are the number of nodes for the branch MB where the node is defined as:

$$\mathbf{M}_j = \{F_j^1, \ldots, F_j^{|\mathbf{M}_j|}\}$$

Each node is a set of focal elements such that F_j^i is adjacent to F_j^{i+1} for $i = 1, \ldots, |\mathbf{M}_j| - 1$. If $|\mathbf{M}| > 1$, it is called compound node, which means it is a compound of more than one focal elements because of merging (e.g., see Fig. 4.13). The associate mass for $\mathbf{M}_j$ is given by

$$m_x(\mathbf{M}_j) = \sum_{i=1}^{|\mathbf{M}_j|} m_x(F_j^i) \tag{4.23}$$

where w is the number of merged adjacent focal elements for attribute j.

Based on Eq. (4.8), we can obtain

$$P(C_t|x) = \prod_{r=1}^{|MB|} m_{x_r}(\mathbf{M}_r) \tag{4.24}$$

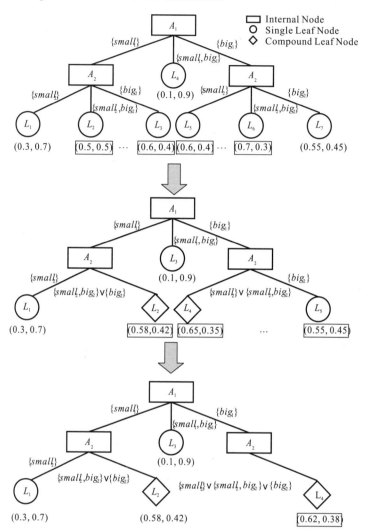

Fig. 4.13 An illustration of forward branch merging process. Given the merging threshold 0.1, branches L_2 and L_3 are firstly merged into new merged branch L_2 and branches L_5 and L_6 are merged into a new branch L_4. There is one more step merging of the new L_4 and L_5 because these branches have close probabilities less than or equal to the threshold probability 1. Finally, the original LDT with 7 branches is merged into a new LDT with 4 branches only

Therefore, based on Eqs. (4.12), (4.13) and (4.23) we use the following formula to calculate the class probabilities given a merged branch.

$$P(C_t|MB) = \frac{\sum_{i \in DB_t} P(C_t|x_i)}{\sum_{i \in DB} P(C_t|x_i)} \tag{4.25}$$

When the merging algorithm is applied in learning a linguistic decision tree, the adjacent branches meeting the merging criteria will be merged and re-evaluated according to Eq. (4.25). Then the adjacent branches after the first round of merging will be examined in a further round of merging, until all adjacent branches cannot be merged further. We then proceed to the next depth. In Fig. 4.13 , leaves L_2 and L_3, L_5 and L_6 are merged in the first round of merging, and the new leaves L_4 and L_5 are then merged further because they still meet the merging criteria in the second round of merging. The merged branches can be represented by compound expressions that will be described in the subsequent sections. The merging is applied as the tree develops from the root to the maximum depth and hence is referred to as forward merging.

4.6.2 Dual-Branch LDTs

Dual-Branch LDTs are a special LDT where each branch grain is two neighboring focal elements. It is a special case of the merged tree introduced in the previous section. Give a focal set with size l, from each node there are $l - 1$ branches. For example, the focal set for a particular attribute x is $\mathbb{F} = \{F_1, \ldots, F_7\}$ $\{\{tiny\}, \{tiny, small\}, \{small\}, \{small, normal\}, \{normal\}, \{normal, large\}, \{large\}\}$. Then we have the branches from the node x: $\mathbb{B}_x = \{B_1, \ldots, B_6\} = \{\{F_1, F_2\}, \{F_2, F_3\}, \{F_3, F_4\}, \{F_4, F_5\}, \{F_5, F_6\}, \{F_6, F_7\}\}$. The LDT with such nodes are referred to as a *dual-branch LDT*. The revised condition of probability of a focal element $F_y \in \mathbb{F}_y$ that is appropriate to describe a goal given the branch B, can be evaluated from a training set DB according to

$$P(F_y|B) = \frac{\sum_{i \in DB_y} \prod_{r=1}^{N} \left(m_{x_{i_r}}(F_j) + m_{x_{i_r}}(F_{j+1})\right)}{\sum_{i \in DB} \prod_{r=1}^{N} \left(m_{x_{i_r}}(F_j) + m_{x_{i_r}}(F_{j+1})\right)} \tag{4.26}$$

Different from the normal LDTs, each branch of the dual-branch LDT has the summed masses of the neighboring focal elements.

4.6.3 Experimental Studies for Forward Merging

We tested the forward merging algorithm on the UCI datasets listed in Table 4.3 with 10 50-50 split experiments and the results are shown in Table 4.7 . Obviously, there is a tradeoff between the algorithm accuracy and the algorithm transparency in terms of the number of leaves. The merging threshold T_m plays an important role in the accuracy-transparency tradeoff problem. Algorithm accuracy tends to increase while algorithm transparency decreases with decreasing T_m and vice versa.

Table 4.7 Comparisons of accuracy and the number of leaves (rules) $|T|$ with different merging thresholds T_m across a set of UCI datasets[9]. The results for $T_m = 0$ are obtained with $N_F = 2$ and results for other T_m values are obtained with N_F values listed in the second column of the table

#	N_F	$T_m = 0$		$T_m = 0.1$		$T_m = 0.2$		$T_m = 0.3$		$T_m = 0.4$	
		Acc.	$|T|$	Acc.	$|T|$	Acc.	$|T|$	Acc.	$|T|$	Acc.	$|T|$
1	2	83.80	77	84.19	51	81.09	25	75.08	10	47.03	1
2	2	73.06	17	71.67	12	71.11	9	59.65	4	61.25	2
3	2	96.43	57	95.80	29	95.74	16	95.63	9	95.49	4
4	3	85.41	345	85.29	445	84.24	203	83.88	104	82.65	57
5	3	65.69	329	62.84	322	64.04	190	44.31	86	35.41	49
6	2	76.71	37	78.68	31	78.55	22	78.42	18	68.49	11
7	3	76.52	31	78.37	35	78.44	23	77.85	12	72.22	7
8	3	82.95	11	81.28	24	80.77	18	80.64	15	80.77	13
9	3	88.98	45	87.90	78	88.47	41	89.20	30	89.20	26
10	3	96.00	21	95.47	23	95.20	18	95.20	14	94.27	10
11	2	58.73	83	56.30	43	55.90	11	57.34	4	57.92	3
12	2	76.12	27	75.31	20	74.45	5	73.85	3	65.10	1
13	2	86.54	615	88.46	516	85.58	337	81.73	93	49.04	6
14	3	95.33	67	93.78	80	94.11	50	93.56	36	89.67	24

The number of fuzzy sets N_F in the merging algorithm is also a key parameter. Compared to $N_F = 3$, setting $N_F = 2$ can achieve better transparency, but for some datasets, with $N_F = 2$, the accuracy is greatly reduced although the resulting trees have significantly fewer branches. For example, Figs. 4.14 and 4.15 show the change in test accuracy and the number of leaves (or the number of rules interpreted from a LDT) for different T_m on the Breast-w dataset. Fig. 4.14 is with $N_F = 2$ and Fig. 4.15 with $N_F = 3$. Fig. 4.14 shows that the accuracy is not greatly influenced by merging, but the number of branches is greatly reduced. This is especially true for the curve marked by '+' corresponding to $T_m = 0.3$ where applying forward merging, the best accuracy (at the depth 4) is only reduced by approximately 1%, whereas, the number of branches is reduced by roughly 84%. However, in Fig. 4.15 , at the depth 4 with $T_m = 0.3$, the accuracy also reduces about 1% but the number of branches only reduces by 55%. So, for this dataset, we should choose $N_F = 2$ rather than $N_F = 3$.

However, this is not always the case. For the dataset Iris, the change in accuracy and the number of branches against depth with $N_F = 2$ and $N_F = 3$ is shown in Figs. 4.16 and 4.17 , respectively. As we can see from Fig. 4.16 , by applying the forward merging algorithm, the accuracy is greatly changed. The best accuracy with

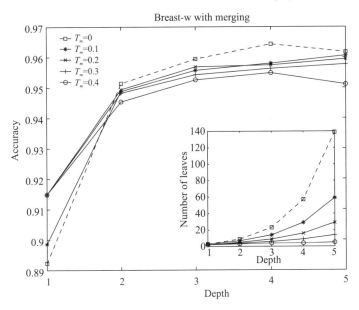

Fig. 4.14 The change in accuracy and number of leaves as T_m varies in the Breast-w dataset with $N_F = 2$

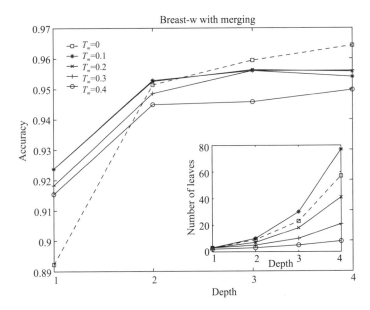

Fig. 4.15 The change in accuracy and number of leaves as T_m varies in the Breast-w dataset with $N_F = 3$. While the dot trial $T_m = 0$ is with $N_F = 2$

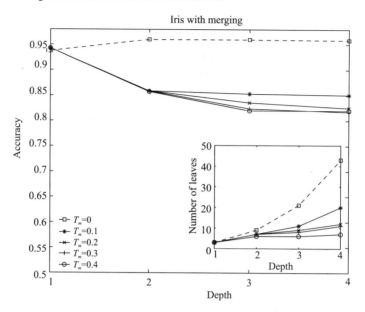

Fig. 4.16 The change in accuracy and number of leaves as T_m varies in the Iris dataset with $N_F = 2$

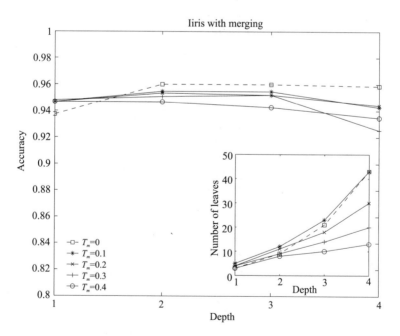

Fig. 4.17 The change in accuracy and number of leaves as T_m varies in the Iris dataset with $N_F = 3$. While the dot trial $T_m = 0$ is with $N_F = 2$

merging is roughly 10% worse than with the non-merging algorithm. But for $N_F = 3$, as we can see from Fig. 4.17 , the accuracy is not that greatly reduced compared to $N_F = 2$, and we still obtain a reduced number of branches, compared to the accuracy for $T_m = 0$ obtained from $N_F = 2$. In this case we should prefer $N_F = 3$.

Table 4.7 shows the results with optimal N_F and different T_m ranging from 0 to 0.4, where $T_m = 0$ represents no merging. Acc represents the average accuracy from 10 runs of experiments and $|T|$ is the average number of rules (leaves). Unless otherwise stated, the results obtained in this section are with the threshold probability set to $T = 1$. The results for T_m from 0.1 to 0.4 are obtained at the depth where the optimal accuracy is found when $T_m = 0$. As we can see from the table, for most cases, the accuracy before and after merging is not significantly different but the number of branches is dramatically reduced. In some cases, the merging algorithm even outperforms the LID3 without merging. The possible reason for this is because the merging algorithm generates self-adapting granularities based on class probabilities. Compared to other methods that discretize attributes independently, merging may generate a more reasonable tree with more appropriate information granules.

4.6.4 ROC Analysis for Forward Merging

In this section, we will use ROC analysis to study the forward merging algorithm for LDTs. Six binary datasets from the UCI machine learning repository are tested here: *Breast-Cancer, Wisconsin-Cancer, Heart-C, Heart, Heptitis* and *Pima Indian*[9]. Descriptions of these datasets including the number of examples, the number of attributes (features) and whether the attributes are a mixture of Num. and Nom., is shown in Table 4.3 . The LDT parameters for each data set are set individually: the number of fuzzy sets used for discretization (N_F) is also shown in Table 4.8 . The maximum depth for the Breast-Cancer dataset is 2 and for the other five data sets is 3. These parameter settings are based on a few test-and-trail experiments[10]. For each data set, the examples were equally divided into two subsets, one for training and the other one for the test. This is referred to as a 50-50 split experiment.

Table 4.8 shows the average AUC and standard deviation from 10 runs of 50-50 split experiments by applying merging with the merging threshold T_m ranging from 0 (no merging) to 0.3. The average size of the trees $|T|$ from 10 runs of experiments is also shown in the table, where the size of the tree is in terms of the number of branches (this also corresponds to the the number of rules that can be extracted from an LDT). According to the t-test with confidence level 0.9, the AUC values for the merged LDTs are not reduced significantly compared to the non-merging case. Indeed for some data sets, (e.g., Breast-Cancer) the merged trees even performs a little better than non-merged trees, although no statistically significant differences are found. On the other hand, the tree sizes are reduced significantly. These facts can be seen from FigS. 4.18 and 4.19 . Fig. 4.18 shows the accuracy comparison and Fig. 4.19 shows the comparison of the number of branches, respectively. The possible reason for this is that the merging algorithm generates self-adapting granularities based on class probabilities. Compared to other methods that discretize attributes independently, merging may generate more reasonable trees with more appropriate information granules. However, this claim still needs more investigation.

Table 4.8 Mean AUC values with standard deviation of six data sets with different merging thresholds

Data	N_F	$T_m = 0$		$T_m = 0.1$		$T_m = 0.2$		$T_m = 0.3$	
		AUC	$\|T\|$	AUC	$\|T\|$	AUC	$\|T\|$	AUC	$\|T\|$
Breast-Cancer	3	73.69±7.73	13	71.45±7.12	11	74.29±8.44	9	81.11±3.25	4
Wisconsin-Cancer	3	98.76±0.72	44	99.02±0.54	12	98.69±0.59	9	98.99±0.60	7
Heart-C	2	85.36±2.58	35	84.02±3.46	32	84.79±3.39	25	84.32±4.38	17
Heart-S	2	84.41±3.64	29	85.16±2.90		281.12±15.05	19	82.36±5.71	11
Heptitis	2	73.26±6.89	19	73.99±5.36	11	74.80±4.83	9	74.25±5.99	7
Pima Indian	2	81.08±0.97	27	81.92±1.79	14	74.74±15.13	5	81.90±4.84	2

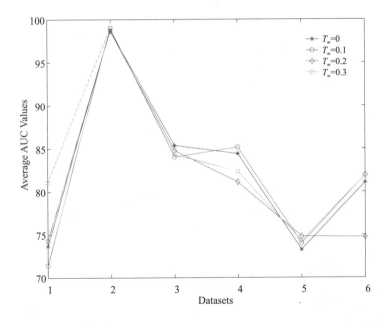

Fig. 4.18 Comparison between non-merged trees and merged trees with T_m ranging from 0.1 to 0.3 on the given test data in terms of accuracy

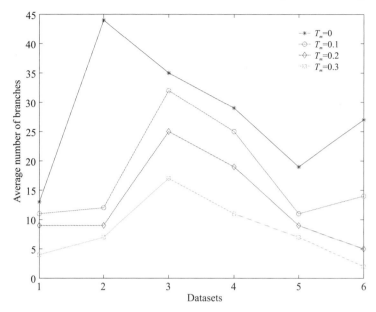

Fig. 4.19 Comparison between non-merged trees and merged trees with T_m ranging from 0.1 to 0.3 on the given test data in terms of the number of branches

4.7 Linguistic Reasoning

As we have known from Chapter 3, the main logical connectives for fuzzy labels are interpreted as follows: $\neg L$ means that L is not an appropriate label, $L_1 \wedge L_2$ means that both L_1 and L_2 are appropriate labels, $L_1 \vee L_2$ means that either L_1 or L_2 are appropriate labels, and $L_1 \rightarrow L_2$ means that L_2 is an appropriate label whenever L_1 is. In this section we use label semantics to provide a linguistic interpretation for LDTs and merged LDTs. We also use this framework to show how LDTs can be used to classify data with linguistic constraints on attributes. In addition, a method for classification of fuzzy data is proposed and supported with empirical studies of a toy problem.

4.7.1 Linguistic Interpretation of an LDT

Based on the α-function (Definition 3.12), a branch of a linguistic decision tree in random set forms (i.e. $\{small\}$, $\{small, medium\}$, $\{medium\}$) can be represented by a linguistic rule that joined by logical connectives (i.e., $\neg large$)[5]. The motivation of this mapping is shown in Fig. 4.20. Given a focal set $\{s, m\}$ this states that the labels appropriate to describe the attribute are exactly *small* and *medium*. Hence, they

---

[5] By applying the α-function, the logical expression for $\{small\}$, $\{small, medium\}$, $\{medium\}$ is $\neg large$, see Section 3.4.3.

include s and m and exclude all other labels that occur in focal sets that are supersets of $\{s,m\}$. Given a set of focal sets $\{\{s,m\},\{m\}\}$ this provides the information that the set of labels is either $\{s,m\}$ or $\{m\}$ and hence the sentence providing the same information should be the disjunction of the α sentences for both focal sets (see Section 3.4.3).

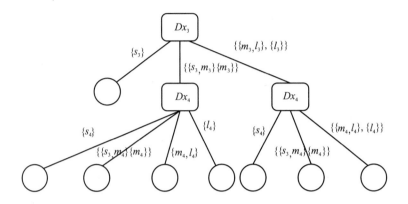

Fig. 4.20 A merged linguistic decision tree for the Iris problem

As discussed in the last section, a merged LDT was obtained from a real-world dataset Iris at the depth 2 when $T_m = 0.3$ and where $\mathbb{L}_j = \{small_j\ (s_j),\ medium_j\ (m_j),\ large_j\ (l_j)| j = 1,\ldots,4\}$ (see Fig 4.21).

$MT_{iris} = \{MB_1, MB_2, MB_3, MB_4, MB_5, MB_6, MB_7, MB_8\} =$
$\{\langle\langle\{s_3\}\rangle, 1.0000, 0.0000, 0.0000\rangle$
$\langle\langle\{\{s_3,m_3\},\{m_3\}\},\{s_4\}\rangle, 1.0000, 0.0000, 0.0000\rangle$
$\langle\langle\{\{s_3,m_3\},\{m_3\}\},\{\{s_4,m_4\},\{m_4\}\}\rangle, 0.0008, 0.9992, 0.0000\rangle$
$\langle\langle\{\{s_3,m_3\},\{m_3\}\},\{m_4,l_4\}\rangle, 0.0000, 0.5106, 0.494\rangle$
$\langle\langle\{\{s_3,m_3\},\{m_3\}\},\{l_4\}\rangle, 0.0000, 0.0556, 0.9444\rangle$
$\langle\langle\{\{m_3,l_3\},\{l_3\}\},\{s_4\}\rangle, 0.3333, 0.3333, 0.3333\rangle$
$\langle\langle\{\{m_3,l_3\},\{l_3\}\},\{\{s_4,m_4\},\{m_4\}\}\rangle, 0.000, 0.8423, 0.1577\rangle$
$\langle\langle\{\{m_3,l_3\},\{l_3\}\},\{\{m_4,l_4\},\{l_4\}\}\rangle, 0.000, 0.0913, 0.9087\rangle\}$

We can then translate this tree into a set of linguistic expressions as follows:

$MT_{iris} = \{$
$\langle\langle s_3 \wedge \neg(m_3 \vee l_3)\rangle, 1.0000, 0.0000, 0.0000\rangle$
$\langle\langle m_3 \wedge \neg l_3, s_4 \wedge \neg(m_4 \vee l_4)\rangle, 1.0000, 0.0000, 0.0000\rangle$
$\langle\langle m_3 \wedge \neg l_3, m_4 \wedge \neg l_4\rangle, 0.0008, 0.9992, 0.0000\rangle$
$\langle\langle m_3 \wedge \neg l_3, \neg s_4 \wedge m_4 \wedge l_4\rangle, 0.0000, 0.5106, 0.4894\rangle$
$\langle\langle m_3 \wedge \neg l_3, \neg(s_4 \vee m_4) \wedge l_4\rangle, 0.0000, 0.0556, 0.9444\rangle$

$\langle\langle l_3, s_4 \wedge \neg(m_4 \vee l_4)\rangle, 0.3333, 0.3333, 0.3333\rangle$
$\langle\langle l_3, m_4 \wedge \neg l_4\rangle, 0.000, 0.8423, 0.1577\rangle$
$\langle\langle l_3, l_4\rangle, 0.000, 0.0913, 0.9087\rangle\}$

Furthermore, the tree itself can be rewritten as a set of fuzzy rules. For example branch 2 corresponds to the rule:

IF Attribute 3 is medium but not large and Attribute 4 is only small, THEN the class probabilities given these branches are (1.0000, 0.0000, 0.0000).

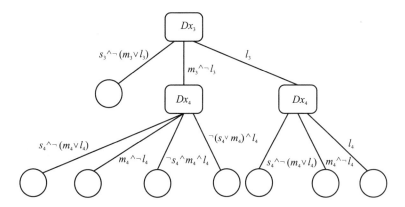

Fig. 4.21 A merged linguistic decision tree in logical expressions for the LDT shown in Fig. 4.20

4.7.2 Linguistic Constraints

Here we consider that the linguistic constraints take the form of $\theta = \langle x_1$ is $\theta_1, \ldots, x_n$ is $\theta_n\rangle$, where θ_j represents a label expression based on $\mathbb{L}_j : j = 1, \ldots, n$. Consider the vector of linguistic constraint $\theta = \langle \theta_1, \ldots, \theta_n\rangle$, where θ_j is the linguistic constraint on attribute j. We can evaluate a probability value for class C_t conditional on this information using a given linguistic decision tree as follows. The mass assignment given a linguistic constraint θ is evaluated by

$$\forall F_j \in \mathbb{F}_j \quad m_{\theta_j}(F_j) = \begin{cases} \dfrac{pm(F_j)}{\sum_{F_j \in \lambda(\theta_j)} pm(F_j)} & \text{if} : F_j \in \lambda(\theta_j) \\ 0 & \text{otherwise} \end{cases} \quad (4.27)$$

where $pm(F_j)$ is the prior mass for focal elements $F_j \in \mathbb{F}_j$ derived from the prior distribution $p(x_j)$ on Ω_j as follows:

$$pm(F_j) = \int_{\Omega_j} m_x(F_j)p(x_j)\mathrm{d}x_j \quad (4.28)$$

Usually, we assume that $p(x_j)$ is the uniform distribution over Ω_j so that

$$pm(F_j) \propto \int_{\Omega_j} m_x(F_j)\mathrm{d}x_j \qquad (4.29)$$

More details of the calculation of mass assignment given a linguistic constraint are given in Example 4.3. For branch B the probability of B given θ is evaluated by

$$P(B|\theta) = \prod_{r=1}^{|B|} m_{\theta_{j_r}}(F_{j_r}) \qquad (4.30)$$

where $|B|$ is the number of nodes in branch B. By Jeffrey's rule[11], we can obtain

$$P(C_t|\theta) = \sum_{v=1}^{|T|} P(C_t|B_v)P(B_v|\theta) \qquad (4.31)$$

Example 4.3 *Given the LDT in Example 4.2, suppose we know that for a particular data element "x_1 is not large and x_2 is small". We then can translate this knowledge into the following linguistic constraint vector:*

$$\theta = \langle \theta_1, \theta_2 \rangle = \langle \neg large_1, small_2 \rangle$$

By applying the λ-function (Definition 3.10), we can generate the associated label sets, so that:

$$\lambda(\neg large_1) = \{\{small_1\}\}$$
$$\lambda(small_2) = \{\{small_2\}, \{small_2, large_2\}\}$$

Suppose the prior mass assignments are

$$pm_1 = \{small_1\} : 0.4, \{small_1, large_1\} : 0.3, \{large_1\} : 0.3$$
$$pm_2 = \{small_2\} : 0.3, \{small_2, large_2\} : 0.2, \{large_2\} : 0.5$$

From this, according to Eq. (4.27) we obtain that,

$$m_{\theta_1} = \{small_1\} : 0.4/0.4 = \{small_1\} : 1$$
$$m_{\theta_2} = \{small_2\} : 0.3/(0.3 + 0.2), \{small_2, large_2\} : 0.2/(0.2 + 0.3)$$
$$= \{small_2\} : 0.6, \{small_2, large_2\} : 0.4$$

This gives

$$P(B_1|\theta) = m_{\theta_1}(\{small_1\}) \times m_{\theta_2}(\{small_2\}) = 1 \times 0.6 = 0.6$$
$$P(B_2|\theta) = m_{\theta_1}(\{small_1\}) \times m_{\theta_2}(\{small_2, large_2\}) = 1 \times 0.4 = 0.4$$
$$P(B_3|\theta) = P(B_4|\theta) = P(B_5|\theta) = P(B_6|\theta) = P(B_7|\theta) = 0$$

Hence, according to Jeffrey's rule

$$P(C_1|\theta) = \sum_{v=1}^{7} P(B_v|\theta)P(C_1|B_v) = \sum_{v=1,2} P(B_v|\theta)P(C_1|B_v)$$
$$= 0.6 \times 0.3 + 0.4 \times 0.5 = 0.38$$
$$P(C_2|\theta) = \sum_{v=1}^{7} P(B_v|\theta)P(C_2|B_v) = \sum_{v=1,2} P(B_v|\theta)P(C_2|B_v)$$
$$= 0.6 \times 0.7 + 0.4 \times 0.5 = 0.62$$

The methodology for classification under linguistic constraints allows us to fuse the background knowledge in linguistic form into classification. This is one of the advantages of using high-level knowledge representation language models such as label semantics.

4.7.3 Classification of Fuzzy Data

In previous discussions LDTs have only been used to classify crisp data where objects are described in terms of precise attribute values. However, in many real-world applications limitations of measurement accuracy mean that only imprecise values can be realistically obtained. In this section we introduce the idea of fuzzy data and show how LDTs can be used for classification in this context.

Formally, a fuzzy database is defined to be a set of elements or objects each described by linguistic expressions rather than crisp values. In other words

$$FD = \{\langle \theta_1(i), \ldots, \theta_n(i) \rangle : i = 1, \ldots, N\}$$

Currently, there are very few benchmark problems of this kind with fuzzy attribute values. This is because, traditionally, only crisp data values are recorded even in cases where this is inappropriate. Hence, we have generated a fuzzy database from a toy problem where the aim is to identify the interior of a figure of eight shape. Specifically, a figure of eight shape was generated according to the equation

$$x = 2^{(-0.5)}(sin(2t) - sin(t)) \tag{4.32}$$
$$y = 2^{(-0.5)}(sin(2t) + sin(t)) \tag{4.33}$$

where $t \in [0, 2\pi]$ (See Fig. 4.23). Points in $[-1.6, 1.6]^2$ are classified as legal if they lie within the 'eight' shape (marked with $\times$) and illegal if they lie outside (marked with points).

To form the fuzzy database we first generated a crisp database by uniformly sampling 961 points across $[-1.6, 1.6]^2$. Then each data vector $\langle x_1, x_2 \rangle$ was converted to a vector of linguistic expressions $\langle \theta_1, \theta_2 \rangle$ as follows: $\theta_j = \theta_{R_j}$ where

$$R_j = \{F \in \mathbb{F}_j : m_{x_j}(F) > 0\}$$

An LDT was then learnt by applying the LID3 algorithm to the crisp database. This tree was then used to classify both the crisp and fuzzy data. The results are shown in Table 4.9 and the results with $N_F = 7$ are shown in Fig. 4.22 .

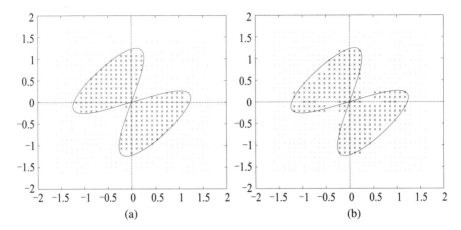

Fig. 4.22 Classification of crisp dataset (a) and fuzzy data without masses (b), where each attribute is discretized uniformly by 7 fuzzy sets

Table 4.9 Classification accuracy based on crisp data and fuzzy data of the "eight" problem

	$N_F = 3$	$N_F = 4$	$N_F = 5$	$N_F = 6$	$N_F = 7$
Crisp Data	87.72%	94.17%	95.94%	97.29%	98.54%
Fuzzy Data	79.29%	85.85%	89.39%	94.17%	95.01%

As we can see from Table 4.9 , our model gives a reasonable approximation of the legal data area, though it is not as accurate as testing on crisp data. The accuracy increases with N_F the number of fuzzy sets used for discretization. These results show that the LDT model can perform well in dealing with fuzzy and ambiguous data. Here the "eight" problem is also used for testing classification with linguistic constraints in the following example.

Example 4.4 *Suppose an LDT is trained on the "eight" database where each attribute is discretized by five fuzzy sets uniformly: verysmall (vs), small (s),medium (m), large (l) and verylarge (vl). Further, suppose we are given the following description of data points:*

$$\theta_1 = \langle x\, is\, vs \vee s \wedge \neg m, y\, is\, vs \vee s \wedge \neg m \rangle$$
$$\theta_2 = \langle x\, is\, m \wedge l, y\, is\, s \wedge m \rangle$$
$$\theta_3 = \langle x\, is\, s \wedge m, y\, is\, l \vee vl \rangle$$

Experimental results obtained based on the approach introduced in Section 4.7 are as follows:

$$Pr(C_1|\theta_1) = 1.000 \quad Pr(C_2|\theta_1) = 0.000$$
$$Pr(C_1|\theta_2) = 0.000 \quad Pr(C_2|\theta_2) = 1.000$$
$$Pr(C_1|\theta_3) = 0.428 \quad Pr(C_2|\theta_3) = 0.572$$

As we can see from Fig. 4.23 , the above 3 linguistic constraints roughly correspond to the areas 1, 2 and 3, respectively. By considering the occurrence of legal and illegal examples within these areas, we can verify the correctness of our approach.

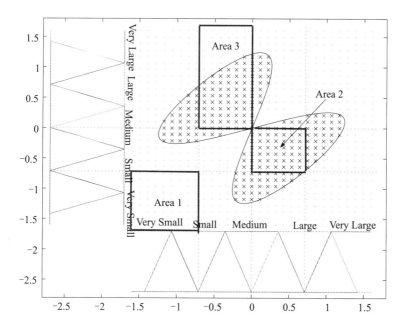

Fig. 4.23 Testing on the "eight" problem with linguistic constraints θ, where each attribute is discretized by 5 trapezoidal fuzzy sets: *very small, small, medium, large and very large*

4.8 Summary

In this chapter, a decision tree learning algorithm is proposed based on label semantics. Unlike classical decision trees, the new algorithm uses probability estimation based on linguistic labels. The linguistic labels are based on fuzzy discretization using a number of different methods including uniform partitioning, a percentile-based partitioning and an entropy-based partitioning. We found that the percentile-based discretization and entropy-based discretization outperform uniform discretization, but no statistical significance was found. By testing our new model on real-world datasets and compared with three well-known machine learning algorithms, we found that LID3 outperformed C4.5 on all given datasets and outperforms Naive Bayes on datasets with numerical attributes only. Also it has equivalent classification accuracy and better transparency when compared to back propagation Neural Networks.

In order to obtain compact trees, a forward merging algorithm was proposed and the experimental results show that the number of branches can be greatly reduced without a significant loss in accuracy. Finally, we introduce the method of interpreting a linguistic decision tree into a set of linguistic rules joined by logical connectives. The methods for classification with linguistic constraints and fuzzy data classification are discussed, supported by a test on toy problems. In the subsequent chapter, we will focus on extending the LDT model from classification problems to prediction problems.

References

[1] Quinlan J. R.: Induction of decision trees, Machine Learning, 1: pp. 81-106. (1986).

[2] Quinlan J. R.:C4.5: Programs for Machine Learning, San Mateo: Morgan Kaufmann. (1993).

[3] Mitchell T.: Machine Learning, McGraw-Hill, New York. (1997).

[4] Berthold M., Hand D. J.: Ed. , Intelligent Data Analysis, Springer-Verlag, Berlin Heidelberg. (1999).

[5] Peng Y., Flach P. A.: Soft discretization to enhance the continuous decision trees, Integrating Aspects of Data Mining, Decision Support and Meta-Learning, C. Giraud-Carrier, N. Lavrac and S. Moyle, editors, pp. 109-118, ECML/PKDD'01 workshop. (2001).

[6] Baldwin J. F., Lawry J., Martin T. P.: Mass assignment fuzzy ID3 with applications. Proceedings of the Unicom Workshop on Fuzzy Logic: Applications and Future Directions, pp. 278-294, London. (1997).

[7] Janikow C. Z.: Fuzzy decision trees: issues and methods, IEEE Trans. on Systems, Man, and Cybernetics-Part B: Cybernetics, 28/1: pp. 1-14. (1998).

[8] Olaru C., Wehenkel L., A complete fuzzy decision tree technique, Fuzzy Sets and Systems, 138: pp.221-254. (2003).

[9] Blake C., Merz C. J.: UCI machine learning repository.

[10] Qin Z., Lawry J.: A tree-structured model classification model based on label semantics, Proceedings of the 10th International Conference on Information Processing and Management of Uncertainty in Knowledge-based Systems (IPMU-04), pp. 261-268, Perugia, Italy. (2004).

[11] Jeffrey R. C.: The Logic of Decision, Gordon & Breach Inc., New York. (1965).

[12] Provost F., Domingos P.: Tree induction for probability-based ranking, Machine Learning, 52, pp. 199-215. (2003).

[13] Witten I. H., Frank E.: Data Mining: Practical Machine Learning Tools and Techniques with Java Implementations, Morgan Kaufmann. (1999).

5

Linguistic Decision Trees for Prediction

Prediction is very difficult, especially if it's about the future.

– Niels Bohr (1885–1962)

5.1 Prediction Trees

In the last chapter, the LDT model was introduced for classification and its performance on a range of benchmark data sets was investigated and compared to a number of well known classifiers such as Naive Bayes and BP-neural networks. In this chapter, a methodology for extending LDTs to prediction problem is proposed and the performance of LDTs are compared to other state of the art prediction algorithms such as a Support Vector Regression (SVR) system and Fuzzy Semi-Naive Bayes on a variety of data sets, that include some real-world prediction problems such as sunspot prediction and flood forecasting. The merging algorithm proposed for classification LDTs is also extended to allow for the generation of compact prediction trees.

To date, classification problems have been much more widely studied in machine leaning and pattern recognition than prediction (regression) problems. For example, in the most popular machine learning repository — UCI Machine Learning Repository[1], most datasets concern classification but not prediction. However, in many real-world applications, problems ranging from financial analysis to flood forecasting, are prediction problems.

Consider the tree learning models. From early discrete decision trees such as ID3[2] and C4.5[3] to a variety types of fuzzy decision trees as well as the linguistic decision tree model proposed in the last chapter, most tree induction models are designed for classification but not for prediction[4–7]. However, there is some research on regression trees, for example Breiman *et al.*'s CART algorithm[8]. Based on the introduction of the LDT model in the last chapter, the output of an LDT is a probability distribution on classes in stead of a discrete class label. Such a classifier is referred to as a probabilistic classifier. This provides the possibility of extending it from classification to prediction where the probability distribution will be used to obtain predicted numerical values. In this chapter, we will extend the LDT model to handle prediction problems.

5.2 Linguistic Prediction Trees

Consider a database for prediction

$$DB = \{\langle x_1(i), \ldots, x_n(i), x_t(i) \rangle | i = 1, \ldots, |DB|\}$$

where $x_1, \ldots, x_n$ are potential explanatory attributes and x_t is the continuous target attribute. Given a new instance $x_i = (x_1(i), \ldots, x_n(i))$, we hope to prediction with a model ϕ:

$$\phi(x) \rightarrow \hat{x}_t \tag{5.1}$$

When using the LDT model, the data processing steps are as the same as introduced in the previous chapters. Unless otherwise stated, trapezoidal fuzzy sets with 50% overlap are used to discretize each continuous attribute (x_t as well) universe and assume the focal sets are $\mathbb{F}_1, \ldots, \mathbb{F}_n$ and $\mathbb{F}_t$. For the target attribute x_t:

$$\mathbb{F}_t = \{F_t^1, \ldots, F_t^{|\mathbb{F}_t|}\}$$

For other attributes: x_j:

$$\mathbb{F}_j = \{F_j^1, \ldots, F_j^{|\mathbb{F}_j|}\}$$

The inventive step is, the focal elements for the target attribute can be regarded as class labels. Hence, the LDT[①] model for prediction has the following form:

Definition 5.1 (*Linguistic prediction tree*) *A linguistic decision tree for prediction is a set of branches with associated probability distribution on the target focal elements of the following form:*

$$T = \{\langle B_1, P(F_t^1|B_1), \ldots, P(F_t^{|\mathbb{F}_t|}|B_1) \rangle, \ldots,$$
$$\langle B_{|T|}, P(F_t^1|B_{|T|}), \ldots, P(F_t^{|\mathbb{F}_t|})|B_{|T|}) \rangle\}$$

where $F_t^1, \ldots, F_t^{|\mathbb{F}_t|}$ are the target focal elements (i.e., the focal elements for the target attribute or the output attribute.

Fig. 5.1 gives a sample a linguistic prediction tree where each leaf is associated with a probability distribution on the focal elements of the target attribute. Given the example in Fig. 5.1 ,

$$\mathbb{F} = \{F_1, \ldots, F_6\}$$

---

① We will use the same term of "LDT" for representing both linguistic decision trees (for classification) and linguistic prediction trees.

A Linguistic Prediction Tree

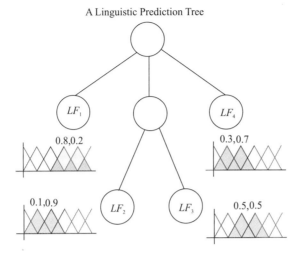

Fig. 5.1   A linguistic prediction tree example: each leaf is associated with a probability distribution on the focal set of the target attribute x_t. Each focal element is represented by a trianglar fuzzy membership function

We can consider the prediction problem as a classification problem with 6 classes. The probability distributions associated with LF_i (for $i = 1, 2, 3$ and 4) are:

$$P(LF_1) = \{F_4 : 0.8,\ F_5 : 0.2\}$$
$$P(LF_2) = \{F_2 : 0.1,\ F_3 : 0.9\}$$
$$P(LF_3) = \{F_3 : 0.5,\ F_4 : 0.5\}$$
$$P(LF_4) = \{F_2 : 0.3,\ F_3 : 0.7\}$$

5.2.1 Branch Evaluation

Intuitively, we may like to view the target focal elements as imprecise class labels. The essential difference is that these "class labels" overlap each other and this must be taken into account when evaluating branch probabilities. At the training stage, for a particular instance $x_i \in \Omega_1 \times, \ldots, \times \Omega_n$, where $x_i \rightarrow x_t(i)$ (i.e., $x_t(i)$ is the predicted value for the instance x_i) for $i = 1, \ldots, |DB|$, there may be several corresponding target focal elements rather than just one. By using linguistic translation on x_t, we can obtain:

$$x_t \rightarrow m_{x_t} = F_t^j : \ j \in \{1, \ldots, |\mathbb{F}_t|\}$$

The degree to which x_i belonging to a particular target focal element F_t^j is measured by ξ_i^j defined by:

$$\xi_i^j = m_{x_t(i)}(F_t^j) \tag{5.2}$$

where $j = 1, \ldots, |\mathbb{F}_t|$. From Eq. (5.2), we can see that ξ_i^j is just the associated mass of F_t^j given $x_t(i)$. Hence, we can write the corresponding target focal elements with a membership for x_i are as follows:

$$x_i \rightarrow \langle F_t^1 : \xi_i^1, \ldots, F_t^{|\mathbb{F}_t|} : \xi_i^{|\mathbb{F}_t|} \rangle \tag{5.3}$$

However, since we have made an assumption of 50% overlapping on fuzzy sets, then it follows that, at most two of the values $\{\xi^1, \ldots, \xi^{|\mathbb{F}_t|}\}$ are non-zero. We can also view ξ as an indicator: if and only if $\xi_i^j > 0$, F_t^j is one of the corresponding target focal elements for the data element x_i, otherwise, it is not. The probability of a branch given a data element is evaluated based on on Eq. (4.8):

$$P(B|x) = \prod_{r=1}^{|B|} m_{x_r}(F_r)$$

Based on the class probability calculation for classification problems (see Eq. (4.12)). The probability of F_t^j given B is evaluated as follows:

$$P(F_t^j|B) = \frac{\sum_{i \in DB} \xi_i^j P(B|x_i)}{\sum_{i \in DB} P(B|x_i)} \tag{5.4}$$

where $F_t^j \in \mathbb{F}_t$. By combining Eqs. (5.2) and (5.4):

$$P(F_t^j|B) = \frac{\sum_{i \in DB} P(B|x_i) m_{x_t(i)}(F_t^j)}{\sum_{i \in DB} P(B|x_i)} \tag{5.5}$$

Eq. (5.5) is a general version of Eq. (4.12). In classification problems, the target labels are discrete, thus ξ is either 0 or 1:

$$\xi_i^j = \begin{cases} 1 & i \in DB_j \\ 0 & \text{otherwise} \end{cases} \tag{5.6}$$

where DB_j represents the subset of instances that in the class j. This means that in classification problems:

$$\sum_{i \in DB_j} P(B|x_i) = \sum_{i \in DB} \xi_i^j P(B|x_i)$$

In case of the dominator $\sum_{i \in DB} P(B|x_i) = 0$, we use the following equation:

$$P(F_t^j|B) = \frac{1}{|\mathbb{F}_t|} \tag{5.7}$$

When the dominator equals to zero, it means this branch covers no data and we do not have any discriminate information on classes, so we just simply assign this branch a probability which is equal over all the classes.

Considering the classification problem, Eq. (4.16) can be modified to obtain the probabilities of target focal elements given a data element $x \in \Omega_1 \times \ldots \times \Omega_n$ based on an LDT according to the Jeffrey's rule[9]:

$$P(F_t^j|x) = \sum_{v=1}^{|T|} P(F_t^j|B_v)P(B_v|x) \tag{5.8}$$

The following example illustrates how such probabilities can be evaluated from a toy database described by Table 5.1 .

Table 5.1 A small-scale training linguistic database for prediction, where the values are the associated masses for the corresponding focal elements on 5 given data elements

# Instance	Attribute 1 (x_1)			Attribute 2 (x_2)			Target Attribute (x_t)		
	$\{s_1\}$	$\{s_1,l_1\}$	$\{l_1\}$	$\{s_2\}$	$\{s_2,l_2\}$	$\{l_2\}$	$\{s_t\}$	$\{s_t,l_t\}$	$\{l_t\}$
1	0.4	0.6	0	0	0.7	0.3	0.9	0.1	0
2	0.2	0.8	0	0.5	0.5	0	0	0.8	0.2
3	0	0.9	0.1	1	0	0	0	1	0
4	0.3	0.7	0	1	0	0	0.7	0.3	0
5	0	0.2	0.8	0.3	0.7	0	1	0	0

Example 5.1 *Consider a problem with 2 potential explanatory attributes x_1, x_2 and one target attribute x_t, where $\mathbb{L}_1 = \{small_1(s_1), large_1(l_1)\}$, $\mathbb{L}_2 = \{small_2(s_2), large_2(l_2)\}$ and $\mathbb{L}_t = \{small_t(s_t), large_t(l_t)\}$. We assume the focal elements defined on the attributes are $\mathbb{F}_1 = \{\{s_1\}, \{s_1,l_1\}, \{l_1\}\}$, $\mathbb{F}_2 = \{\{s_2\}, \{s_2,l_2\}, \{l_2\}\}$ and $\mathbb{F}_t = \{\{s_t\}, \{s_t,l_t\}, \{l_t\}\}$. The training database obtained by applying linguistic translation is shown in Table 5.1 . If we are given a branch of the form:*

$$B = \langle\langle\{s_1\}, \{s_2\}\rangle, P(\{s_t\}|B), P(\{s_t,l_t\}|B), P(\{l_t|B\})\rangle$$

The probabilities of target focal elements are evaluated according to Eq. (5.5) as follows:

$$
\begin{aligned}
P(\{s_t\}|B) &= \frac{\sum_{i=1}^5 m_{x_t(i)}(\{s_t\})\prod_{r=1,2} m_{x_r(i)}(F_r)}{\sum_{i=1}^5 \prod_{r=1,2} m_{x_r(i)}(F_r)} \\
&= \frac{\sum_{i=1,4,5} m_{x_1(i)}(\{s_1\}) \times m_{x_2(i)}(\{s_2\}) \times m_{x_t(i)}(\{s_t\})}{\sum_{i=1}^5 m_{x_1(i)}(\{s_1\}) \times m_{x_2(i)}(\{s_2\})} \\
&= \frac{0.4 \times 0 \times 0.9 + 0.3 \times 1 \times 0.7 + 0 \times 0.3 \times 1}{0.4 \times 0 + 0.2 \times 0.5 + 0 \times 1 + 0.3 \times 1 + 0 \times 0.3} = 0.525
\end{aligned}
$$

$$P(\{s_t, l_t\}, B) = \frac{\sum_{i=1}^{5} m_{x_t}(\{s_t, l_t\}) \prod_{r=1,2} m_{x_r(i)}(F_r)}{\sum_{i=1}^{5} \prod_{r=1,2} m_{x_r(i)}(F_r)}$$

$$= \frac{\sum_{i=1,2,3,4} m_{x_1(i)}(\{s_1\}) \times m_{x_2(i)}(\{s_2\}) \times m_{x_t(i)}(\{s_t, l_t\})}{\sum_{i=1}^{5} m_{x_1(i)}(\{s_1\}) \times m_{x_2(i)}(\{s_2\})}$$

$$= \frac{0.4 \times 0 \times 0.1 + 0.2 \times 0.5 \times 0.8 + 0 \times 1 \times 1 + 0.3 \times 1 \times 0.3}{0.4 \times 0 + 0.2 \times 0.5 + 0 \times 1 + 0.3 \times 1 + 0 \times 0.3} = 0.425$$

$$P(\{l_t\}, B) = \frac{\sum_{i=1}^{5} m_{x_t}(\{l_t\}) \prod_{r=1,2} m_{x_r(i)}(F_r)}{\sum_{i=1}^{5} \prod_{r=1,2} m_{x_r(i)}(F_r)}$$

$$= \frac{\sum_{i=2} m_{x_1(i)}(\{s_1\}) \times m_{x_2(i)}(\{s_2\}) \times m_{x_t(i)}(\{l_t\})}{\sum_{i=1}^{5} m_{x_1(i)}(\{s_1\}) \times m_{x_2(i)}(\{s_2\})}$$

$$= \frac{0.2 \times 0.5 \times 0.2}{0.4 \times 0 + 0.2 \times 0.5 + 0 \times 1 + 0.3 \times 1 + 0 \times 0.3} = 0.05$$

5.2.2 Defuzzification

As discussed in the last section, for a given value $x = \langle x_1, \ldots, x_n \rangle$ we need to estimate the target value $\hat{x}_t$ (i.e., $x_i \rightarrow \hat{x}_t$). This is achieved by initially evaluating the probabilities on target focal elements: $P(F_t^1|x), \ldots, P(F_t^{|\mathbb{F}_t|}|x)$ as described above. We then take the estimate of x_t, denoted $\hat{x}_t$, to be the expected value:

$$\hat{x}_t = \int_{\Omega_t} x_t \, p(x_t|x) \, dx_t \tag{5.9}$$

where:

$$p(x_t|x) = \sum_{j=1}^{|\mathbb{F}_t|} p(x_t|F_t^j) \, P(F_t^j|x) \tag{5.10}$$

and

$$p(x_t|F_t^j) = \frac{m_{x_t}(F_t^j)}{\int_{\Omega_t} m_{x_t}(F_t^j) \, dx_t} \tag{5.11}$$

so that, we can obtain:

$$\hat{x}_t = \sum_j P(F_t^j|x) \, E(x_t|F_t^j) \tag{5.12}$$

where:

$$E(x_t|F_t^j) = \int_{\Omega_t} x_t \, p(x_t|F_t^j) \, dx_t = \frac{\int_{\Omega_t} x_t \, m_{x_t}(F_t^j) \, dx_t}{\int_{\Omega_t} m_{x_t}(F_t^j) \, dx_t} \tag{5.13}$$

In practice the calculation of Eq. (5.13) can be illustrated by the following example.

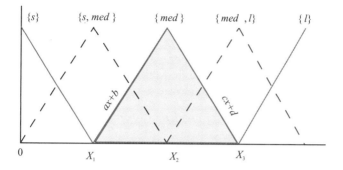

Fig. 5.2 Illustration of calculating the expected value for focal elements

Example 5.2 *Suppose that the output space x_t is partitioned with a set of class labels $\mathbb{L}_t = \{small(s),\ medium(med),\ large(l)\}$. From this we can obtain mass assignment values across the focal sets of $\mathbb{L}_t$. For example, suppose the $m_x(\{med\})$ (see Fig. 5.2) is defined by*

$$f(x) = \begin{cases} ax+b & X_1 \le x < X_2 \\ cx+d & X_2 \le x < X_3 \\ 0 & otherwise \end{cases} \tag{5.14}$$

The expected value for the focal element $\{med\}$ is evaluated as follows:

$$E(x_t|\{med\}) = \frac{f(x)}{A} \tag{5.15}$$

where A is the area covered by $f(x)$ as represented by the dark triangle in Fig. 5.2 . The area of the triangle can be obtained by multiplying the base and one-half the height. Here the height is 1 so that $A = \frac{X_3-X_1}{2}$. $f(x)$ is the function of $m_x(\{med\})$ (see Fig. 5.2):

$$f(x) = \int_{X_1}^{X_2} x(ax+b) + \int_{X_2}^{X_3} x(cx+d)$$

$$= \left[\frac{ax^3}{3} + \frac{bx^2}{2}\right]_{X_1}^{X_2} + \left[\frac{cx^3}{3} + \frac{dx^2}{2}\right]_{X_2}^{X_3}$$

$$= X_2^3\left(\frac{a}{3} - \frac{c}{3}\right) + X_2^2\left(\frac{b}{2} - \frac{d}{2}\right) - X_1^3\frac{a}{3} - X_1^2\frac{b}{2} + X_3^3\frac{c}{3} + X_3^2\frac{d}{2}$$

So that,

$$E(x_t|\{med\}) = \frac{f(x)}{A} = \frac{2}{X_3 - X_1}\left[X_2^3\left(\frac{a}{3} - \frac{c}{3}\right) + X_2^2\left(\frac{b}{2} - \frac{d}{2}\right)\right.$$

$$\left. - X_1^3\frac{a}{3} - X_1^2\frac{b}{2} + X_3^3\frac{c}{3} + X_3^2\frac{d}{2}\right]$$

5.2.3 Linguistic ID3 Algorithm for Prediction

In this section, the Linguistic ID3 (LID3) for prediction is introduced. This is modified from the LID3 for classification described in the previous chapter. The corresponding definitions are modified from classification problems to take account of the overlapping focal classes as follows:

Definition 5.2 (*Branch entropy for prediction*) *For a branch $B = \langle F_1, \ldots, F_{|B|} \rangle$ the entropy of B is given by*

$$E(B) = -\sum_{j=1}^{|\mathbb{F}_t|} P(F_t^j | B) \log_2 P(F_t^j | B) \tag{5.16}$$

Now, given a particular branch B suppose we want to expand it with the attribute x_j. The evaluation of this attribute will be given based on the expected entropy defined as follows:

$$EE(B, x_j) = \sum_{F_j \in \mathbb{F}_j} E(B \cup F_j) \cdot P(F_j | B) \tag{5.17}$$

where $B \cup F_j$ represents the new branch obtained by appending the focal element F_j to the end of branch B. The probability of F_j given B can be calculated as follows:

$$P(F_j | B) = \frac{\sum_{i \in DB} P(B \cup F_j | x_i)}{\sum_{i \in DB} P(B | x_i)} \tag{5.18}$$

so that the Information Gain (IG) obtained by expanding branch B with attribute x_j in the same way as the classification is as follows:

$$IG(B, x_j) = E(B) - EE(B, x_j) \tag{5.19}$$

The basic difference from classification is in the output space: in classification, the outputs are discreet classes, while in prediction, overlapping focal elements are acted as classes. The class probabilities for the evaluation of branch entropy and expected entropy must to be adopted to take account of this fact. In next section we adopt the merging algorithm described in Chapter 4 to the prediction case.

5.2.4 Forward Branch Merging for Prediction

One of the inherent disadvantages of tree induction algorithms is overfitting. There are many pruning algorithms proposed, a good review of which is given in Reference [5]. Here we present an alternate approach of using "forward merging" instead of "pruning" to generate compact trees. In this section, a branch merging algorithm for the prediction LDT model is discussed. The basic idea is that, we employ breadth-first search in developing an LDT, at each depth. The adjacent branches which give similar probabilities on target focal elements are merged into one branch according to a merging threshold:

Definition 5.3 (*Merging threshold for prediction trees*) *In a linguistic decision tree, if the maximum difference between the probabilities of target focal elements on two adjacent branches B_1 and B_2 is less than or equal to a given merging threshold T_m, then the two branches can be merged into one branch. Formally, if*

$$T_m \geq \max_{F_t \in \mathbb{F}_t}(|Pr(F_t|B_1) - Pr(F_t|B_2)|) \tag{5.20}$$

where $\mathbb{F}_t = \{F_t^1, \ldots, F_t^{|\mathbb{F}_t|}\}$ are focal elements for the target attribute, then B_1 and B_2 can be merged into one branch MB.

$$MB = \langle \mathbf{M}_1, \ldots, \mathbf{M}_{|MB|} \rangle$$

where $\mathbf{M}_j = \{F_j^1, \ldots, F_j^{|\mathbf{M}_j|}\}$ is a set of focal elements such that F_j^i is adjacent to F_j^{i+1} for $i = 1, \ldots, |\mathbf{M}_j| - 1$. The associate mass for $\mathbf{M}_j$ is given by

$$m_x(\mathbf{M}_j) = \sum_{i=1}^{|\mathbf{M}_j|} m_x(F_j^i) \tag{5.21}$$

where w is the number of merged focal elements for attribute j. The probability of a merged branch given a data element $x \in \Omega \times \ldots \times \Omega$ can be evaluated by

$$P(MB|x) = \prod_{r=1}^{|MB|} m_{x_r}(\mathbf{M}_r) = \prod_{r=1}^{|MB|} \left(\sum_{i=1}^{|\mathbf{M}_r|} m_{x_r}(F_r^i) \right) \tag{5.22}$$

where $|MB|$ is the length of the merged branch MB and $|\mathbf{M}_r|$ for $r = 1, \ldots, |MB|$ is the number of merged nodes of the attribute r. Based on Eqs. (4.12), (4.13), (5.2), (5.21) and (5.22), we use the following equation to evaluate the probabilities on target focal elements given a merged branch.

$$P(F_t^j|MB) = \frac{\sum_{i \in DB} \xi_i^j P(MB|x)}{\sum_{i \in DB} P(MB|x)} \tag{5.23}$$

And, the following equation is used when doing classification with a merged LDT:

$$P(F_t^j|x) = \sum_{v=1}^{|T|} P(F_t^j|MB_v)P(MB_v|x) \tag{5.24}$$

As we have discussed in the previous chapter, when the merging algorithm is applied in learning a linguistic prediction tree, the adjacent branches meeting the merging criteria will be merged and re-evaluated according to Eq. (5.23). Then the adjacent branches after the first round of merging will be examined in a further round of merging, until all adjacent branches cannot be merged further. We then proceed to the next depth. For example, Fig. 5.3 shows that leaves LF_2 and LF_3 are merged in the first round of merging, and LF_4 and $\{LF_2, LF_3\}$ are then merged further $\{LF_2, LF_3, LF_4\}$ if they meet the merging criteria in the second round of merging.

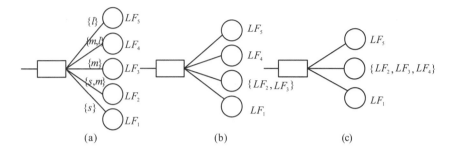

Fig. 5.3 A schematic illustration of tree merging

5.3 Experimental Studies

In this section, a range of benchmark prediction problems are tested with the LID3 algorithm. The prediction results obtained are compared with several state of the art prediction algorithms such as Support Vector Regression System (SVR), Fuzzy Naive Bayes and Fuzzy Semi-Naive Bayes (FSNB)[10,14]. In this experiment, we use ε-Support Vector Regression System (ε-SVR) with a Gaussian kernel and an ε-insensitive loss function[12]. The SVR results presented here are obtained by using a Matlab toolbox for SVM implemented by Gunn[13] and the parameter settings for each problem are based on empirical research on these problems by Randon[14].

Fuzzy Naive Bayes is another linguistic model based on label semantics (see Chapter 6) and Fuzzy Semi-Naive Bayes presented here is modified from Fuzzy Naive Bayes by weakening the independence assumption of Naive Bayes (more details are available in[10,14]). The results of Fuzzy Naive Bayes and FSNB presented in his paper are the best results so far from a set of systematic research[14].

Two kinds of measures are used here for evaluating the prediction performance: Average Error (AVE) and Mean Square Error (MSE), which are defined as follows:

(1) The Average Error scales the error according to the range of output (target attribute) space is used for evaluating the algorithms' performance: Given the output universe defined by $\Omega_t = [a, b]$ and a training set DB, AVE is the average modulus error taken as a percentage of the length of the output universe, formally:

$$AVE = \frac{\sum_{i \in DB} |\hat{x}_t(i) - x_t(i)|}{|DB|(b - a)} \tag{5.25}$$

where $|DB|$ represents the number of instances in DB. The standard deviation across DB is given by

$$\sigma_E = \sqrt{\frac{1}{|DB|} \sum_{i \in DB} (\varepsilon_i - AVE)^2} \tag{5.26}$$

where:

$$\varepsilon_i = \frac{|\hat{x}_t - x_t|}{b - a}$$

(2) The Mean Square Error is calculated as follows:

$$MSE = \frac{1}{|DB|} \sum_{i \in DB} (\hat{x}_t(i) - x_t(i))^2 \qquad (5.27)$$

With standard deviation across DB given by

$$\sigma_{SE} = \sqrt{\frac{1}{|DB|} \sum_i (e_i - MSE)^2} \qquad (5.28)$$

where:

$$e_i = (\hat{x}_t - x_t)^2 \qquad (5.29)$$

5.3.1 3D Surface Regression

In this toy problem, 529 points were uniformly generated describing a surface defined by equation

$$z = \sin(x \times y) \qquad (5.30)$$

where $x, y \in [0, 3]$ as shown in Fig. 5.4 . 2209 points are sampled uniformly as the test set. The attributes are discretized uniformly by fuzzy labels, the results in the AVE

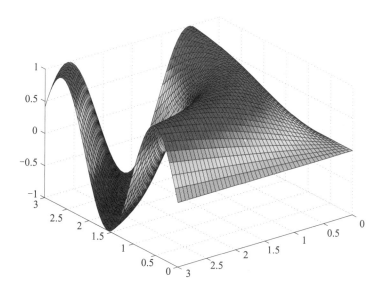

Fig. 5.4 The original surface of function $z = \sin(x \times y)$

Table 5.2 Average error for the $\sin(x \times y)$ problem with different number of fuzzy sets (represented by N_F) for discretization in input and output space, respectively

N_F	Training Error				Test Error			
Input	4	5	6	7	4	5	6	7
4	7.4290	7.4296	7.4254	7.4419	7.1827	7.1834	7.1785	7.1955
5	4.8314	4.8316	4.8262	4.8456	4.6772	4.6777	4.6695	4.6892
6	3.2266	3.2265	3.2160	3.2357	3.1890	3.1895	3.1776	3.1986
7	2.1734	2.1711	2.1653	2.1864	2.1560	2.1555	2.1464	2.1684

Table 5.3 Mean square error the $\sin(x \times y)$ problem with different number of fuzzy sets (represented by N_F) for discretization on input and output space, respectively

N_F	Training Error				Test Error			
Input	4	5	6	7	4	5	6	7
4	0.0325	0.0325	0.0325	0.0326	0.0303	0.0303	0.0303	0.0304
5	0.0147	0.0147	0.0147	0.0148	0.0134	0.0134	0.0134	0.0135
6	0.0070	0.0071	0.0071	0.0071	0.0065	0.0065	0.0065	0.0065
7	0.0033	0.0033	0.0033	0.0034	0.0031	0.0031	0.0031	0.0032

Table 5.4 Comparisons of prediction models in average error on the $\sin(x \times y)$ problem

	Fuzzy Naive Bayes	**FSNB**	**ε-SVR**	**LID3**
$AVE \pm \sigma_E$	16.042 ± 12.817	2.815 ± 2.268	1.452 ± 0.746	2.146 ± 1.795

are measured with different numbers of fuzzy labels which are respectively defined on input and output space are listed in Table 5.2 . The results in *MSE* measure are shown in Table 5.3 .

It is surprising to see that the number of fuzzy sets used for output (i.e., z) space does not cause a great difference in error. On the contrary, the resulting model is very sensitive to the number of fuzzy sets for inputs (i.e., x and y). The more the fuzzy sets used for discretization, the more accurate the prediction surface we can obtain. This monotonicity is of course partly dependent on the noise free nature of the data in this case. Fig. 5.5 shows the predicted surfaces and the error surfaces, where the input space is discretized with 5, 6 and 7 fuzzy sets, respectively. As we can see from the figures,the more the fuzzy sets that we used, the more accurate surface was generated.

We now compare these results to those obtained from the ε-SVR with the parameters: $\sigma = 1$, $\varepsilon = 0.05$, $C = \infty$ (justificatioin for this parameter can be found

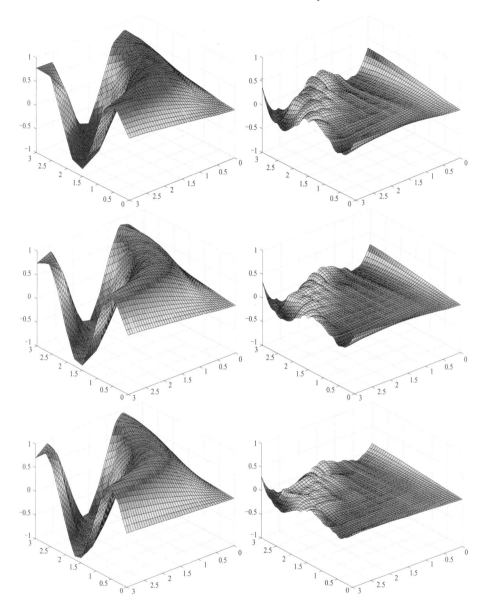

Fig. 5.5 Prediction surfaces (left-hand figures) and error surfaces (right-hand figures) where input spaces are discretized by 5 (upper figures), 6 (middle figures) and 7 (bottom figures) fuzzy sets, respectively

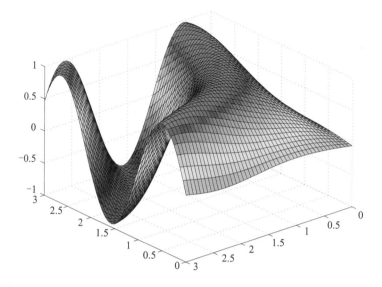

Fig. 5.6 The prediction surface by ε-SVR with a Gaussian RBF kernel on the $z = \sin(x \times y)$ problem

in Reference [14]). The test errors are shown in Table 5.4 . Compared to ε-SVR, LID3 is slightly worse. As we can see from Fig. 5.6 , the ε-SVR has a very good approximation to the original surface. By comparing Figs. 5.4 and 5.5 , we can see that LID3 cannot accurately capture the small 'tail' on the left, while the ε-SVR can. Table 5.4 also shows the results of fuzzy Naive Bayes and Fuzzy Semi-Naive Bayes. Among them, LID3 (7 fuzzy labels for the input and 6 labels for the output) is the second best. For such a function regression problems, higher accuracy could be obtained by increasing the number of fuzzy labels discretized for the input space. However, the computing complexity will be increased exponentially with the number of fuzzy labels.

5.3.2 Abalone and Boston Housing Problem

These two problems are taken from the UCI repository[1]. The Abalone database concerns the problem of predicting the age of abalone from physical measurements. Abalones are a type of shellfish, the age of which can be accurately determined by cutting the shell through the cone, staining it, and counting the number of rings through a microscope, which is a laborious and time consuming task. The Boston Housing problem contains data on housing values in the suburbs of Boston, USA. The data set contains 506 instances and 13 continuous attributes (including the target attribute) and one binary attribute.

In our experiments, the instances for each data set are randomly split into two parts with approximately the same number of instances, one for training and the other for the test (i.e., 50-50 split experiments, see Section 4.4). The test errors from 10 runs of 50-50 split experiments on the two data sets are shown in Table 5.5 with the results obtained for the Abalone prediction test set by applying ε-SVR with a Gaussian RBF kernel with parameters: $\sigma = 1$, $\varepsilon = 0.05$ and $C = 5$. The results of LID3 are obtained from the LDTs are based on 3 uniformly distributed fuzzy labels and generated at the depth 5. For the Boston Housing problem the ε-SVR parameters are $\sigma = 3$, $\varepsilon = 0.05$ and $C = 10$. The LID3 results are obtained by the LDTs with 5 uniformly distributed fuzzy labels at the depth 3. The standard deviation (Std.) in Table 5.5 is the standard deviation of AVE across the experiments.

Table 5.5 Prediction results in AVE from 10 runs 50-50 split experiments for abalone prediction and the Boston Housing prediction problem, respectively

Prediction Model	Abalone			Boston Housing		
	AVE %	σ_E(%)	Std.	AVE %	σ_E(%)	Std.
Fuzzy Naive Bayes	7.9660	7.2010	0.6638	8.2437	9.0864	0.5034
FSNB	7.0141	6.9277	0.5225	7.7059	8.9876	0.5766
ε-SVR	5.6921	6.0034	0.0894	5.4508	6.7989	0.3874
LID3	6.4327	6.3247	0.3145	8.2022	8.1502	0.4579

From Table 5.5 , we can see that ε-SVR has the best performance on these two data sets. LID3 is the second best in the Abalone prediction problem. But it does not perform very well in the Boston Housing problem where LID3 gives the equivalent average errors to Fuzzy Naive Bayes.

5.3.3 Prediction of Sunspots

This problem is taken from the Time Series Data Library[15] and contains data of sunspot numbers between the years 1700–1979. For this experiment the data was organized as described in Reference [6] using a sliding window and the validation set of 35 examples (1921-1955) was merged into the test set of 24 examples (1956-1979). This is because a validation set is not required in this framework. Hence, a training set of 209 examples (1712-1920) and a test set of 59 examples (1921-1979) are used. The input attributes are x_{T-12} to x_{T-1} (the data for previous 12 years) and the output (target) attribute is x_T, i.e., one-year-ahead.

The experimental results for LID3, ε-SVR, Fuzzy Naive Bayes[14] and Fuzzy Semi-Naive Bayes in the AVE measure are shown in Table 5.6 , where the parameter setting for ε-SVR is $\sigma = 3$, $\varepsilon = 0.05$, $C = 5$ and the results for FSNB are the best results from a range of FSNB parameter settings[14]. Results of LID3 present here are obtained from LDTs discretized by 4 fuzzy labels by a percentile-based method (both on input and output spaces) and at the depth of 5. The comparisons between the predictions made by SVR and LDT together with the original data are shown in Fig. 5.9 , where the data on the left (1712-1921) are for training data and on the right are (1921-1979) for the test.

Table 5.6 Prediction results in AVE on the sunspot prediction problem

Prediction Model	AVE (%)		$\sigma_E(\%)$		|LDT|
	Training	Test	Training	Test	(LDT only)
Fuzzy Naive Bayes	9.5514	13.0588	10.7682	13.0213	-
FSNB	5.1301	10.9064	5.4943	9.5208	-
ε-SVR	5.6988	8.9337	5.8328	9.7766	-
LID3	3.7557	8.6793	3.1859	8.8876	5731
LID3 $(T_m = 0.05)$	3.9146	8.8925	3.3100	8.9437	2285
LID3 $(T_m = 0.10)$	4.1259	8.9649	3.5013	9.1994	1493
LID3 $(T_m = 0.15)$	4.9315	9.8419	4.3850	10.1869	757
LID3 $(T_m = 0.20)$	5.9327	9.8341	5.1525	10.7063	204
LID3 $(T_m = 0.25)$	7.2166	10.5858	5.9409	10.3711	81
LID3 $(T_m = 0.30)$	14.0175	18.9539	12.4700	19.1159	5

Table 5.7 Prediction results in MSE on the sunspot prediction problem

Prediction Model	AVE (%)		$\sigma_E(\%)$		|LDT|
	Training	Test	Training	Test	(LDT only)
Fuzzy Naive Bayes	493.91	810.74	1223.15	1630.48	-
FSNB	134.70	499.66	364.86	723.58	-
ε-SVR	266.81	418.13	545.27	913.95	-
LID3	57.824	532.73	101.86	1117.90	5731
LID3 $(T_m = 0.05)$	62.650	549.12	110.95	1077.70	2285
LID3 $(T_m = 0.10)$	69.807	569.60	120.94	1139.00	1493
LID3 $(T_m = 0.15)$	103.82	692.63	197.23	1326.30	757
LID3 $(T_m = 0.20)$	147.20	729.56	316.19	1520.10	204
LID3 $(T_m = 0.25)$	208.29	756.15	496.02	1498.60	81
LID3 $(T_m = 0.30)$	839.13	2501.70	1555.00	4398.50	5

Table 5.6 shows the results (in AVE) of LID3 obtained by applying forward branch merging where the merging threshold varies from 0.05 to 0.30 and Table 5.7 shows the results in MSE. From these tables, we can see that ε-SVR gives the best results and the LID3 gives the second best. If we increase the merging threshold T_m, the size of LDT (i.e., the number of branches) is reduced greatly while the error rate only changes slightly. For example, compare $T_m = 0$ (no merging) and $T_m = 0.25$, with the tree reduced about 98.6% in size and the error rate only

increasing 1.91%. The prediction peformance for merged LDTs (with $T_m = 0.2$ and $T_m = 0.25$) compared with non-merged LDTs are shown in Figs. 5.7 and 5.8. When $T_m = 0.20$, the prediction performance is not significantly influenced compared to non-merged trees (see Fig. 5.9). However, the prediction performance is greatly worse when $T_m = 0.25$ than $T_m = 0.20$ (see the bottom of Fig. 5.8, there is a bad regression).

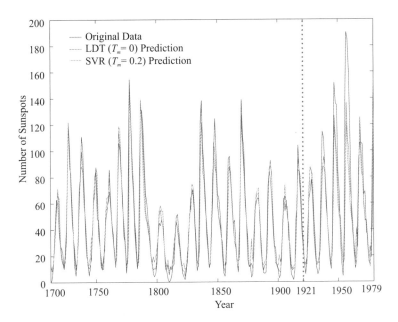

Fig. 5.7   The prediction results obtained from LID3 without merging and LID3 with $T_m = 0.2$, where the data on the left (1712–1921) are for training and the right (1921–1979) are for test

Fig. 5.10 also shows the scatter plot of the actual sunspot number against the predicted number on 59 test data by using fuzzy Naive Bayes, fuzzy semi-Naive Bayes, ε-SVR, non-merged LDT, the merged LDT with $T_m = 0.05$ and the merged LDT with $T_m = 0.25$. In these graphs, for an error free prediction all points will fall on the line defined by $y = x$. Roughly, from the illustration, we can see that SVR and non-merged LDT have better performance, because predicted values are distributed closer to $y = x$ than the other two models.

5.3.4 Flood Forecasting

In this section, a flood forecasting problem is investigated. We attempt to model the stream flow characteristics of a river. The database we shall investigate here describes the Bird Creek river basin in Oklahoma, USA. The data was collected to

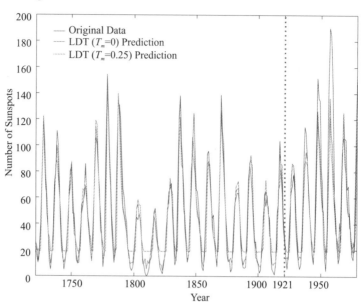

Fig. 5.8   The prediction results obtained from LID3 without merging and LID3 with $T_m = 0.25$, where the data on the left (1712–1921) are for training and the right (1921–1979) are for test

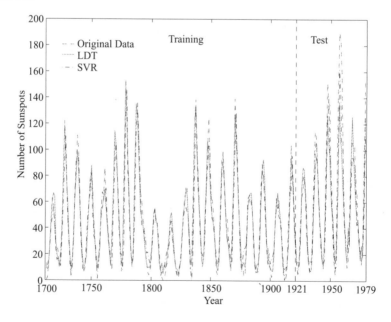

Fig. 5.9   The prediction results obtained from SVR and LID3 without merging, where the data on the left (1712–1921) are for training and the right (1921–1979) are for test

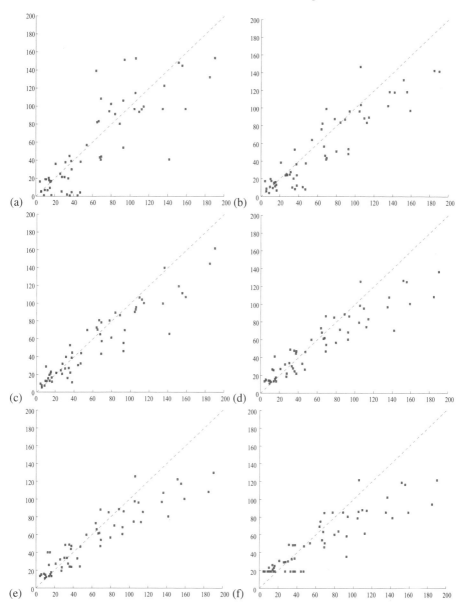

Fig. 5.10 Scatter plot showing original data verses prediction data on the sunspot prediction problem. From the upper left to the bottom right figures: (a) fuzzy Naive Bayes; (b) fuzzy semi-Naive Bayes; (c) support vector regression; (d) linguistic prediction tree; (e) merged linguistic prediction tree with $T_m = 0.05$; (f) merged linguistic prediction tree with $T_m = 0.25$

form part of a real-time hydrological model inter-comparison exercise conducted in Vancouver, Canada in 1987 and reported by the World Meteorological Organization (WMO) in 1992. Fig. 5.11 shows the Bird-Creek river basin [17].

The database describing the Bird Creek catchment area gives information on two attributes: the average rainfall (U) given in mm, derived from 12 rainfall gauges situated in or near the catchment area and the river's stream flow (Y) given in m^3/s, measured using a continuous stage recorder. Both values were recorded in the database at 6 hour intervals from October 1955 to November 1974. In this thesis only a subset of the original database is used for modelling. This is comprised of 2,090 training records of rainfall and stream flow values from November 1972, 00:00, to April 1974, 06:00 and 1,030 test records of rainfall and stream flow values from November 1974, 12:00 hours, to December 1974, 12:00 hours [14].

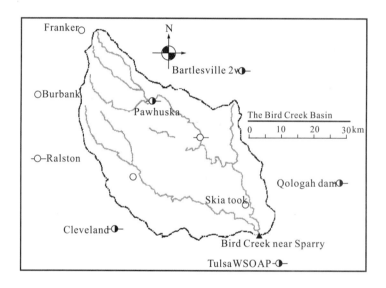

Fig. 5.11 The Bird Creek drainage basin [17]

Flood forecasting is a typical problem of prediction and several models had been developed based on the Bird-Creek data. Clukie and Han [18] extensively developed the Weather Radar Information Processor System (WRIP) [19], which is a well-known rainfall-runoff modeling system. In this research, the LDT model is applied by using a windowing technique to obtain the required prediction of the stream flow 36 hours ahead (i.e., Y_{T+6}).

The window technique is described as follows: The model is first initialized with rainfall values, U_{T-2} to U_T and stream flow values Y_{T-2} to Y_T, and optimized to predict the stream flow value Y_{T+1}, We then feedback the newly predicted stream flow value $\widehat{Y}_{T+1}$, along with the real rainfall value for U_{T+1}. We now run the model using rainfall values, U_{T-1} to U_{T+1} and stream flow values Y_{T-1} to $\widehat{Y}_{T+1}$ and predict the stream flow at Y_{T+2}. This process is then repeated four more times until we obtain a prediction for the stream flow at Y_{T+6} (36 hours in advance). Fig. 5.12 gives an illustration of the windowing process.

The results obtained from LID3 are compared with the results of Fuzzy Semi-Naive Bayes and ε-SVR. The results in terms of average errors are shown in Table 5.8 , where the results of ε-SVR are based on parameters: $\sigma = 3$, $\varepsilon = 0.05$ and $C = 5$. The LID3 results are obtained based on the linguistic translation by which each attribute is discretized uniformly by 3 fuzzy labels and the LDT extends with a maximum depth 6.

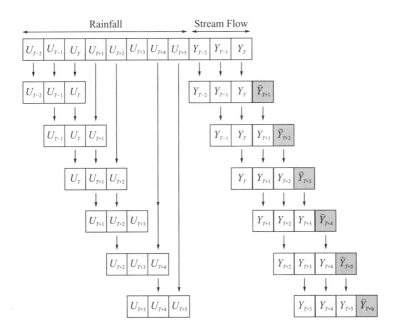

Fig. 5.12 The windowing technique for the flood forecasting problem

As we can see from Table 5.8 , LID3 outperforms the other models on this problem. However, the size of the LDT is still very large (2133 branches without merging). By applying forward merging, the errors increase only slightly while the number of branches are significantly reduced. With $T_m = 0.30$, the LID3 still gives better accuracy to Fuzzy Semi-Naive Bayes. However, the tree has only 108 branches and compared to LID3 without merging, the tree size has been reduced nearly 94%. The performance on the test set can be seen from Fig. 5.13 . Although LID3 over-estimates at some peaks, it still captures the original data well.

Table 5.8 Average errors with standard deviations on test set of the flood forecasting problem

Prediction Model	AVE %	$\sigma_E(\%)$	$|LDT|$
Fuzzy Naive Bayes	2.9922	7.3017	-
FSNB	2.9219	7.1798	-
ε-SVR	3.3555	7.6602	-
LID3	2.5625	6.9160	2133
LID3 $(T_m = 0.05)$	2.5596	6.8865	815
LID3 $(T_m = 0.10)$	2.5576	6.1244	652
LID3 $(T_m = 0.15)$	2.6523	6.9574	389
LID3 $(T_m = 0.20)$	2.7932	6.9225	225
LID3 $(T_m = 0.25)$	2.7935	6.9258	203
LID3 $(T_m = 0.30)$	2.8227	7.0835	118
LID3 $(T_m = 0.35)$	2.9368	7.5019	79
LID3 $(T_m = 0.40)$	2.9769	7.7628	37

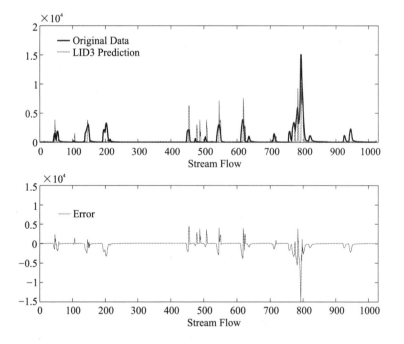

Fig. 5.13 The stream flow prediction with a merged LDT with $T_m = 0.3$

5.4 Query Evaluation

Intuitively, $\lambda(\theta)$ corresponds to those subsets of $\mathbb{F}$ identified as being possible values of D_x by expression θ. In this sense, the imprecise linguistic restriction "x is θ" on x corresponds to the strict constraint $D_x \in \lambda(\theta)$ on D_x[20].

Example 5.3 *Given a variable h representing John's height and* $\mathbb{L}_h = \{$*very short, short, medium, tall, very tall*$\}$*, suppose we are told that "John is **not very tall** but it is **medium to tall**". This constraint can be interpreted as the logical expression*

$$\theta_h = \neg very\ tall \wedge (medium \vee tall)$$

According to definition 3.10*, the possible label sets of the given linguistic constraint* θ_h *are*

$$\lambda(\theta_h) = \lambda(\neg very\ tall \wedge (medium \vee tall)) = \{\{medium\},\{medium,tall\},\{tall\}\}$$

Two kinds of queries are discussed here: single queries and compound queries and the evaluation methods are given in the subsequent sections.

5.4.1 Single Queries

A single query $F_t : \langle \theta_1,\ldots,\theta_n \rangle$ represents the question: Do elements satisfying θ have a value of x_t with description F_t? Consider the vector of linguistic expression $\theta = \langle \theta_1,\ldots,\theta_n \rangle$, where θ_j is the linguistic expression on attribute j. The probability value for F_t conditional on this information using a given a linguistic decision tree can be evaluated through the following steps:

$$m_{\theta_j}(F_j) = \begin{cases} \dfrac{pm(F_j)}{\sum_{F_j \in \lambda(\theta_j)} pm(F_j)} & F_j \in \lambda(\theta_j) \\ = 0 & \text{otherwise} \end{cases} \tag{5.31}$$

where $pm(F_j)$ is the prior mass for focal elements $F_j \in \mathbb{F}_j$ derived from the prior distribution $p(x_j)$ on Ω_j as follows:

$$pm(F_j) = \int_{\Omega_j} m_x(F_j)p(x_j)dx_j \tag{5.32}$$

Usually, we assume that $p(x_j)$ is the uniform distribution over Ω_j so that

$$pm(F_j) \propto \int_{\Omega_j} m_x(F_j)dx_j \tag{5.33}$$

For example, given $\mathbb{L}_x = \{small,large\}$ and x is *small* (i.e., $\theta = small$). By applying the λ function (Definition 3.10), we can generate the possible label sets for x, so that:

$$\lambda(\theta) = \lambda(small) = \{\{small\}, \{small, large\}\}$$

Suppose the prior mass assignments are

$$pm = \{small\} : 0.3, \{small, large\} : 0.2, \{large\} : 0.5$$

According to Eq. (5.31) we then obtain,

$$
\begin{aligned}
m_\theta &= \{small\} : 0.3/(0.3+0.2), \{small, large\} : 0.2/(0.2+0.3) \\
&= \{small\} : 0.6, \{small, large\} : 0.4
\end{aligned}
$$

Hence, $m_\theta(\{small\}) = 0.6$ and $m_\theta(\{small, large\}) = 0.4$ according to the given the linguistic constraint $\theta = small$. For branch B the probability of B given θ is evaluated by

$$P(B|\theta) = \prod_{r=1}^{|B|} m_{\theta_r}(F_r) \qquad (5.34)$$

and therefore, by the Jeffrey's rule [9]

$$P(F_t|\theta) = \sum_{v=1}^{|LDT|} P(F_t|B_v)P(B_v|\theta) \qquad (5.35)$$

5.4.2 Compound Queries

A compound query $\theta_t : \langle \theta_1, \ldots, \theta_n \rangle$ represents the question: Do elements satisfying θ have a value of x_t satisfies the linguistic expression θ_t? Given a linguistic expression $\theta = \langle \theta_1, \ldots, \theta_n \rangle$, where θ_j for $j = 1, \ldots, n$ is the linguistic expression on attribute j, and θ_t (the linguistic expression on the target attribute). The evaluation method for compound queries is based on the single queries.

$$P(\theta_t|\theta) = \sum_{F_t \in \lambda(\theta_t)} P(F_t|\theta) \qquad (5.36)$$

Example 5.4 Consider the $y = \sin(x \times y)$ problem, 7 fuzzy labels are defined on input attributes (i.e., x and y) and target attribute z, respectively. $\mathbb{L}_x = \mathbb{L}_y = \mathbb{L}_z = \{extremely\ small(es),\ very\ small(vs),\ small(s),\ medium(m),\ large(l),\ very\ large(vl),\ extremely\ large(el)\}$. From this we obtain the focal elements describing each attribute: $\mathbb{F}_x = \mathbb{F}_y = \mathbb{F}_z = \{\{es, vs\}, \{vs\}, \{vs, s\}, \{s\}, \{s, m\}, \{s, m\}, \{m\}, \{m, l\}, \{m, l\}, \{l, vl\}, \{vl\}, \{vl, el\}\}$.

Suppose we are given:
$\theta_x = \neg\ very\ small \land small \land \neg\ medium$
$\theta_y = \neg\ large \land (very\ large \lor extremely\ large)$

Given the query for evaluation $F_z^i : \langle \theta_x, \theta_y \rangle$ for $i = 1 : |\mathbb{F}_z|$. According to the above

Eqs. (5.31), (5.34) and (5.35), we obtain:

$$P(\{es,vs\}|\theta) = P(\{vs\}|\theta) = P(\{s\}|\theta) = P(\{s,m\}|\theta) = 0$$
$$P(\{m\}|\theta) = 0.0003, \; P(\{m,l\}|\theta) = 0.0006, \; F = P(\{l\}|\theta) = 0.0152,$$
$$P(\{l,vl\}|\theta) = 0.1646, \; P(\{vl\}|\theta) = 0.2125, \; P(\{vl,el\}|\theta) = 0.2338$$

Suppose the query for evaluation is a compound query

$$\theta_z = \neg large \wedge very \; large$$

. According to the λ-function, we obtain:

$$\lambda(\theta_z) = \{\{very \; large\}, \{very \; large, extremely \; large\}\}$$

Then, according to Eq. (5.36) we obtain:

$$P(\theta_z|\langle \theta_x, \theta_y \rangle) = P(\{vl\}|\langle \theta_x, \theta_y \rangle) + P(\{vl,el\}|\langle \theta_x, \theta_y \rangle) = 0.2125 + 0.2338 = 0.4463$$

5.5 ROC Analysis for Prediction

Currently, all the ROC analysis research is for classification problems. However, in many real-world applications ranging from financial analysis to flood forecasting (e.g., Section 5.3.4) are prediction problems. Hence, it is interesting to consider extend to the ROC analysis to predictors? This is the motivation of this research. A prediction model can be easily used as a classifier by setting a decision threshold. Usually, a good prediction model can be a good classifier as well. However, not all classifiers can be used for prediction. Hence, prediction is at least as important as classifications in machine learning and data mining. In this section, some initial investigations are presented where we only consider predictors based on defuzzification with two fuzzy labels on probabilistic classifiers. This is where the universe of the variable for prediction is discretized by two focal elements (see linguistic decision tree for prediction) acting as class labels, and the final prediction is obtained by defuzzification.

5.5.1 Predictors and Probabilistic Classifiers

Consider a prediction problem where the output space or target attribute t is numeric. For each instance x (a multi-dimensional vector) the aim is to predict the corresponding target value t (i.e., $x_i \rightarrow \hat{t_i}$). Suppose we discretize the output universe with m focal elements [2]: $F_1, \ldots, F_m$. We can consider each fuzzy set as a single

---

[2] The ROC curve for prediction has not necessarily to be in label semantics framework, where $F_1, \ldots, F_m$ are focal elements. We can generalize it by considering $F_1, \ldots, F_m$ as fuzzy sets.

class label which has weights denoted by ξ and each instance can be mapped to a representation as follows:

$$x_i \rightarrow \langle F_1 : \xi_1, \ldots, F_m : \xi_m \rangle$$

where $\sum_{i=1}^{m} \xi_i = 1$. We then can use an arbitrary probabilistic classifier to obtain a series of conditional probabilities on target fuzzy sets given a test instance x: $P(F_1|x), \ldots, P(F_m|x)$. The estimate of t, denoted by $\hat{t}$, to be the expected value:

$$\hat{t} = \int_{\Omega} t \, p(t|x) \, dt \tag{5.37}$$

where,

$$p(t|x) = \sum_{j=1}^{m} p(t|F_j) \, P(F_j|x) \tag{5.38}$$

and

$$p(t|F_j) = \frac{M_t(F_j)}{\int_{\Omega_t} M_t(F_j) \, dt} \tag{5.39}$$

where $M_x(F_j)$ is the membership of x belonging to fuzzy set (or label) F_j. Hence we obtain:

$$\hat{t} = \sum_{j=1}^{m} P(F_j|x) \, E(t|F_j) \tag{5.40}$$

where,

$$E(t|F_j) = \frac{\int_{\Omega_t} t \, M_t(F_j) \, dt}{\int_{\Omega_t} M_t(F_j) \, dt} \tag{5.41}$$

where the process of calculating $E(x_t|F_j)$ is also called defuzzification in some other literature. More details about obtaining a predictor from a probabilistic classifier are available in Reference [21] and Chapter 5.

From the above we can see that, by fuzzifying the continuous target attribute t into intervals which could be considered as class labels, any probabilistic classifiers can be extended to a prediction model. However, we need to notice that the class labels are not discrete but overlap each other and there are many different degrees of overlapping. For example, Fig. 5.14 shows four different possible overlapping. In this paper, we only consider the simplest case that $m = 2$, where one fuzzy label is represented by $-$ and the other by $+$. In the following paper, unless otherwise stated, we will use the fuzzy labels with 50% overlapping (Fig. 5.14 -d), it satisfying:

$$\forall i : P(-|x_i) + P(+|x_i) = 1$$

The basic difference between such predictors and normal probabilistic classifiers is that the class labels overlap each other. For a particular instance, it has actual membership probabilities of positives from fuzzy discretization $P(+|x)$ and predicted class probabilities $\hat{P}(+|x)$ from classifiers. In the following context, unless otherwise stated, we will focus on the membership probabilities of positives and we

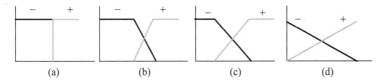

Fig. 5.14 Different degrees of overlapping between two fuzzy labels that are used as class labels

---

Algorithm 4: ROC Curve for Classification Problems

- Given a test set of size Γ, rank the instances on decreasing predicted membership scores of the "positive" class $\hat{p}_i$, where $i \in \{1, 2, \ldots, \Gamma\}$.
- $TP_0 = 0$, $FP_0 = 0$
- FOR $i = 1 : \Gamma$, DO:
  $TP_i = TP_{i-1} + p_i/n_+$, $FP_i = FP_{i-1} + (1 - p_i)/n_-$
- Starting from $(0,0)$, for $i = 1 : \Gamma$, draw the curve by joining (FP_{i-1}, TP_{i-1}) and (FP_i, TP_i) successively

---

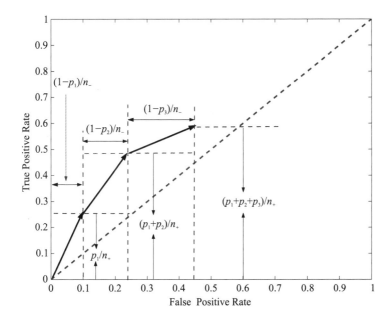

Fig. 5.15 An illustration of drawing ROC curve (the black arrows) and AUC calculation by adding a new point

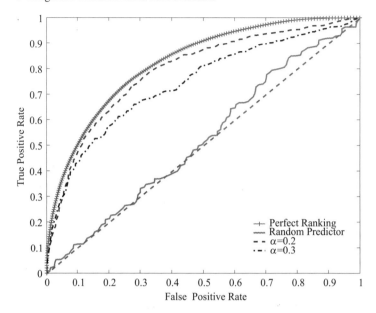

Fig. 5.16 ROC curves for a prefect-ranking predictor, a random predictor, and two predictors obtained from a perfect ranking predictor corrupted by different levels of noise

write $P(+|x_i)$ as p_i and $\hat{P}(+|x_i)$ as $\hat{p}_i$. For example, given the original membership scores and predicted scores, how can we draw the ROC curve? A simple and practical method based on discrete class labels is proposed as follows:

In the Algorithm 4, n_+ represents the sum of positive parts on all examples, it is obtained by:

$$n_+ = \sum_{i=1}^{\Gamma} p(i|+) = \sum_{i=1}^{\Gamma} p(i) \tag{5.42}$$

Similarly, we can obtain:

$$n_- = \sum_{i=1}^{\Gamma} p(i|-) = \sum_{i=1}^{\Gamma} (1 - p(i)) = \Gamma - n_+ \tag{5.43}$$

Fig. 5.15 shows a set of ROC curves on a real-world prediction problem: the curve marked with "+" represents a perfect ranking, which means that given a ranked list decreasing with $\hat{p}_i$ (i.e., $\hat{p}_1 \geq \ldots \geq \hat{p}_\Gamma$), the relation $p_1 \geq \ldots \geq p_\Gamma$ holds. The curves marked with $\alpha = 0.2$ represents a perfect ranking predictor corrupted by a uniform distributed noise in the range of [0, 0.2], denoted by $U[0,0.2]$. So that the predicted probabilities are:

$$\forall i \quad \hat{p}_i = p_i \pm \varepsilon \qquad \varepsilon \sim U[0, \alpha]$$

The random classifier is a random guess that follows:

$$\forall i \quad \hat{p}_i \sim U[0,1]$$

As we can see from those curves, they exhibit similar properties as with discrete labels, the only difference is that the maximum value for prediction is not 1. This will be discussed in details in the next section.

5.5.2 AUC Value for Prediction

Fig. 5.15 gives an illustration of the drawing a ROC curve for such prediction problems. We need to notice that the optimal point is not (1,0) for predictions (i.e., AUC value is always less than 1). The reason for this is because we use overlapping fuzzy labels. ROC analysis reflects the separation of positive and negative examples by a classifier. In this case, no matter how good a classifier is, it still cannot completely separate the positives and negatives because they are overlapped to each other. The different overlapping degrees will result in different maximum AUC values. Fig. 5.16 depicts the ROC curves with maximum AUC values on the fuzzy labels with different overlapping degrees shown in Fig. 5.14 . In the legend, the AUC values that are calculated by the method that will be discussed in the following part of this section.

Consider the ranking list on decreasing membership scores in the way we draw the ROC curves. The first example of the ranking list is the one with the highest predicted score $\hat{p}_1$ with original score of p_1. By adding this example to the ROC space, the area under the ROC curve is a triangle with side lengths of $(1-p_1)/n_-$ and p_1/n_+, respectively (see Fig. 5.17). So that:

$$AUC_1 = \frac{p_1(1-p_1)}{2n_+n_-} \tag{5.44}$$

By adding a new example with score of p_2, the ROC curve is extended and a new area in trapezoidal shape is added so that the current AUC becomes:

$$AUC_2 = \frac{1}{n_+n_-}\left[\frac{p_1(1-p_1)}{2} + (1-p_2)\frac{p_1+(p_1+p_2)}{2}\right]$$

Similarly, by adding the third point:

$$AUC_3 = \frac{1}{n_+n_-}\left[\frac{p_1(1-p_1)}{2} + (1-p_2)\frac{p_1+(p_1+p_2)}{2}\right.$$
$$\left. + (1-p_3)\frac{(p_1+p_2)+(p_1+p_2+p_3)}{2}\right]$$

By successively adding the kth example ($k \neq 1$), we can obtain:

$$AUC_k = \frac{1}{2n_+n_-}\sum_{i=1}^{k}(1-p_i)\left(2\sum_{j=1}^{i-1}p_j + p_i\right) \tag{5.45}$$

Eq. (5.45) can be rearranged and the AUC value for prediction on a test set with L examples is:

$$AUC = \frac{1}{2n_+n_-} \left[\sum_{i=1}^{L} p_i(1-p_i) + 2C \right] \tag{5.46}$$

where,

$$C = \sum_{i=2}^{L} \sum_{j=1}^{i-1} p_j(1-p_i) \tag{5.47}$$

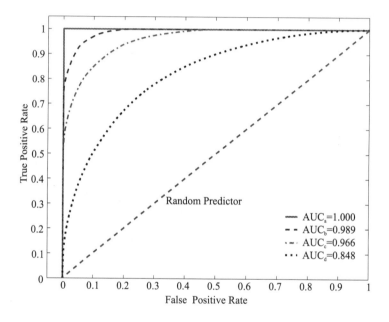

Fig. 5.17 ROC curves with maximum AUC values given fuzzy labels on different degrees of overlapping in figure 5.14

Consider the Eq. (5.46), the first term $\sum_{i=1}^{L} p_i(1-p_i)$ is invariant to different rankings. Now we only consider the term C to investigate the relation between AUC value and example ranking. Term C can be separated into two terms $A_i = 1 - p_i$ and $B_i = \sum_{j=1}^{i-1} p_j$ so that $C = \sum_i A_i B_i$. Suppose we have the following ranking of examples according to the B terms:

$$R_p : \cdots 1 - p_k, 1 - p_{k+1} \cdots$$

if we swap the positions of these two examples to:

$$R_x : \cdots 1 - p_{k+1}, 1 - p_k \cdots$$

Suppose $p_k \geq p_{k+1}$. Such swapping is referred to as bad swapping, because R_p is more desirable than R_x for a better ranking. The swapping will result in a change in AUC values, if we define:

$$D(R_p) = \sum_{i=2}^{k+1} A_i B_i = (1 - p_k)T + (1 - p_{k+1})(T + p_k)$$

$$D(R_x) = \sum_{i=2}^{k+1} A_i B_i = (1 - p_{k+1})T + (1 - p_k)(T + p_{k+1})$$

where $T = \sum_{j=1}^{k-1} p_j$ and according to Eq. (5.47) we obtain:

$$C(R_p) = D(R_p) + \sum_{i=k+2}^{L} \sum_{j=1}^{i-1} p_j(1 - p_i)$$

$$C(R_x) = D(R_x) + \sum_{i=k+2}^{L} \sum_{j=1}^{i-1} p_j(1 - p_i)$$

The latter terms for $C(R_p)$ and $C(R_x)$ have identical values. Therefore, according to Eq. (5.46), we can calculate the change in AUC values by exchanging these two examples as follows:

$$AUC(R_p) - AUC(R_x) = \frac{1}{n_+ n_-}[C(R_p) - C(R_x)]$$

$$= \frac{1}{n_+ n_-}[D(R_p) - D(R_x)] = \frac{p_k - p_{k+1}}{n_+ n_-} \geq 0$$

where the equality holds when $p_k = p_{k+1}$. If we suppose $p_k \leq p_{k+1}$, such a swapping then becomes a *good swapping*, the AUC values will be increased by the same value. For example, we start from a perfect ranking R_p shown in Table 5.9 . We can obtain:

$$n_- = \sum_i n_i = 0.2 + 0.4 + 0.6 + 0.8 + 1 = 3$$

$$n_+ = 5 - 3 = 2$$

By swapping 0.8 and 0.6, we obtain the change in AUC as follows:

$$\frac{p_k - p_{k+1}}{n_+ n_-} = \frac{(1 - 0.6) - (1 - 0.8)}{2 \times 3} = 0.0333$$

So that the new AUC value for the rearranged list is

$$AUC(R_{x_1}) = AUC(R_p) - 0.0333 = 0.8000$$

Based on the new ranking list R_{x_1}, swap 0.8 and 0.4, and we then can obtain a new ranking list R_{x_2}, such that:

$$\frac{p_k - p_{k+1}}{n_+ n_-} = \frac{(1 - 0.4) - (1 - 0.8)}{2 \times 3} = 0.0667$$

$$AUC(R_{x_2}) = AUC(R_{x_1}) - 0.0667 = 0.7333$$

Similarly, we can obtain another bad ranking list R_{x_3} by such swapping (i.e., bad swapping) and the AUC values will keep decreasing.

Table 5.9 AUC values with different rankings by exchanging examples from the perfect ranking, where $n_i = 1 - p_i$

	n_1	n_2	n_3	n_4	n_5	$\frac{p_k - p_{k+1}}{n_+ n_-}$	AUC
R_p	0.2	0.4	0.6	0.8	1.0	0	0.8333
R_{x_1}	0.2	0.4	0.8	0.6	1.0	0.0333	0.8000
R_{x_2}	0.2	0.8	0.4	0.6	1.0	0.0667	0.7333
R_{x_3}	0.2	0.8	0.4	1.0	0.6	0.0667	0.6667

5.6 Summary

In this chapter, the methodology of using LDT to do prediction (or LPT) was proposed and tested on several benchmark problems such as function regression, time series prediction and real-world forecasting applications. By empirical studies, we show that the LDT model has equivalent prediction ability compared to several state of the art prediction model such as ε-SVR and Fuzzy Semi-Naive Bayes. A forward merging has been described to increase transparency without great sacrifices in accuracy. Finally, we discuss the method to evaluate linguistic queries by LDT and tested this on a toy problem. Lastly, an extension of using ROC analysis for prediction is proposed.

Similar to the LDT model in the last chapter, we are not arguing that the LPT model is the best algorithm in terms of accuracy. Although we cannot say the LDT model outperform others, we may say that LDT model has equivalent prediction performance compared to other prediction algorithms. On the other hand, the LDT model has better transparency in the following two aspects: (a) Unlike other black-box prediction models, an LDT can be interpreted as a set of linguistic rules, which may provides the information as to how the predictions are made. (b) The high-level knowledge representation structure of the LDT model allows us to evaluate linguistic queries based on the label semantics framework.

References

[1] Blake C., Merz C. J.: UCI machine learning repository.

[2] Quinlan J. R.: Induction of decision trees, Machine Learning, 1: pp. 81-106. (1986).

[3] Quinlan J. R.:C4.5: Programs for Machine Learning, San Mateo: Morgan Kaufmann. (1993).

[4] Janikow C. Z.: Fuzzy decision trees: issues and methods, IEEE Trans. on Systems, Man, and Cybernetics-Part B: Cybernetics, 28(1): pp. 1-14. (1998).

[5] Olaru C., Wehenkel L.: A complete fuzzy decision tree technique, Fuzzy Sets and Systems, 138: pp. 221-254. (2003).

[6] Peng Y., Flach P. A.: Soft discretization to enhance the continuous decision trees, Integrating Aspects of Data Mining, Decision Support and Meta-Learning, C. Giraud-Carrier, N. Lavrac and S. Moyle, editors, pp. 109-118, ECML/PKDD'01 workshop. (2001).

[7] Yuan Y., Shaw M. J.: Induction of fuzzy decision trees, Fuzzy Sets and Systems, 69: pp. 125-139. (1995).

[8] Breiman L., Friedman J. H.: Classification and Regression Trees, Wadsworth Inc. (1984).

[9] Jeffrey R. C.: The Logic of Decision, Gordon & Breach Inc., New York. (1965).

[10] Randon N. J., Lawry J.: Linguistic modelling using a semi-Naive Bayes framework, IPMU-2002, Annecy, France. (2002).

[14] Randon N. J.: Fuzzy and Random Set Based Induction Algorithms, PhD Thesis, Department of Engineering Mathematics, University of Bristol. (2004).

[12] Vapnik V.: Statistical Learning Theory, New York: Wiley, (1998).

[13] Gunn S. R.: Support vector machines for classification and regression. Technical Report of Departartment of Electronics and Computer Science, University of Southampton. (1998).

[14] Randon N. J.: Fuzzy and Random Set Based Induction Algorithms, PhD Thesis, Department of Engineering Mathematics, University of Bristol. (2004).

[15] Hyndman R., Akram M.: Time series Data Library. Monash University. http://www-personal.buseco.monash.edu.au/~hyndman/TSDL/index.htm.

[16] Weigend A. A., Huberman B. A., Rumelhart D. E.: Predicting sunspots and exchange rates with connectionist networks, In M. Casdagli and S. Eubank, Editors, Non-linear Modelling and Forecasting, SFI Studies in the Science of Complexity, Proceedings, Vol. XII, pp. 395-432, Addison-Wesley. (1992).

[17] Han D., Cluckie I. D., Karbassioun D., Lawry J., Krauskopf B.: River flow modelling using fuzzy decision trees, Water Resources Management, 16(6), pp. 431-445. (2002).

[18] Cluckie I. D., Han D.: Dendritic river modelling system in WRIP, Fifth International Symposium on Hydraulically Application of Weather Radar, Heian-Kaikan, Keyoto, Japan. (2001).

[19] Han D.: Weather Radar Information Processing and Real-Time Flood Forecasting, PhD Thesis University of Salford. (1991).

[20] Lawry J., Hall J. W., Bovey R.: Fusion of expert and learnt knowledge in a framework of fuzzy labels, Journal of Approximate Reasoning, 36: pp. 151-198. (2004).

[21] Qin Z., Lawry J.: Prediction trees using linguistic modelling, to appear in the Proceedings of International Fuzzy Association World Congress-05, September 2005, Beijing, China. (2005).

6

Bayesian Methods Based on Label Semantics

Intuition is a poor guide when facing probabilistic evidence.

– Dennis V. Lindley

6.1 Introduction

In previous chapters, we have introduced the Linguistic Decision Tree model and shown how this model can be used for classification and prediction. However, for some complex problems, good probability estimations can only be obtained by deep LDTs, which have low transparency. In such cases, how can we build a model which has a good probability estimation but which uses compact LDTs? In this chapter, two hybrid learning models are proposed combining the LDT model and the fuzzy Naive Bayes classifier. In the first model, an unlabeled instance is classified according to the Bayesian estimation given a single LDT. In the second model, a set of disjoint LDTs are used as Bayesian estimators. Experimental studies show that the first new hybrid models has both better accuracy and transparency when compared to fuzzy Naive Bayes and LDTs at shallow tree depths. The second model is shown to have equivalent performance to the LDT model.

Most tree induction models are designed for classification but not for prediction. Trees that estimate the probability of class membership are also referred to as Probability Estimation Trees (PETs)[1], where probability of a particular class given a branch is calculated by the proportion of data belonging to this class to all the data covered by the branch. For the linguistic decision tree, the probability of a branch belonging to a particular class is evaluated based on the proportion of data in this class relative to all the data covered by the linguistic expressions of the branch. Therefore, the LDT model can be regarded as a probability estimation tree model based on fuzzy labels. The LDT model has been shown to be an effective model for both classification and prediction. However, for complex problems, good probability estimations can only be obtained by deep LDTs, which have a poor transparency. In such cases, how can we build a model which has a good probability estimation with compact LDTs (i.e., LDTs with shallow depths or with a lesser number of branches)? This question motivates the research presented in this chapter.

Naive Bayes is a well known and much studied algorithm in machine learning. It is a simple, effective and efficient learning method. Although Naive Bayes classification makes the unrealistic assumption that the values of the attributes of an instance are conditionally independent given the class of the instance, this model is remarkably successful in practice. In this chapter, an extended version of Naive Bayes based on label semantics is introduced. Two new hybrid models are proposed combining the Naive Bayes classifier and linguistic decision trees and tested on a number of UCI datasets [2].

6.2 Naive Bayes

Bayesian learning[①] provides a probabilistic approach to inference based on the Bayes theorem. It is one of the most important and commonly used learning algorithm because it provides a quantitative approach to weighing the evidence supporting the alternative hypothesis. So-called "naive" Bayesian classification is the optimal method of supervised learning if the attributes are conditionally independent given the classes. Although this assumption is almost always violated in practice, Naive Bayesian learning is remarkably effective in practice [4].

Given a test instance that is presented, the learner is asked to predict its class according to the evidence provided by the training data. We define c as a random variable denoting the class of an instance: $x = \langle x_1, \ldots, x_n \rangle$ as a vector of variables denoting the observed attribute values; $\mathbb{C}$ represents the set of classes; Suppose $y = \langle y_1, \ldots, y_n \rangle$ is a particular observed attribute value vector (a particular instance); and $x = y$ as shorthand for $x_1 = y_1 \land x_2 = y_2 \land \ldots \land x_n = y_n$. This dependence

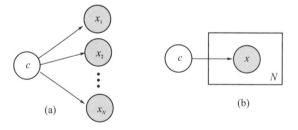

(a)   (b)

Fig. 6.1   Graphical representations of the Naive Bayes classifier. The dependency relationships in subfigure (a) can be simplified to subfigure (b) where the plate represents the duplications

---

① Bayesian learning is a broad research area and it has become the main stream of machine learning [3]. In this book, we employ a different approach for handling uncertainty so that only the Naive Bayes classifier is introduced.

relationship can be represented by directed graphs shown in Fig. 6.1 . Naive Bayes is also considered as one of the simplest probabilistic graphical models.

6.2.1 Bayes Theorem

Expected classification error can be minimized by choosing

$$\arg\max_{c}(P(c = C|x = \mathbf{y}))$$

according to Bayes's theorem:

$$P(H|D) = \frac{P(D|H)}{H} \tag{6.1}$$

where H is the hypothesis and D represents the data or evidence. Given a particular class $C_j \in \mathbb{C}$, we can obtain:

$$P(c = C_j|x = \mathbf{y}) = \frac{P(x = \mathbf{y}|c = C_j)P(c = C_j)}{P(x = \mathbf{y})} \tag{6.2}$$

$$= \frac{P(x = \mathbf{y}|c = C_j)P(c = C_j)}{\sum_j P(x = \mathbf{y}|c = C_j)P(c = C_j)} \tag{6.3}$$

Since the denominator in Eq. (6.2) is invariant across classes, we can consider it as a normalization parameter Z. So, Eq. (6.4) is as follows:

$$P(c = C_j|x = \mathbf{y}) = \frac{P(x = \mathbf{y}|c = C_j)P(c = C_j)}{Z} \tag{6.4}$$

so that:

$$P(c = C_j|x = \mathbf{y}) \propto P(x = \mathbf{y}|c = C_j)P(c = C_j) \tag{6.5}$$

Now suppose we assume for each variable x_i that its outcome is independent of the outcome of all other variables x_j, given C_j. Formally, we assume that,

$$P(x_1 = y_1|x_2 = y_2 \wedge \dots \wedge x_n = y_n, c = C_j) = P(x_1 = y_1|c = C_j) \tag{6.6}$$

and so on for x_2 through x_n. The $P(x_1 = y_1 \wedge \dots \wedge x_n = y_n|c = C_j)$ equals to:

$$P(x_1 = y_1|c = C_j)P(x_1 = y_1|c = C_j)\dots P(x_n = y_n|c = C_j) = \prod_{i=1}^{n} P(x_i = y_i|c = C_j)$$

In discrete cases (i.e., the training data is not continuous), the above product can be estimated from given training data as follows:

$$\hat{P}(x_i = y_i|c = C_j) = \frac{count(x_i = y_i \wedge c = C_j)}{count(c = C_j)} \tag{6.7}$$

For a qualitative attribute, its probabilities can be estimated from corresponding frequencies. For a quantitative attribute, either probability density estimation or discretization can be employed to estimate its probabilities. Under probability density estimation, if the assumed density is not a proper estimate of the true density, the Naive Bayes classification accuracy tends to degrade[5]. Yang and Webb[6] argue that as long as the attribute independence assumption holds and discretization satisfies $P(c = C_j|x^* = \mathbf{y}^*) = P(c = C_j|x = \mathbf{y})$ (where instance $\mathbf{y}_i^*$ is the discretized version of instance x), discretization will result in Naive Bayes classifiers delivering probability estimates directly proportional to those that would be obtained if the correct probability density function were employed. Some other arguments about the independent assumption and discretization of continuous attribute universes can be found in References [7] and [8].

6.2.2 Fuzzy Naive Bayes

In the label semantics framework, suppose we are given focal set $\mathbb{F}_j$ for each attribute x_j. Assuming that attribute x_j is numeric with a continuous universe Ω_j, then the likelihood of x_j given C_t can be represented by a density function $p(x_j|C_t)$ determined from the database DB_t and prior density according to Jeffrey's rule[9].

$$\forall F \in \mathbb{F}_j \qquad p(x_j|C_t) = \sum_{F \in \mathbb{F}_j} p(x_j|F)P(F|C_t) \tag{6.8}$$

From the Bayes theorem:

$$p(x_j|F) = \frac{P(F|x_j)p(x_j)}{P(F)} = \frac{m_{x_j}(F)p(x_j)}{pm(F)} \tag{6.9}$$

where according to Section 3.4.1:

$$pm(F) = \int_{\Omega_j} P(F|x_j)p(x_j)\mathrm{d}x_j = \frac{\sum_{x \in DB} m_{x_j}(F)}{|DB|} \tag{6.10}$$

Substituting Eq. (6.9) in Eq. (6.8) and re-arranging gives

$$p(x_j|C_t) = p(x_j) \sum_{F \in \mathbb{F}_j} m_{x_j}(F) \frac{P(F|C_t)}{pm(F)} \tag{6.11}$$

Also $P(F|C_t)$ can be derived from DB_k according to

$$P(F|C_t) = \frac{\sum_{x \in DB_k} m_{x_j}(F)}{|DB_k|} \tag{6.12}$$

Given a Naive Bayes classifier as follows

$$P(C_t|x) \propto \prod_j P(x_j|C_t)P(C_t) \tag{6.13}$$

where $P(x_j|C_t)$ is evaluated by Eq. 6.8. This model is referred to as fuzzy Naive Bayes (FNB).

6.3 Fuzzy Semi-Naive Bayes

The main advantage of using Semi-Naive Bayes over Naive Bayes is that it allows us to solve non-decomposable problems such as XOR by weakening the independence assumption of Naive Bayes. However, in order to utilize Semi-Naive Bayes it is necessary to find effective groupings of attributes within which dependencies must be taken into account. In this chapter, we present and evaluate a number of heuristic search algorithms for finding such groups of attributes.

Given a set of attributes: $x_1, x_2, \ldots, x_n$, they are partitioned into subsets $S_1, \ldots, S_w$ where $w \geq n$ and for each S_i a joint mass assignment m_{ij} is determined as follows: Suppose, w.l.o.g $S_i = \{x_1, \ldots, x_v\}$ then the joint mass assignment is

$$\forall T_1 \times \ldots \times T_v \in 2^{\mathbb{L}_1} \times \ldots \times 2^{\mathbb{L}_v} \tag{6.14}$$

$$m_{ij}(T_1, \ldots, T_v) = \frac{1}{|DB_j|} \sum_{k \in DB} \prod_{r=1}^{w} m_{rj}(T_i : x_i \in S_r) \tag{6.15}$$

Hence the prototype describing C_j is defined as $\langle m_{ij}, \ldots, m_{wj} \rangle$. A prototype of this form naturally defines a joint mass assignment m_j on the whole cross product space $2^{\mathbb{L}_1} \times \ldots \times 2^{\mathbb{L}_n}$ conditional on C_j as follows:

$$\forall T_1 \times \ldots \times T_n \in 2^{\mathbb{L}_1} \times \ldots \times 2^{\mathbb{L}_n} m_j(T_1, \ldots, T_n) = \prod_{r=1}^{w} m_{r,j}(T_i : x_i \in S_r) \tag{6.16}$$

In this formulation we are encoding variable dependence within the variable groupings $S_i : i = 1, \ldots w$, and assuming independence between the groups.

In order to estimate classification probabilities given input vectors of real attribute values we need a mechanism for mapping from mass assignments on label space onto density functions on attribute space.

Definition 6.1 (Conditional density given a mass assignment)
Let x be a variable into Ω with prior distribution $p(x)$, $\mathbb{L}$ be a set of labels for x and m be a posterior mass assignment for the set of appropriate labels of x inferred from some database DB. Then the posterior distribution of x conditional on m is given by

$$\forall x \in \Omega, \; p(x|m) = p(x) \sum_{S \subseteq \mathbb{L}} \frac{m(S)}{pm(S)} m_x(S) \tag{6.17}$$

where pm(S) is the prior mass assignment generated by the prior distribution $p(x)$ according to

$$pm(S) = \int_{\Omega} m_x(S) p(x) dx \tag{6.18}$$

This definition is motivated by the following argument based on the theorem of total probability which is for a mass assignment, describing variables x on Ω.

We now consider methods for finding attribute groupings that increase discrimination in the model. Two measures have been proposed in Reference [10]:

Definition 6.2 (Importance measure) *Let the joint mass assignment for S_i given C_j be denoted $m_{i,j}$. For any input vector S_i the probability of class C_j can be estimated using Bayes theorem where*

$$P(C_j|S_i) = \frac{p(S_i|m_{i,j})|C_j|}{p(S_i|m_{i,j})|C_j| + p(S_i|m_{i,\neg j})|C_{\neg j}|} \tag{6.19}$$

where $m_{i,\neg j}$ denotes the mass assignments for S_j given $\neg C_j$. The importance measured of group S_i for class C_j is then defined by

$$IM_j(S_i) = \frac{\sum_{k \in DB_j} P(C_j|S_i(k))}{\sum_{k \in DB} P(C_j|S_i(k))} \tag{6.20}$$

Effectively, $IM_j(S_i)$ is a measure of the importance of the set of variables S_i as discriminators of C_j from the other classes.

Definition 6.3 (Correlation measure) *Let $\mathbb{F}_1$ be the focal sets for S_1 and $\mathbb{F}_2$ the focal sets for S_2. Now let $m_{1,2,j}$ be the joint mass of $S_1 \cup S_2$ given C_j*

$$C(S_1, S_2) = \sqrt{\frac{1}{|\mathbb{F}_1||\mathbb{F}_1|} \sum_{R \subseteq \mathbb{F}_1} \sum_{T \subseteq \mathbb{F}_2} (m_{1,2,j}(R,T) - m_{1,j}(R)m_{2,j}(T))^2} \tag{6.21}$$

Here a threshold must be used to determine whether attributes should be grouped. The nearer the correlation measure gets to 1 the higher the correlation between attribute groups.

We tested our models with a real-world problem taken from the Time Series Data Library[11] and contains data of sunspot numbers between the years 1700-1979. The input attributes are x_{T-12} to x_{T-1} (the data for the previous 12 years) and the output (target) attribute is x_T, i.e., one-year-ahead. The experimental results for LID3, Fuzzy Naive Bayes, Semi-Naive Bayes and ε-SVR[12] are compared in Fig. 5.10. We can see the results are quite comparable. In these graphs, for an error free prediction all points will fall on the line defined by $y = x$. Roughly, from the illustration, we can see that SVR and non-merged LDT have better performance, because predicted values are distributed closer to $y = x$ than the other two models.

Using a somewhat weaker version of this assumption Konoenko proposed a form of Semi-Naive Bayes whereby the set of attributes $\{x_1, \ldots, x_n\}$ is partitioned into groups of correlated attributes $S_1, \ldots, S_m$ where $m \leq n$[13]. Conditional independence is then assumed between the attribute groups so that the Naive Bayes classifier defined by Eq. (6.13) becomes

$$P(x|C_t) = P(x_1,\ldots,x_n|C_t) \propto \prod_{i=1}^{m} P(S_i|C_t) \qquad (6.22)$$

The evaluation of $P(S|C_t)$ can be described as follows: Suppose $S = \{x_1,\ldots,x_k\}$, so that the likelihood $P(x_1,\ldots,x_k|C_t)$ is calculated as follows:

$$P(S|C_t) = P(x_1,\ldots,x_k) \sum_{F_1 \in \mathbb{F}_1} \cdots \sum_{F_k \in \mathbb{F}_k} \frac{m(F_1,\ldots,F_k|C_t)}{pm(F_1,\ldots,F_k)} \prod_{i=1}^{k} m_{x_i}(F_i) \qquad (6.23)$$

which is an extension of Eq. (6.11) in k-dimensional case, where

$$m(F_1,\ldots,F_k|C_t) = \frac{1}{DB} \sum_{i \in DB_t} \prod_{j=1}^{k} m_{x_j(i)}(F_j) \qquad (6.24)$$

and

$$pm(F_1,\ldots,F_k) = \frac{\prod_{j=1}^{k} \int_{\Omega_j} m_{x_j} dx_j}{\prod_{j=1}^{k} \int_{\Omega_j} dx_j} \qquad (6.25)$$

which is the extension of Eq. (6.10). Clearly then Naive Bayes is a special case of Semi-Naive Bayes when $S_i = \{x_i\} : i = 1\ldots,n$. Randon[14] and Lawry[10,15] propose a number of search algorithms for identifying the optimal partition of $\{x_1,\ldots,x_n\}$. These are based mainly on the heuristic that attributes should be grouped if and when grouping increases their overall level of importance as an identifier of a given class. These methods are beyond the scope of this thesis.

6.4 Online Fuzzy Bayesian Prediction

All the algorithms we have discussed belong to offline learning where a static model is learned from history data. This type of modeling is appropriate if the underlying dynamics of the system under consideration does not change over time. However, it is not always the case in many real-world problems that evolve over time. In this section, we introduce an online learning using a Bayesian model based on label semantics. The original results of this research were published in Reference [16] and this section is heavily based on this paper as well.

6.4.1 Bayesian Methods

Consider the following formalization of a prediction problem: Given random variables: $x_1,\ldots,x_n,x_{n+1}$ with universes $\Omega_1,\ldots,\Omega_n,\Omega_{n+1}$, suppose that x_{n+1} is dependent on $x_1,\ldots,x_n$ according to some functional relation

$$x_{n+1} = f(x_1,\ldots,x_n)$$

In fuzzy Bayesian models, the appropriateness of using a label L to describe x can be interpreted as the probability that L is valid given value x, i.e.,

$$\forall x \in \Omega \ \mu_L(x) = P(L|x) \tag{6.26}$$

Since there could be more than one labels be appropriate to describe x, and hence we cannot directly define the probability distribution on the set $\mathbb{L} = \{L_1, \ldots, L_n\}$. Instead, we must base our analysis on the set of atoms generated from $\mathbb{L}$, each identifying a possible state of the world by taking the from:

$$\alpha = \bigwedge_{i=1}^{n} \pm L_i \tag{6.27}$$

where,

$$+L_i = L_i, \ -L_i = \neg L_i$$

For example, given two labels: $\mathbb{L} = \{L_1, L_2\}$ then there are for possible items;

$$\alpha_1 = L_1 \wedge L_2, \ \alpha_2 = L_1 \wedge \neg L_2, \ \alpha_3 = \neg L_1 \wedge L_2, \ \alpha_4 = \neg L_1 \wedge \neg L_2$$

In general, there are 2^m items given the cardinality of $|\mathbb{L}| = m$. Let $\mathbb{P}$ denote the set of atoms with non-zero probability [2] for at least some $x \in \Omega$.

For given $x \in \Omega$ the distribution on atoms $P(\alpha|x)$ for $\alpha \in \mathbb{P}$ can be represented by a mass assignment m_x on the power set of $\mathbb{L}$ as follows:

$$\forall S \subseteq \mathbb{P}, \ P(\alpha_S|x) = m_x(S) \tag{6.28}$$

where α_S is the alpha-function (Eq. (3.34) in Definition 3.12) of given S:

$$\alpha_S = \left(\bigwedge_{L \in S} L \right) \wedge \left(\bigwedge_{L \notin S} \neg L \right)$$

For example, given $\mathbb{L} = \{L_1, \ldots, L_n\}$ with 50% overlapping as shown in Fig. 6.2 .

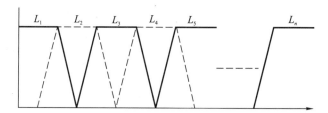

Fig. 6.2 A set of labels $L_1, \ldots, L_n$ with 50% overlapping

---

[2] Given a set of labels $\mathbb{L}$, $\mathbb{P}$ is different from its focal set $\mathbb{F}$ where $\mathbb{P}$ contains the negations of labels. If given some assumptions (e.g., consonance, 50% overlapping and fuzzy linguistic covering), there is a function mapping: $g(\mathbb{F}) \to \mathbb{P}$.

$$P\left(L_1 \wedge L_2 \wedge \bigwedge_{i=3}^{n} \neg L_i | x\right) = m_x(\{L_1, L_2\}) \tag{6.29}$$

where $m_x(S)$ is the probability that the set of all labels appropriate to describe x is S. Given the assumption of 50% overlapping, there are at most two labels that have non-zero probability. In this case, α_S is corresponding to the focal elements of $\mathbb{L}$ and we can obtain $\mathbb{P} = \mathbb{F}$ (see Fig. 6.3). For example:

$$\alpha_1 = L_1 \wedge \neg L_2 \wedge \ldots \wedge \neg L_n = F_1$$

$$\alpha_2 = L_1 \wedge L_2 \wedge \neg L_3 \wedge \ldots \wedge \neg L_n = F_2$$

In the fuzzy Naive Bayes algorithm each input universe is fully covered using trapezoidal fuzzy labels (see Fig. 6.2) and the probability function for the atoms generated as in Fig. 6.3 . Let $\mathbb{P}_i$ denote the atoms generated for variable x_i for $i = 1, \ldots, n$. Then, from the output atom $\alpha_{n+1} \in \mathbb{P}_{n+1}$ and input atom $\alpha_j \in \mathbb{P}$ we infer the conditional probability $P(\alpha_j | \alpha_{n+1})$ from the training database

$$DB = \{\langle x_1(i), \ldots, x_n(i), x_{n+1}(i) : i = 1, \ldots, N\} \tag{6.30}$$

as follows:

$$P(\alpha_j | \alpha_{n+1}) = \frac{\sum_{i \in DB} P(\alpha_j | x_j(i)) P(\alpha_{n+1} | x_{n+1}(i))}{\sum_{i \in DB} P(\alpha_{n+1} | x_{n+1}(i))} \tag{6.31}$$

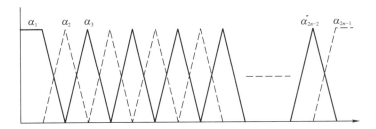

Fig. 6.3 Given the labels in Fig. 6.2 , probability function $P(\alpha|x)$ for atom $\alpha \in \mathbb{P}$ is as the same as focal elements

From this we can use Jeffrey's rule [9] to infer a marginal density conditional on α_{n+1} such that:

$$f(x_j | \alpha_{n+1}) = \sum_{\alpha_j \in \mathbb{P}_j} P(\alpha_j | \alpha_{n+1}) f(x_j | \alpha_j) \tag{6.32}$$

We assume a uniform prior distribution on the input universe Ω_j:

$$\forall x_j \in \Omega_j, \ \alpha_j \in \mathbb{P}_j, \ f(x_j | \alpha_j) = \frac{P(\alpha_j | x_j)}{\int_{\Omega_j} P(\alpha_j | x_j) \mathrm{d}x_j} \tag{6.33}$$

Based on the Bayesian theorem we can obtain the conditional probability $P(\alpha_{n+1}|x_1,\ldots,x_n)$ of each output atom given the input vector $\langle x_1,\ldots,x_n\rangle$ as follows

$$P(\alpha_{n+1}|x_1,\ldots,x_n) = \frac{P(\alpha_{n+1})\prod_{j=1}^n f(x_j|\alpha_{n+1})}{\sum_{\alpha_{n+1}\in\mathbb{P}_{n+1}} P(\alpha_{n+1})\prod_{j=1}^n f(x_j|\alpha_{n+1})} \tag{6.34}$$

Hence, we can obtain a density function on output valves by summing over α_{n+1}, i.e.,

$$P(x_{n+1}|x_1,\ldots,x_n) = \sum_{\alpha_{n+1}\in\mathbb{P}_{n+1}} f(x_{n+1}|\alpha_{n+1})P(\alpha_{n+1}|x_1,\ldots,x_n) \tag{6.35}$$

A estimated output can be obtained by taking the expectation so that:

$$\hat{x}_{n+1} = \int_{\Omega_{n+1}} x_{n+1}f(x_{n+1}|x_1,\ldots,x_n)\mathrm{d}x_{n+1} \tag{6.36}$$

6.4.2 Online Learning

When we consider a dynamic problem, we hope to find the a functional mapping (at time t) from input $\langle x_1,\ldots,x_n\rangle$ to x_{n+1}, formally:

$$g_t : \Omega_1 \times \ldots \times \Omega_n \to \Omega_{n+1}$$

Assuming we are given a training database DB (see Eq. (6.30)) and a new example $x_{i+1} = \langle x_1(i+1),\ldots,x_n(i+1),x_{n+1}(i+1)\rangle$. The conditional probabilities for each output atom can be updated by follows:

$$\tilde{P}(\alpha_j|\alpha_{n+1}) = \frac{|\alpha_{n+1}|P(\alpha_j|\alpha_{n+1}) + wP(\alpha_j|x_j(i+1))P(\alpha_{n+1}|x_{n+1}(i+1))}{|\alpha_{n+1}| + wP(\alpha_{n+1}|x_{n+1}(i+1))} \tag{6.37}$$

where $P(\alpha_j|\alpha_{n+1})$ is the current probability estimate obtained through the current training database DB and $\tilde{P}(\alpha_j|\alpha_{n+1})$ denotes the updated probability by considering the new example x_{i+1}. $|\alpha_{n+1}|$ indicates the degree to which output atom α_{n+1} has been previously encountered during learning given by:

$$|\alpha_{n+1}| = \sum_{k=1}^{i-1} P(\alpha_{n+1}|x_{n+1}(k)) \tag{6.38}$$

Here, w is the learning rate. For example, it can take the value of

$$w(|\alpha_{n+1}|) = \frac{c}{|\alpha_{n+1}|} + 1 \tag{6.39}$$

where c is a constant controlling the level of initial updating. In the absence of any data concerning the atom α_{n+1} conditional probabilities are uniform:

$$P(\alpha_j|\alpha_{n+1}) = \frac{1}{|\mathbb{P}|} : \alpha_j \in \mathbb{P}_j \tag{6.40}$$

Randon *et al.* first apply an online fuzzy Bayesian learning to river flow modeling in order to set up a warning system on flooding. The experimental studies show that the online learning model outperforms the offline fuzzy naive Bayesian model[16].

6.5 Bayesian Estimation Trees

A decision tree, more properly a classification tree, is used to learn a classification function which predicts the value of a target attribute (class attribute) given the values of the independent (input) attributes by a tree-structured model. A node with no split is called a leaf, which is associated with a particular class label. A new unlabeled data is classified by determining which leaf it leads to. Decision tree induction attracts a great attention for its simplicity and effectiveness. Algorithms such as ID3[17], C4.5[18] have been well-known only only in machine learning and but also other scientific communities as well. Traditionally, this setting was sufficient for most of the classification problems and applications. However, more an more applications require some kind of reliability, likelihood or numeric assessment of the quality of each classification. In other words, we do not only want that the model predicts a class value for each example but also that it can be given an estimate of the reliability of each prediction. Such classifiers are usually called soft classifiers[19]. The most general presentation of a soft classifier is a probability estimator, i.e., a model that estimates the probability of a particular class given an unlabeled example. A decision tree classifier is defined as a decision tree with an associated labelling of the leaves with classes. A PET is a decision tree where each leaf is assigned a probability distribution over classes. These probability estimates can for instance be relative frequencies[19]. A thorough study of what are the best methods for PETs would be a successful contribution to machine learning research is given in Reference [1].

6.5.1 Bayesian Estimation Given an LDT

Given a decision tree T is learnt from a training database DB, according to the Bayesian theorem a data element $x = \langle x_1, \ldots, x_n \rangle$ can be classified by

$$P(C_t | x, T) \propto P(x | C_t, T) P(C_t | T) \tag{6.41}$$

We can then divide the attributes into 2 disjoint groups denoted by $x_T = \{x_1, \ldots, x_m\}$ and $x_B = \{x_{m+1}, \ldots, x_n\}$, respectively. x_T is the vector of the variables that are contained in the given tree T and the remaining variables are contained in x_B. Assuming conditional independence between x_T and x_B we obtain:

$$P(x | C_t, T) = P(x_T | C_t, T) P(x_B | C_t, T) \tag{6.42}$$

Because x_B is independent of the given decision tree T and if we assume the variables in x_B are independent of each other given a particular class, we can obtain

$$P(x_B | C_t, T) = P(x_B | C_t) = \prod_{j \in x_B} P(x_j | C_t) \tag{6.43}$$

Now consider x_T. According to Bayes theorem,

$$P(x_T|C_t,T) = \frac{P(C_t|x_T,T)P(x_T|T)}{P(C_t|T)} \qquad (6.44)$$

Combining Eqs. (6.42), (6.43) and (6.44),

$$P(x|C_t,T) = \frac{P(C_t|x_T,T)P(x_T|T)}{P(C_t|T)} \prod_{j \in x_B} P(x_l|C_t) \qquad (6.45)$$

Combining Eqs. (6.41) and (6.45),

$$P(C_t|x,T) \propto P(C_t|x_T,T)P(x_T|T) \prod_{j \in x_B} P(x_j|C_t) \qquad (6.46)$$

Further, since $P(x_T|T)$ is independent from C_t, we have that:

$$P(C_t|x,T) \propto P(C_t|x_T,T) \prod_{j \in x_B} P(x_j|C_t) \qquad (6.47)$$

where $P(x_j|C_t)$ is evaluated according to Eq. (6.11) and $P(C_t|x_T,T)$ is just the probability of class C_t evaluated from the decision tree T according to Eq. (4.16).

The basic idea of using Bayesian estimation given a LDT is to use the LDT as one estimator and the rest of the attributes as other independent estimators. Consider the two extreme cases for Eq. (6.47). If all the attributes are used in building the tree (i.e., $x_T = x$), the probability estimations are from the tree only, that is:

$$P(C_k|x,T) \propto P(C_k|x_T,T)$$

If none of the attributes are used in developing the tree (i.e., $x = x_B$), the probability estimation will become

$$P(C_k|x,T) \propto \prod_{j \in x_B} P(x_j|C_k)$$

which is simply a Naive Bayes classifier. This relation is illustrated by Fig. 6.4 . If we now extend this idea and use a set of small-sized LDTs as estimators, we then have the second hybrid model which is described in the next section.

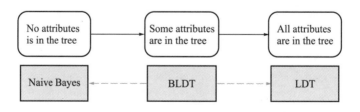

Fig. 6.4 A schematic illustration of the relations among Naive Bayes, BLDT and LDT. BLDT can be consider as a hybrid model between Naive Bayes and LDT

6.5.2 Bayesian Estimation from a Set of Trees

Given a training dataset, a small-sized tree (usually the depth is less than 3) can be learnt based on the method we discussed in the last section. We then learn another tree with the same size based on the remaining attributes, i.e., the attributes which have not been used in previous trees. In this manner, a set of trees can successively be built from training set. We denote this set of trees by $\mathbb{T} = \langle T_1, \ldots, T_W \rangle$ and where the set of attributes x_{T_w} for $w = 1, \ldots, W$ for a partition of $\{x_1, \ldots, x_n\}$ (see Fig. 6.5 for a schematic illustration). For a given unclassified data element x, we can partition it into W groups of a disjoint set of attributes $\langle x_{T_1}, \ldots, x_{T_W} \rangle$. If we assume

$$P(C_t|x) = P(C_t|x_{T_1}, \ldots, x_{T_W}) \approx P(C_t|T_1, \ldots, T_W) \tag{6.48}$$

then, according to the Bayes theorem:

$$P(C_t|\mathbb{T}) = P(C_t|T_1, \ldots, T_W) = \frac{P(T_1, \ldots, T_W|C_t)P(C_t)}{P(T_1, \ldots, T_W)} \tag{6.49}$$

Assuming that the trees are generated independently, then it is reasonable to assume that the groups of attributes are conditionally independent of each other. Hence

$$P(T_1, \ldots, T_W|C_t) = \prod_{w=1}^{W} P(T_w|C_t) \tag{6.50}$$

For a particular tree T_w for $w = 1, \ldots, W$, we have

$$P(T_w|C_t) = \frac{P(C_t|T_w)P(T_w)}{P(C_t)} \tag{6.51}$$

So that,

$$\prod_{w=1}^{W} P(T_w|C_t) = \frac{\prod_{w=1}^{W} P(C_t|T_w) \prod_{i=1}^{W} P(T_w)}{P(C_t)^W} \tag{6.52}$$

Combining Eqs. (6.49), (6.50) and (6.52), we obtain

$$P(C_t|\mathbb{T}) \propto \frac{\prod_{w=1}^{W} P(C_t|T_w) \prod_{w=1}^{W} P(T_w)}{P(C_t)^{W-1}} \tag{6.53}$$

Since $\prod_{w=1}^{W} P(T_w)$ is independent from C_t, we finally obtain:

$$P(C_t|\mathbb{T}) \propto \frac{\prod_{w=1}^{W} P(C_t|T_w)}{P(C_t)^{W-1}} \tag{6.54}$$

where $P(C_t|T_w)$ is evaluated according to Eq. (4.16).

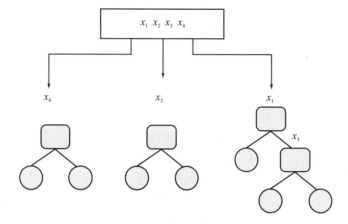

Fig. 6.5 An schematic illustration of Bayesian estimation from a set of linguistic decision trees

6.6 Experimental Studies

We evaluated the hybrid LDT models (Bayesian estimation tree denoted by BLDT) by comparing the performance of a single LDT without Bayesian estimation and Bayesian estimation with a set of trees (denoted by FLDT, i.e., a forest of LDTs) on 10 datasets taken from the UCI Machine Learning repository[2]. The descriptions are shown in Table 6.1 . Unless otherwise stated, attributes are discretized by 2 trapezoidal fuzzy sets with 50% overlap based on percentile-based discretization (see Chapter 4), and classes are evenly split into two sub-datasets randomly, one half for training and the other half for testing. This is referred to as a 50-50 split experiment. For each dataset, we ran a 50-50 experiment with a random split 10 times and the average test accuracies with standard deviations are shown against depths of the trees in Figs. 6.6 and 6.7 . The results for C4.5 [3], Fuzzy Naive Bayes (FNB), FLDT and the best results of LDT and BLDT are shown in Tables 6.2—6.8, where the depth for LDT and BLDT represents the depth at which the best results are obtained.

We also performed t-tests with a confidence level of 90% [4] to compare the models at depth 2 (except for C4.5 and FNB) and the results are shown in Table 6.8 . We can see that BLDT and FLDT models are better than Fuzzy Naive Bayes and C4.5. However, if we compare BLDT and FLDT with LDT, we find that the BLDT model outperforms LDT at shallow depths and the FLDT model has the equivalent performance. equivalent instead of which one is better than another one. From Fig. 6.6 , we found that most of the best results for BLDT are obtained at shallow depths,

---

[3] The results for C4.5 are obtained by WEKA [20] machine toolkit with default settings.

[4] We generally believe that the confidence level of 90% is enough to be significant for comparisons among different learning models given these relatively simple data sets.

Table 6.1 Descriptions of the datasets for experiments selected from the UCI machine learning repository [2]

Dataset	Classes	Size	Attributes	Missing Values
Balance	3	625	4	No
Ecoli	8	336	8	No
Glass	6	214	9	No
Heptitis	2	155	19	Yes
Iris	3	150	4	No
Liver	2	345	6	No
Pima	2	768	8	No
Sonar	2	208	60	No
Wine	3	178	14	No
Wcancer	2	699	9	No

but for LDTs the best results are always obtained with deep trees. Hence, we can conclude that the BLDT model is more efficient than LDT. Compared to BLDT, the FLDT model performs relatively worse and is less efficient. The reasons for this are probably that small trees are not good estimators,but this still needs further investigation.

From Figs. 6.6 and 6.7 , we can see that the BLDT model generally performs better at shallow depths than the LDT model. However, with the increase in the tree depth, the performance of the BLDT model remains constant or decreases, while the accuracy curves for LDT increase. For datasets Balance, Ecoli, Wisconsin-Cancer (Wcancer) and Wine, the BLDT model performs better at most of depths. For Iris and Heptitis, the differences are insignificant at all depths. For Pima, the LDT model performs better than the BLDT model at most depths and the differences are significant. For the rest of the datasets, the accuracy curves cross somewhere in the middle and the differences are not significant.

6.7 Summary

In this chapter we have introduced Bayesian models based on label semantics. Specifically, we discussed the fuzzy Naive Bayes, Semi-Naive Bayes and two hybrid Bayesian models based on the LDT by combining the Naive Bayes classifier and the linguistic decision trees. Through experimental studies, we found that the BLDT (i.e., Bayesian estimation given an LDT) model outperforms the fuzzy Naive Bayes, C4.5 and the linguistic decision tree model at shallow tree depths. However, the FLDT (i.e., using a set of small size LDTs as Bayesian estimators) model outperforms fuzzy Naive Bayes classifier and C4.5 but has equivalent accuracy to

LDTs. Future research will focus on investigating the reasons why FLDTs do not seem to improve on the performance of LDTs at shallow depths.

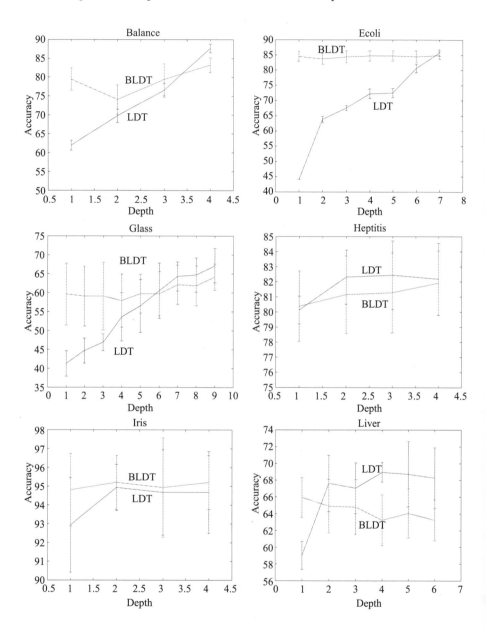

Fig. 6.6 Results for single LDT with Bayesian estimation: Average accuracy with standard deviation on each dataset against the depth of the tree

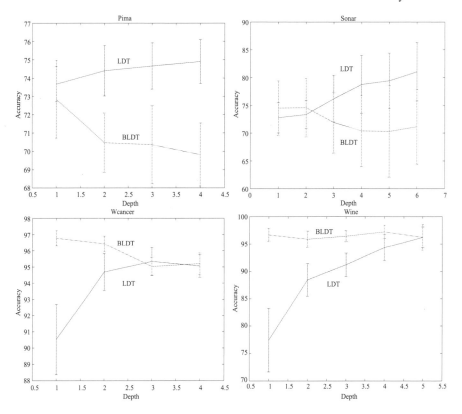

Fig. 6.7 Results for single LDT with Bayesian estimation: Average accuracy with standard deviation on each dataset against the depth of the tree

Table 6.2 Experimental results (average accuracy with standard deviation) on UCI data sets based on PET models with discrete and fuzzy labels, where d represents the depth at which the results were obtained. The best results are highlighted

		Discreet Labels		**Fuzzy Labels**	
Data	*depth*	LDT	BLDT	LDT	BLDT
Balance	1	54.54±1.34	69.04±1.82	62.33±1.60	79.53±1.90
	2	62.25±1.38	71.34±1.89	68.12±1.57	74.76±1.89
	3	68.23±2.56	74.47±3.49	75.01±1.66	77.49±2.20
	4	**80.74±3.47**	**77.74±2.26**	**87.70±1.13**	**81.96±1.79**

		Discreet Labels		Fuzzy Labels	
Data	*depth*	LDT	BLDT	LDT	BLDT
Ecoli	1	51.94±1.75	**79.24±1.88**	44.12±0.00	**84.53±1.60**
	2	70.47±1.88	78.35±1.66	63.88±0.97	83.76±1.82
	3	71.94±2.30	78.47±3.00	67.59±0.76	84.41±2.00
	4	73.53±4.58	77.06±2.63	72.29±1.53	84.76±1.67
	5	73.53±4.58	77.06±2.63	72.53±1.52	84.76±1.67
	6	**73.76±4.52**	77.24±2.34	80.59±1.41	84.47±1.96
	7	73.12±2.32	77.71±1.95	**85.76±1.03**	84.88±1.21
Glass	1	38.81±4.17	61.38±5.16	41.28±3.35	59.63±8.17
	2	40.37±3.72	60.28±3.46	44.68±3.32	59.08±7.92
	3	45.69±5.91	60.64±5.46	46.88±2.22	59.08±8.92
	4	53.67±5.32	**60.92±5.92**	53.58±6.36	57.89±6.98
	5	52.84±3.49	60.00±4.22	56.51±6.96	59.72±5.13
	6	51.83±4.64	58.81±5.65	60.55±7.33	59.72±5.83
	7	51.93±3.36	58.26±5.34	64.31±3.83	62.11±5.21
	8	52.11±3.40	58.72±5.69	64.68±4.54	61.83±5.26
	9	**52.20±3.19**	58.35±5.30	**67.16±4.57**	**64.13±3.47**
Heptitis	1	79.49±0.00	80.51±2.33	80.13±0.91	80.38±2.34
	2	79.62±3.39	**82.05±2.34**	82.31±1.79	81.15±2.57
	3	80.13±4.33	81.03±2.89	**82.44±2.27**	81.28±2.65
	4	**80.38±3.42**	80.77±2.42	82.18±2.38	**81.92±2.13**
Iris	1	92.67±3.34	**92.53±3.57**	92.93±2.52	94.80±1.93
	2	**94.93±2.07**	91.87±4.89	**94.93±1.23**	**95.20±1.43**
	3	94.27±2.60	92.27±3.97	94.67±2.27	94.93±1.64
	4	93.87±2.75	92.67±3.51	94.67±2.18	95.20±1.43
Liver	1	55.66±3.96	**63.24±3.36**	59.02±1.67	**65.95±2.38**
	2	60.81±4.63	61.68±3.79	67.63±3.37	64.91±3.17
	3	60.81±2.40	62.72±4.23	67.05±3.03	64.80±3.25
	4	**61.39±3.71**	62.66±4.48	**68.96±1.18**	63.24±3.02
	5	59.89±3.79	62.72±4.20	68.73±3.90	64.05±2.92
	6	59.65±2.67	62.25±3.61	68.27±3.62	63.24±2.44
Pima	1	73.49±1.58	**71.48±2.52**	73.67±0.96	**72.84±2.12**
	2	**73.52±2.62**	69.77±2.84	74.40±1.37	70.47±1.62
	3	71.80±2.47	69.97±2.98	74.66±1.26	70.36±2.14
	4	68.10±2.20	68.52±2.69	**74.90±1.20**	69.82±1.72
Wisconsin-Cancer	1	90.60±1.83	**96.54±0.39**	90.54±2.17	**96.77±0.47**
	2	93.09±1.12	95.80±0.81	94.69±1.15	96.43±0.47
	3	**94.51±1.16**	94.49±1.04	**95.34±0.85**	95.03±0.56
	4	94.29±0.92	94.26±0.81	95.06±0.70	95.20±0.66
Wine	1	75.89±7.18	**94.22±3.66**	77.44±5.79	96.67±1.17
	2	**87.22±2.41**	92.89±4.03	88.44±2.97	95.89±1.49
	3	85.56±2.92	89.67±3.31	91.22±2.12	96.44±1.02
	4	82.78±3.32	88.00±4.38	94.33±2.37	**97.22±1.20**
	5	85.22±2.87	87.11±1.41	**96.22±1.90**	96.22±2.35

Table 6.3 Experimental results on 10 UCI datasets: average accuracy with standard deviation from 10 runs of random 50-50 split experiments

Database	C4.5 Acc	FNB Acc	LDT Acc	d	BLDT Acc	d	FLDT Acc(d=1)	Acc(d=2)
Balance	79.20±1.53	73.77±2.43	87.70±1.13	4	83.23±1.97	4	66.26±2.81	79.42±1.99
Ecoli	78.99±2.23	76.53±4.19	85.76±1.03	7	84.53±1.60	1	80.18±3.45	78.76±1.60
Glass	64.77±5.10	48.35±6.80	59.17±3.70	9	64.13±3.47	9	52.94±8.74	58.53±5.28
Heptitis	76.75±4.68	80.13±2.28	82.44±2.27	3	81.92±2.13	4	80.26±3.15	79.26±0.41
Iris	93.47±3.23	93.73±2.60	94.93±1.23	2	95.20±1.43	2	93.73±1.89	92.00±3.38
Liver	65.23±3.86	63.35±2.38	68.96±3.18	4	65.95±2.38	1	62.43±4.62	59.65±2.09
Pima	72.16±2.80	72.29±2.25	74.90±1.20	4	72.84±2.12	1	72.40±1.48	66.07±1.04
Sonar	70.38±5.23	74.76±4.96	81.05±5.24	6	74.57±5.26	2	76.48±4.82	75.62±2.21
Wcancer	94.38±1.42	96.74±0.54	95.34±0.85	3	96.77±0.47	1	97.17±0.93	98.77±0.85
Wine	88.09±4.14	96.22±1.67	96.22±1.90	5	97.22±1.20	4	96.11±0.79	98.56±1.66

Table 6.4 Result comparisons (with LDT, BLDT and FLDT are at depth 2) based on t-test with 90% confidence, where "$\sqrt{}$" represents significant better, "$-$" represents equivalence and "$\times$" represents significant worse

#	BLDT vs C4.5	BLDT vs FNB	BLDT vs LDT	FLDT vs C4.5	FLDT vs FNB	FLDT vs LDT
Balance	√	√	√	−	√	√
Ecoli	√	√	√	−	−	√
Glass	−	√	√	−	√	√
Heptitis	√	−	−	−	−	×
Iris	−	−	−	−	−	−
Liver	−	−	−	−	−	×
Pima	−	−	×	−	−	×
Sonar	−	−	−	−	−	−
Wcancer	√	−	√	√	√	√
Wine	√	−	√	√	−	√

Table 6.5 Experimental results based on discrete labels

Data	NB Accuracy	PET Accuracy	depth	BPET Accuracy	depth
Balance	78.45±3.43	80.74±3.47	4	77.74±2.26	4
Ecoli	78.29±2.29	73.76±4.52	6	79.24±1.88	1
Glass	57.06±5.22	52.20±3.19	9	60.92±5.92	4
Heptitis	80.64±2.38	80.38±3.42	4	82.05±2.34	2
Ionosphere	83.30±3.50	82.39±2.32	3	85.28±2.07	3
Iris	92.53±2.96	94.93±2.07	2	92.53±3.57	1
Liver	63.24±2.42	61.39±3.71	4	63.24±3.36	1
Pima	72.06±2.86	73.52±2.62	2	71.48±2.52	1
W-cancer	96.63±0.40	94.51±1.16	3	96.54±0.39	1
Wine	94.33±3.61	87.22±2.41	2	94.22±3.66	1

Table 6.6 Experimental results based on fuzzy labels

Data	FNB Accuracy	LDT Accuracy	depth	BLDT Accuracy	depth
Balance	81.87±2.24	87.70±1.13	4	81.96±1.79	4
Ecoli	76.53±4.19	85.76±1.03	7	84.53±1.60	1
Glass	48.35±6.80	67.16±4.57	9	64.13±3.47	9
Heptitis	80.13±2.28	82.44±2.27	3	81.92±2.13	4
Ionosphere	76.02±3.82	88.47±2.60	2	77.44±4.76	1
Iris	93.73±2.60	94.93±1.23	2	95.20±1.43	2
Liver	63.35±2.38	68.96±3.18	4	65.95±2.38	1
Pima	72.29±2.25	74.90±1.20	4	72.84±2.12	1
W-cancer	96.74±0.54	95.34±0.85	3	96.77±0.47	1
Wine	96.22±1.67	92.66±1.90	5	97.22±1.20	4

Table 6.7 Average accuracy for LDT and FLDT from 10 runs of random 50-50 split experiments

	LDT		FLDT	
Database	Accuracy	depth	Accuracy (depth=1)	Accuracy (depth=2)
Balance	87.70±1.13	4	66.26±2.81	79.42±1.99
Ecoli	85.76±1.03	7	80.18±3.45	78.76±1.60
Glass	59.17±3.70	9	52.94±8.74	58.53±5.28
Heptitis	82.44±2.27	3	80.26±3.15	79.26±0.41
Iris	94.93±1.23	2	93.73±1.89	92.00±3.38
Liver	68.96±3.18	4	62.43±4.62	59.65±2.09
Pima	74.90±1.20	4	72.40±1.48	66.07±1.04
W-cancer	95.34±0.85	3	97.17±0.93	98.77±0.85
Wine	96.22±1.90	5	96.11±0.79	98.56±1.66

Table 6.8 Result comparisons at depth 2 based on t-test with 90% confidence, where "$\sqrt{}$" represents significant better, "$-$" represents equivalence and "$\times$" represents significant worse

BLDT vs. PET	BLDT vs. FNB	BLDT vs. LDT	FLDT vs. PET	FLDT vs. FNB	FLDT vs. LDT	LDT vs. PET
$\sqrt{}$	$\sqrt{}$	$\sqrt{}$	$-$	$\sqrt{}$	$\sqrt{}$	$\sqrt{}$
$\sqrt{}$	$\sqrt{}$	$\sqrt{}$	$-$	$-$	$\sqrt{}$	$\sqrt{}$
$-$	$\sqrt{}$	$\sqrt{}$	$-$	$\sqrt{}$	$\sqrt{}$	$\sqrt{}$
$\sqrt{}$	$-$	$-$	$-$	$-$	$\times$	$\sqrt{}$
$-$	$-$	$-$	$-$	$-$	$\times$	$-$
$-$	$-$	$\times$	$-$	$-$	$\times$	$\sqrt{}$
$-$	$-$	$-$	$-$	$-$	$-$	$-$
$\sqrt{}$	$-$	$\sqrt{}$	$\sqrt{}$	$-$	$\sqrt{}$	$-$
$\sqrt{}$	$-$	$\sqrt{}$	$\sqrt{}$	$\sqrt{}$	$\sqrt{}$	$\sqrt{}$

References

[1] Provost F., Domingos P.: Tree induction for probability-based ranking, Machine Learning, 52, pp. 199-215. (2003).
[2] Blake C., Merz C. J.: UCI machine learning repository.
[3] Jordan M. I.: Learning in Graphical Models, MIT Press. (1999).
[4] Elkan C., Naive bayesian learning. Technical Report No. CS97-557, Department of Computer Science and Engineering, University of California, San Diego. (1997).

[5] Pazzani M. J.: An iterative improvement approach for the discretization of numeric attributes in Bayesian classifiers, Proceedings of the 1st International Conference on Knowledge Discovery and Data Mining, pp. 228-233. (1995).

[6] Yang Y., Webb G. I.: On why discretization works for naive-bayes classifiers, Proceedings of 16th Australian Joint Conference on Artificial Intelligence. (2003).

[7] Hsu C. -N., Huang H. -J., Wong T. -T.: Implications of the Dirichlet assumption for discretization of continuous variables in Naive Bayesian classifiers, Machine Learning, 53, pp. 235-263. (2003).

[8] Zhang H., Ling C. X.: A fundamental issue of Naive Bayes, Proceedings of 2003 Canadian Artificial Intelligence Conference. (2003).

[9] Jeffrey R. C.: The Logic of Decision, Gordon & Breach Inc., New York. (1965).

[10] Randon N. J., Lawry J.: Classification and query evaluation using modelling with words. Information Sciences, 176, pp. 438-464, (2006).

[11] Hyndman R., Akram M.: Time series Data Library. Monash University. http://www-personal.buseco.monash.edu.au/~hyndman/TSDL/index.htm.

[12] Gunn S. R.: Support vector machines for classification and regression. Technical Report of Departartment of Electronics and Computer Science, University of Southampton. (1998).

[13] Konoenko I.: Semi-Naive Bayesian classifier, Proceedings of EWSL-91 6th European Workshop on Learning, Springer, pp. 206-219. (1991).

[14] Randon N. J.: Fuzzy and Random Set Based Induction Algorithms, PhD Thesis, Department of Engineering Mathematics, University of Bristol. (2004).

[15] Randon N. J., Lawry J.: Linguistic modelling using a semi-Naive Bayes framework, IPMU-2002, Annecy, France. (2002).

[16] Randon N. J., Lawry J., Cluckie I. D.: Online learning for fuzzy Bayesian prediction, Soft Methods in Probability and Statistics (SMPS) Advances in Soft Computing, 6: pp. 405-412.

[17] Quinlan J. R.: Induction of decision trees, Machine Learning, 1: pp. 81-106. (1986).

[18] Quinlan J. R.:C4.5: Programs for Machine Learning, San Mateo: Morgan Kaufmann. (1993).

[19] Ferri C., Flach P. A., Hernández-Orallo J.: Improving the AUC of probabilistic estimation trees, Proceedings of ECML-03, LNAI 2837, pp. 121-132. (2003).

[20] Witten I. H., Frank E.: Data Mining: Practical Machine Learning Tools and Techniques with Java Implementations, Morgan Kaufmann. (1999).

7

Unsupervised Learning with Label Semantics

Things of a kind come together. People of a mind fall into the same group.

– Chinese Proverb

7.1 Introduction

Unsupervised learning is a class of problems in machine learning where the goal is to determine how data is structured and organized. It is distinguished from supervised learning, semi-supervised learning and reinforcement learning in that the learner is given only unlabeled data. Unsupervised learning is closely related to the problem of density estimation in statistics. However unsupervised learning also encompasses many other techniques that seek to summarize and explain key features of the data[1]. In this section, we will mainly discuss two sorts of unsupervised learning models based on label semantics, probability estimation and clustering.

Probability density estimation is used to construct an unobservable underlying probability density function (PDF) based on randomly sampled data. The approaches to density estimation are usually classified as parametric and non-parametric. In parametric estimation, it is assumed that the underlying PDF $f(x)$ belongs to a family distribution characterized by parameters $\theta = \{\theta_1, \ldots, \theta_m\}$. A density estimate $\hat{f}$ is then obtained by computing from the data an estimate $\hat{\theta}$ of the parameters θ and having

$$\hat{f} = f(x|\hat{\theta})$$

Non-parametric approaches do not assume a particular family of distributions. In this chapter, we will first discuss how to use label semantics for non-parametric density estimation based on given observed data. Then, we will consider the clustering of these unlabeled data within the label semantics framework. Particularly, we use a new proposed distance measurement to cluster imprecise concepts and data.

Cluster analysis is considered as the most important form of unsupervised learning. It deals with finding similar patterns in a collection of unlabeled data. A cluster is therefore a collection of objects which are "similar" and are "dissimilar" to the objects belonging to other clusters. Another kind of clustering is conceptual clustering. Two or more objects belong to the same cluster if this one defines a concept common to all objects. In other words, objects are grouped according to their fit to descriptive concepts, not according to simple similarity measures.

7.2 Non-Parametric Density Estimation

In statistics, kernel density estimation is a non-parametric method of estimating the probability density function of a random variable. Kernel density estimates[2] are closely related to histograms, although the former have several advantages. In Fig. 7.1 , we compare the construction of histogram and kernel density estimators, using these 6 data points: $x_1 = -2.1$, $x_2 = -1.3$, $x_3 = -0.4$, $x_4 = 1.9$, $x_5 = 5.1$, $x_6 = 6.2$. For the histogram, first the horizontal axis is divided into sub-intervals or bins which cover the range of the data (e.g., Fig. 7.1 (a)). In this case, we have 6 bins each of width 2. For the kernel density estimate, we place a normal kernel with variance $\delta = 2.25$ (see Fig. 7.1 (b)) on each of the data points x_i. The kernels are summed to make the kernel density estimate (solid curve). The smoothness of the kernel density estimate is evident compared to the discreteness of the histogram. This discrete appearance is a result of the inherent statistical inefficiency of histograms as compared to kernel estimators.

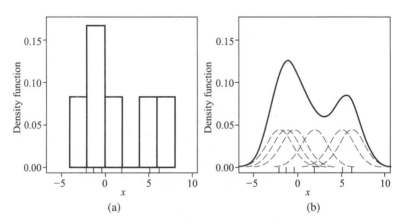

(a)   (b)

Fig. 7.1 Kernel density estimation using normal kernels with variance $\delta = 2.25$. This figure is originally from Reference [2]

Definition 7.1 *Let $D = \{X_1, \ldots, X_n\}$ be a sample of data where the underlying variable x takes values in a closed interval $\Omega = [l, u] \subset \mathbb{R}$ according to an unknown density function $f(x)$. Let $\mathbb{L}$ be a set of labels forming a full linguistic covering (Definition 3.5) of the universe Ω. The density estimate $\hat{f}(\cdot)$ is obtained* *by conditioning on the mass obtained from D, m_D, assuming a uniform prior distribution on Ω, that is*

$$\forall x \in \Omega, \ \hat{f}(x) = p(x|m_D) = C_\Omega \sum_{S \subset \mathbb{L}} \frac{m_D(s)}{pm(S)} m_x(S) \tag{7.1}$$

where C_Ω is the constant function of the uniform density in Ω, m_D is the mass assignment conditional on the information provided by D (see Definition 3.8), $pm(\cdot)$ is the prior mass assignment generated by the uniform distribution and m_x is the mass assignment for $x \in \Omega$ determined from $\{\mu_L(x) : L \in \mathbb{L}\}$

Definition 7.2 *A measure of the discrepancy of the density estimator $\hat{f}(x)$ from the true density $f(x)$ at a single point is the mean square error*

$$MSE_x(\hat{f}) = E[\hat{f}(x) - f(x)]^2 \tag{7.2}$$

The proposed estimate is consisted with MSE under certain regularity conditions[3]:

Theorem 7.1 *Let f be a C^2 function with bounded derivatives and let $\mathbb{L}$ be a uniform full linguistic covering of Ω. Then $\forall x \in \Omega$, $\hat{f}$ is consistent in the MSE, that is, if m denotes the number of labels in $\mathbb{L}$ and n the sample size*

$$m \to \infty, \frac{n}{m} \to \infty \Rightarrow MSE_x(\hat{f}) \to 0 \tag{7.3}$$

The proof is very similar to that of binned kernel estimators, using the decomposition of MSE as a combination of bias and variance at x, $MSE_x(\hat{f}) = E[\hat{f}(x) - f(x)]^2 - Var[\hat{f}(x)]$. Given the smoothness of f, both the bias and the variance can be rewritten using a Taylor series expansion. The resulting expressions can be seen to be bounded by functions that converge to 0 as the number of labels tends to infinity.

Example 7.1 *This example is modified from[3]. Given an function of mixed Gaussian:*

$$f(x) = \frac{1}{2}(\mathcal{N}(2,3) + \mathcal{N}(8,0.5)) \tag{7.4}$$

We have generated 100 random samples. We use 5 trapezoidal shape fuzzy labels {very small (vs)}, {small (s)}, {medium (m)}, {large (l)} and {very large (vl)} that cover the sampling universe $[-2, 10]$ using the percentile method. For these labels, the mass assignment conditional on the sample DB is given by:

$$m_{DB} = \{vs\} : 0.151, \{vs, s\} : 0.107, \{s\} : 0.12, \{s, m\} : 0.043, \{m\} : 0.063,$$

$$\{m, l\} : 0.165, \{l\} : 0.095, \{l, vl\} : 0.151, \{vl\} : 0.105$$

Fig. 7.2 shows the estimated PDF against the original function of Eq. (7.4). The estimated values of the sample data $\hat{f}(x_i) : i = 1, \ldots, 100$ are also labelled on the graph. The MSE is:

$$MSE = \frac{1}{100} \sum_{i=1}^{100} [f(x_i) - \hat{f}(x_i)]^2 = 9.13 \times 10^{-7}$$

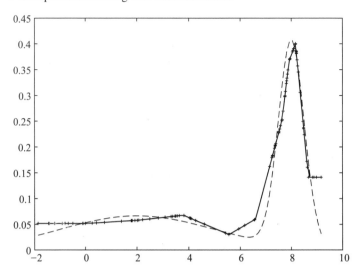

Fig. 7.2 Estimated density using label semantics: the target function f (dashed line), $\hat{f}$ (solid lines) and samples DB that are denoted by "+"

7.3 Clustering

Clustering algorithms can be applied in many fields, such as marketing, bio-informatics, video analysis and so on[4]. Hence, in past decades, many classical clustering algorithms, for example K-means, Fuzzy K-means, hierarchical clustering algorithms, have been proposed and some of them have been successfully applied in resolving practical problems. They group the "similar" objects into one cluster. In this sense, the clustering result is depend heavily on the distance measure between objects. Euclidean distance and Mahalanobis distance are two of the most used distance measures. Other (dis)similarity measures may be used for some particular data type. For example, Kullback-Leibler (KL) distance is good for measuring the divergence between two probability distributions. But its unsymmetrical properties make it unsuitable to be a good universal measure of data distance. In the literature, the objects handled by these classical clustering algorithms are restricted to numerical data, though they could be high-dimensional complex data. However, what we hope to cluster is not limited to numerical data, it could be some high-level knowledge of imprecise concepts or linguistic descriptions[5].

Unfortunately, these objects can not be well handled by the existing clustering algorithms. The main reason is that there is no good metric for measuring dissimilarity between numerical data and linguistic descriptions[6,7]. In this chapter, we proposed a novel distance measure which can measure the distance between numeral data and logical expressions of linguistic labels based on Label Semantics[8]. This new measure makes it possible to cluster a set of objects including numerical data, concepts, and linguistic descriptions, by modifying the distance measure based on the classical K-means clustering algorithms.

7.3.1 Logical Distance

Based on the theory of fuzzy sets, many similarity/dissimilarity measures[6,7] have been proposed for measuring the degree of similarity between fuzzy sets. But those measures are not proper for dealing with the similarity/dissimilarity measures between logical expressions which are concepts based on given linguistic variables. Label semantics focus on the decision making process, an intelligent agent must go through in order to identify which labels or logical expressions can actually be used to describe an object or value. For this reason, the appropriateness degree is proposed for measuring the appropriateness of using a particular subset of labels to describe an object or value. One step further, we present a measure to evaluate the dissimilarity of logical expressions based on the mass assignments which can quantize the divergences between logical expressions. This measure is also extendable to measure distance between any two granular sets.

Definition 7.3 (Distance between data points) *Given two data points x_1 and x_2 from an multi-dimensional universe Ω which is fully covered by n labels $\mathbb{L} = \{L_1, \ldots, L_n\}$, then the distance between x_1 and x_2 in this linguistic label space is defined by:*

$$D(x_1, x_2) = \sum_{i=0}^{R-1} D(\mathbf{u}_i, \mathbf{u}_{i+1}) \tag{7.5}$$

where

$$D(\mathbf{u}_i, \mathbf{u}_{i+1}) = \sum_{S \in \lambda(\mathbb{L})} (m_{\mathbf{u}_i}(S) - m_{\mathbf{u}_{i+1}}(S))^2 \tag{7.6}$$

$$\mathbf{u}_i = x_1 + \frac{i}{R}(x_2 - x_1) \tag{7.7}$$

Fig. 7.3 intuitively explains the above definition. To calculate the distance between two data points, we divide the distance between them into R ($R > 0$) pieces and calculate the dissimilarity $D(\mathbf{u}_i, \mathbf{u}_{i+1})$ between two neighboring points $(\mathbf{u}_i, \mathbf{u}_{i+1})$ in the space of linguistic labels. The overall dissimilarity $D(x_1, x_2)$ is the sum of the above R pieces of dissimilarity. Thus the accuracy of the distance measure will be improved with the increase in the value of R. As we can easily see, this measure can be generalized to calculate the dissimilarity between any granular sets or a data point to a granular set. In addition, this distance measure has two important properties.

Theorem 7.2 *The distance defined by Eq. (7.5) is symmetric.*

$$D(x_i, x_j) = D(x_j, x_i) \tag{7.8}$$

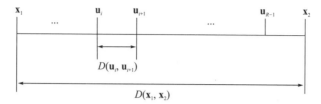

Fig. 7.3 Illustration of calculating the distance between two data points. The overall dissimilarity between x_1 and x_2 is the aggregated dissimilarity of all the neighboring points $\mathbf{u}_i$ and $\mathbf{u}_{i+1}$ for $i \in R$

Theorem 7.3 *If given* $x_1 < x_2 < x_3^{\,①}$, *then*

$$D(x_1, x_3) \geq D(x_1, x_2) \tag{7.9}$$

Theorem 7.3 demonstrates that this measure has non-negative correlation with the distance of $\mathbf{x}$.

Proof

$$D(x_2, x_1) = \lim_{M \to \infty} \sum_{m'=1}^{M} D(u', v') \tag{7.10}$$

where

$$u' = x_2 + \frac{m'}{M}(x_1 - x_2) = x_1 + \frac{M - m'}{M}(x_2 - x_1) \tag{7.11}$$

$$v' = x_2 + \frac{m' - 1}{M}(x_1 - x_2) = x_1 + \frac{M - m' + 1}{M}(x_2 - x_1) \tag{7.12}$$

$M - m' + 1$ has the same value domain. Thus

$$D(u', v') = D(v, u) \tag{7.13}$$

In addition, because of the symmetry of D defined by Eq. (7.6), the following conclusion can be deduced

$$D(x_2, x_1) = D(x_1, x_2) \tag{7.14}$$

So the distance between variables is symmetric.

Theorem 7.3 demonstrates that this measure has non-negative correlation with the distance of x, which can be easily proved as follows:

Proof

$$D(x_1, x_2) = \lim_{M \to \infty} \sum_{m=1}^{M} D(u, v) \tag{7.15}$$

---

① if $dim(x) > 2$, we define: $x_1 \geq x_2$ if $d(x_1, 0) \geq d(x_2, 0)$, where $d(\cdot)$ is the Euclidean distance.

where

$$u = x_1 + \frac{m}{M}(x_2 - x_1) \tag{7.16}$$

$$v = x_1 + \frac{m-1}{M}(x_2 - x_1) \tag{7.17}$$

$$D(x_1, x_3) = \lim_{M \to \infty} \sum_{m=1}^{M} D(u', v') \tag{7.18}$$

where

$$u' = x_1 + \frac{m}{M}(x_3 - x_1) \tag{7.19}$$

$$v' = x_1 + \frac{m-1}{M}(x_3 - x_1) \tag{7.20}$$

obviously,

$$\forall m, u' - v' > u - v \tag{7.21}$$

because $D(u', v') >= D(u, v)$, thus

$$D(x_1, x_3) \geq D(x_1, x_2) \tag{7.22}$$

Now proof of Theorem 7.3 has been completed.

Given a data point x_0 and a linguistic label set $S \in \mathbb{F}$ that covers a continuous area $\delta(S)$ on the universe Ω, the distance between $\mathbf{x_0}$ and S is defined as follows:

$$D(x_0, S) = \frac{\int_{\delta(S)} D(x_0, x)\mathrm{d}x}{\delta(S)} \tag{7.23}$$

Furthermore, the distance of sets of labels which is used to measure the divergence between them can be defined as follows:

Definition 7.4 (Distance between sets of labels) *Given two sets of labels $S_i, S_j \in \mathbb{F}$ and S_i covering a continuous area $\delta(S_i)$ and S_j covering a continuous area $\delta(S_j)$. Then the distance between these two sets is defined as*

$$D(S_i, S_j) = \frac{\int_{\delta(S_i)} \int_{\delta(S_j)} D(x_i, x_j)dx_i dx_j}{\delta(S_i)\delta(S_j)} \tag{7.24}$$

where $x_i \in \delta(S_i), x_j \in \delta(S_j)$, and when $i = j$:

$$D(S_i, S_j) = D(S_i, S_i) = 0 \tag{7.25}$$

For the symmetry of the distance between two variables, it is obviously that the distance of the sets of labels is also symmetric. As we have discussed in Section 3.2, λ-function provides a way of mapping from logical expressions of labels to random set descriptions of labels. So we also can define the distance between two logical expressions as the following.

Definition 7.5 (Distance between logical expressions) *Given   two   logical expressions* $\theta, \varphi \in LE$, *then the distance between* θ *and* φ *is*

$$D(\theta, \varphi) = \frac{1}{pr} \sum_{i=1}^{r} \sum_{j=1}^{p} D(S_i^{\theta \wedge \neg \varphi}, S_j^{\varphi})$$

$$-\frac{1}{qt} \sum_{k=1}^{t} \sum_{l=1}^{q} D(S_k^{\varphi \wedge \neg \theta}, S_l^{\theta}) \tag{7.26}$$

where p, q, r, t *respectively represent the cardinality of label set* $\mathbb{S}^{\varphi}$, $\mathbb{S}^{\theta}$, $\mathbb{S}^{\theta \wedge \neg \varphi}$, $\mathbb{S}^{\varphi \wedge \neg \theta}$, *where:*

$$S_i^{\theta} \in \mathbb{S}^{\theta} = \{S | S \in \lambda(\theta)\}, i = 1, 2, ..., q$$

$$S_j^{\varphi} \in \mathbb{S}^{\varphi} = \{S | S \in \lambda(\varphi)\}, j = 1, 2, ..., p$$

$$S_k^{\theta \wedge \neg \varphi} \in \mathbb{S}^{\theta \wedge \neg \varphi} = \{S | S \in \lambda(\theta) \bigcap \overline{\lambda(\varphi)}\}, k = 1, 2, ..., r$$

$$S_l^{\varphi \wedge \neg \theta} \in \mathbb{S}^{\varphi \wedge \neg \theta} = \{S | S \in \lambda(\varphi) \bigcup \overline{\lambda(\theta)}\}, l = 1, 2, ..., t$$

When $\mathbb{S}^{\varphi \wedge \neg \theta} = \emptyset$,

$$D(\theta, \varphi) = \frac{1}{pr} \sum_{i=1}^{r} \sum_{j=1}^{p} D(S_i^{\theta \wedge \neg \varphi}, S_j^{\varphi}) \tag{7.27}$$

When $\mathbb{S}^{\theta \wedge \neg \varphi} = \emptyset$,

$$D(\theta, \varphi) = \frac{1}{qt} \sum_{k=1}^{t} \sum_{l=1}^{q} D(S_k^{\varphi \wedge \neg \theta}, S_l^{\theta}) \tag{7.28}$$

The above logical expression is one dimensional, which can be used by agents to describe one of the features of the object. If we have a multi-dimensional objects, linguistic rule can be used to described the object such as "*x* is *big* AND *y* is *medium* $\wedge$ *large*". Based on the definition of logical expressions (Definition 3.9), a linguistic rule is a rule that can be represented as a multi-dimensional logical expressions of linguistic labels.

Definition 7.6 (Multi-dimensional logical expressions of labels) $MLE^{(n)}$ *is the set of all multi-dimensional label expressions that can be generated from the logical label expression* $LE_j : j = 1, ..., n$ *and is defined recursively by*

(i) If $\theta \in LE_j$ *for* $j = 1, ..., n$ *then* $\theta \in MLE^{(n)}$.

(ii) If $\theta, \varphi \in MLE^{(n)}$ *then* $\neg \theta, \theta \wedge \varphi, \theta \vee \varphi, \theta \rightarrow \varphi \in MLE^{(n)}$

Similarly we could give the definition of distance between two $MLE^{(n)}$.

Definition 7.7 (Distance between multi-dimensional logical expressions) *Given two n-dimensional logical expressions: Φ, Ψ with*

$$\Phi = \theta_{D_1} \wedge \theta_{D_2} \wedge \ldots \wedge \theta_{D_n}$$

$$\Psi = \varphi_{D_1} \wedge \varphi_{D_2} \wedge \ldots \wedge \varphi_{D_n}$$

where θ_{D_i}, φ_{D_i} respectively means the logical expressions in dimension D_i. Hence, the distance between Φ and Ψ is defined as follows:

$$D(\Phi, \Psi) = \sqrt{\sum_{i=1}^{n} |D(\theta_{D_i}, \varphi_{D_i})|^2} \tag{7.29}$$

7.3.2 Clustering of Mixed Objects

Based on the above dissimilarity measure, the distance between objects including numerical data, concepts and linguistic description can be easily measured. Further more, a set of these objects can be grouped into clusters using clustering algorithms.

K-means is one of the simplest unsupervised learning algorithms that solve clustering problem[9]. The procedure follows a simple way to group a given data set to a certain number of clusters. Suppose that we have n sample feature vectors $x_1, x_2, \ldots, x_N$, where each element is a d-dimensional real vector, a K-means algorithm aims to partition the observations into K sets $(K \leq N)$ $\mathbf{S} = \{S_1, S_2, \ldots, S_K\}$ so as to minimize the within-cluster sum of squares J:

$$J = \arg \min_{\mathbf{S}} \sum_{i=1}^{K} \sum_{x_j \in S_i} \left\| x_j - \mu_i \right\|^2 \tag{7.30}$$

where μ_i is the mean of points in S_i.

The most common algorithm uses an iterative refinement technique. Due to its ubiquity it is often called the K-means algorithm; Given an initial set the algorithm proceeds by alternating between two steps[10]: Assignment step: Assign each observation to the cluster with the closest mean.

$$S_i^{(t)} = \left\{ \mathbf{x}_j : \left\| \mathbf{x}_j - \mu_i^{(t)} \right\| \leq \left\| \mathbf{x}_j - \mu_{i*}^{(t)} \right\| \text{ for all } i^* = 1, \ldots, K \right\}$$

Update step: Calculate the new means to be the centroid of the observations in the cluster.

$$\mu_i^{(t+1)} = \frac{1}{|S_i^{(t)}|} \sum_{\mathbf{x}_j \in S_i^{(t)}} \mathbf{x}_j$$

The algorithm is deemed to have converged when the assignments no longer change.

Fig. 7.4 gives a schematic illustration of mixed objects clustering where the ellipses represent some imprecise concepts that can could be interpreted into linguistic labels or other granularity. Such mixed objects can be clustered by combining the classical clustering algorithms with our proposed distance measure. Formally, suppose we are given an unlabeled data set $\mathbf{o}_1,\ldots,\mathbf{o}_n$, in which there are numerical data, labels (concepts) and logical expressions (linguistic description). Now we focus on clustering them using a K-means algorithm. The algorithm is as the same as the classical K-means clustering and the pseudo-code is shown in Table 7.1 .

Table 7.1 Generalized K-means algorithm for clustering vague concepts and data

Given unlabeled data set $DB = \{\mathbf{o}_i : i = 1,\ldots,N\}$ in $\mathbb{R}^d$ and cluster number $K > 0$, $p = 0$, $\varepsilon > 0$
Randomly initialize the K cluster centers $\mu_1,\ldots,\mu_K$.

While (TRUE): $p++$

    Step 1: For each $i \in \{1,\ldots,N\}$, determine the cluster for all objects in DB:

        $\mathbf{o}_i \leftarrow \mu_j$, if: $D(\mathbf{o}_i, \mu_j^{(p-1)})=\min\{D(\mathbf{o}_i, \mu_k^{(p-1)}) : k = 1,\ldots,K \}$

    Step 2: Compute the cluster centers $\mu_i^{(p)}$ which satisfy:

        $\sum_{\mathbf{o}_j \in S_i} D(\mu_i^{(p)}, \mathbf{o}_j)=\min\{ \sum_{\mathbf{o}_j \in S_i} D(x,\mathbf{o}_j) \}$

Until $|\mu^{(p)}\text{-}\mu^{(p-1)}| < \varepsilon$.

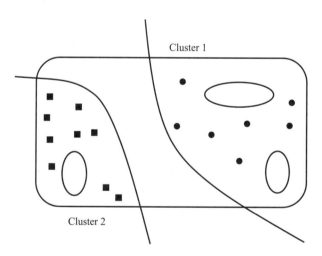

Fig. 7.4 A schematic illustration of mixed objects clustering

There are two points which are worthy of highlighting in . First and the most important, we adopted the new proposed distance metric in the last section as the distance measure of these mixed objects. The novel distance definition makes it possible to cluster data and imprecise concepts represented by linguistic labels. Second, in the algorithm implementation, the center of each cluster should be numerical data but not logical expressions.

7.4 Experimental Studies

In this section we did two experiments to verify the new proposed measure and the clustering problem. The first experiment is to illustrate the properties of the proposed logical distance measure. The second experiments shows image scene clustering based on a benchmark problem.

7.4.1 Logical Distance Example

Color of an object is a vague concept and largely depends on the observer's subjective belief. The human eye can distinguish about 10 million different colors but we only use a very limited number of words to describe them. There is no general principle for human beings to decide using the most appropriate word such as yellow or red to describe the color of an object. However, people know the difference between these colors, which is difficult to be define by some specific numerical value. We often make classifications based on these vague and subjective differences among objects. We can use the method proposed in this research to quantize these differences in order to let the agents have the ability to distinguish different objects.

HSV color space can be well visualized by the conical representation model that accords with human beings' visual features. Fig. 7.5 shows three linguistic labels defined on the Hue (H) value. Based on Definition 3.6, we can infer that the focal set is

$$\mathbb{F} = \{\{r\}, \{r,o\}, \{o\}, \{o,y\}, \{y\}\}$$

The distances between these label sets based on Definition 7.4 is calculated and shown in Table 7.2 , from which we can clearly see the symmetric property of this distance measure.

Table 7.2   Distances between sets of labels defined on H values

	$\{r\}$	$\{r,o\}$	$\{o\}$	$\{o,y\}$	$\{y\}$
$\{r\}$	0	0.0288	0.0626	0.0950	0.1246
$\{r,o\}$	0.0288	0	0.0354	0.0673	0.0968
$\{o\}$	0.0626	0.0354	0	0.0336	0.0626
$\{o,y\}$	0.0950	0.0673	0.0336	0	0.0304
$\{y\}$	0.1246	0.0968	0.0626	0.0304	0

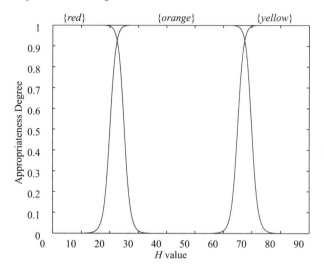

Fig. 7.5 Three linguistic labels: red (*R*), orange (*O*) and yellow (*Y*). They are defined by bell-shape fuzzy sets on the Hue (*H*) values

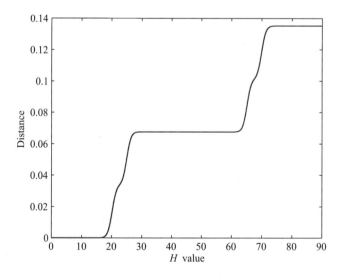

Fig. 7.6 Distance between variables with $x_0 = 0$, x_1 varying from 0 to 90

Given the same example above, if there is an imprecise concept of the color that is not orange, or formally denoted by θ:

$$\theta = \neg orange$$

There are also two other descriptions for the colors φ and γ:

$$\varphi = red \lor orange$$

$$\gamma = red$$

According to Definition 3.10, the possible label sets of the given logical expressions θ, γ and φ are calculated as follows:

$$\lambda(\neg o) = \{\{r\}, \{y\}\}$$

$$\lambda(r) = \{\{r\}, \{r, o\}\}$$

$$\lambda(o) = \{\{r, o\}, \{o\} \{o, y\}\}$$

so that

$$\lambda(\theta) = \{\{r\}, \{y\}\}$$

$$\lambda(\varphi) = \{\{r\}, \{r, o\}, \{o\} \{o, y\}\}$$

$$\lambda(\gamma) = \{\{r\}, \{r, o\}\}$$

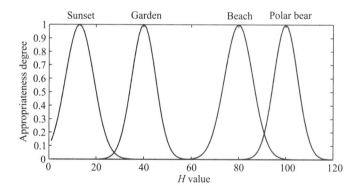

Fig. 7.7 Four image labels are predefined on the HSV space. This is the mapping of the labels on the Hue (H) axis

Then, according to Definition 7.5 and Table 7.2 , we could calculate all the distances and fill in Table 7.3 . It is illustrated that distances between LEs are symmetric and could reasonably reflect the logical divergences between LEs.

Table 7.3 Distances between each two logical expressions θ, φ and γ defined on H values

	$\theta = \neg orange$	$\varphi = red \vee orange$	$\gamma = red$
$\theta = \neg orange$	0	0.1413	0.1735
$\varphi = red \vee orange$	0.1413	0	0.0650
$\gamma = red$	0.1735	0.0650	0

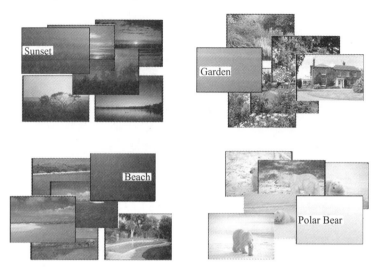

Fig. 7.8 Sample results of images and linguistic labels clustering. Linguistic labels *sunset, garden, beach* and *polar bear* are areas of color in HSV space. For each cluster, four images and one label (the colored shape on the top of the stack of images) are shown

7.4.2 Images and Labels Clustering

To show how to use our proposed approach to cluster data and an imprecise concept, we built a toy application which can cluster images and image labels which are defined based on the image global color feature. One hundred images are evenly picked from four categories of the Corel image data set[11,12]. We then artificially designed four linguistic labels "sunset", "beach", "garden", and "polar bear" based on their colors. These labels can be considered as the linguistic descriptors of images which convey the semantics of images (see Fig 7.6). Fig. 7.7 shows the mappings of these predefined labels on the Hue (H) axis. The original labels are 3-dimensional granularity in the HSV space.

Low-level image features, such as color and texture, are useful information to describe images in this experiment. For each image, the only feature we used is the global average of HSV color because we only hope to show how to use the proposed approach to cluster mixed objects. Actually in practice the features extraction is very important and the clustering algorithms are always only one step of the procedure. Thus after artificially designing the image labels and extracting image color feature, the data set needs to be clustered with one hundred images and the above four image labels which are represented by granularity on HSV space. Fig. 7.9 illustrates the flow chart of our experiment.

The experimental results are shown in Table 7.4 . In the future work, such linguistic labels can be used as constraints to guide clustering process by using high-level knowledge. It allows us to develop a new human-machine interface by using linguistic labels.

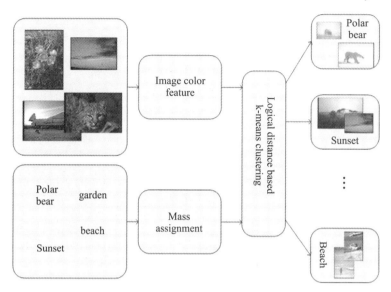

Fig. 7.9 Flow chat of the image classification experiment

Table 7.4 Performance of the image clustering

	sunset	beach	garden	polar bear
Performance	72%	60%	64%	96%

The sample results are shown in Fig. 7.8 . In the future work, such linguistic labels can be used as constraints guide clustering process by using high-level knowledge. It allows us to develop a new human-machine interface by using linguistic labels.

7.5 Summary

In this chapter we discussed unsupervised learning based on label semantics. We mainly introduced the methods for probability density estimation and clustering. We proposed a novel clustering algorithm by employing a new distance measure based on label semantics. The new algorithm can be used to cluster data and imprecise concepts. The distance defined in linguistic label space differs from the other measures by focusing on the difference in logical meanings the objects convey. It has the ability to measure the linguistic divergence between numerical data and concepts which are presented in the form of linguistic labels. Experimental studies on a toy image clustering problem showed that our approach is effective in grouping data and linguistic labels reasonably, because the new proposed measure is calculated by considering the accumulated dissimilarities alone the trials connecting to imprecise concepts. It is extendable to measuring distance between any granularity.

References

[1] http://en.wikipedia.org/wiki/Unsupervised_learning, accessed on March 30, (2011).

[2] http://en.wikipedia.org/wiki/Kernel_density_estimation, accessed on Feb 12, (2011).

[3] Lawry J., Gonzalez-Rodriguez I.: Non-parametric density estimation based on label semantics, Soft Methods for Handling Variability and Imprecision, (SMPS 2008). (2008).

[4] Wan T., Qin Z.: A new technique for summarizing video sequences through histogram evolution, Proceedings of International Conference on Signal Processing and Communications (SPCOM), pp. 1-5. (2010).

[5] Qin Z., Lawry J.: LFOIL: Linguistic rule induction in the label semantics framework. Fuzzy Sets and Systems 159(4): pp. 435-448. (2008).

[6] Hyung L. K., Song Y. S., Lee K. M.: Similarity measure between fuzzy sets and between elements, Fuzzy Sets and System, 62, pp. 291-293. (1994)

[7] Li D. -F.: Some measures of dissimilarity in intuitionistic fuzzy structures, Journal of Computer and System Sciences, 8, pp. 115-122. (2004).

[8] Lawry J.: A framework for linguistic modelling, Artificial Intelligence, 155: pp. 1-39. (2004).

[9] MacQueen J. B.: Some methods for classification and analysis of multivariate observations, Proceedings of 5th Berkeley Symposium on Mathematical Statistics and Probability, University of California Press, pp. 281-297. (1967).

[10] http://en.wikipedia.org/wiki/K-means_clustering, accessed on March 15, (2011).

[11] Carneiro G., Chan A. B., Moreno P. J., Vasconcelos N.: Supervised learning of semantic classes for image annotation and retrieval, IEEE Transactions on Pattern Analysis and Machine Intelligence, 29 (3), pp. 394-410. (2006).

[12] Lavrenko V., Manmatha R., Jeon J.: A model for learning the semantics of pictures, Proceedings of NIPS. (2004).

[13] Provost F., Domingos P.: Tree induction for probability-based ranking, Machine Learning, 52, pp. 199-215. (2003).

8

Linguistic FOIL and Multiple Attribute Hierarchy for Decision Making

Most of the fundamental ideas of science are essentially simple, and may, as a rule, be expressed in a language comprehensible to everyone.

— Albert Einstein (1879-1955)

8.1 Introduction

Rule induction has been well accepted as a transparent learning system for its interpretable rules in decision making. In this chapter, a new linguistic rule induction algorithm is proposed by incorporating label semantics into the FOIL (First-Order Inductive Learning) algorithm. The latter is a well-known first-order rule induction algorithm in Inductive Logical Programming (ILP) proposed by Quinlan[1]. The new algorithm is guided by information based heuristics in accordance with label semantics. Some benchmark problems are tested and the results show that the new algorithm has comparable accuracy with linguistic rules. In the second part of this chapter, the multiple attribute decision making based on linguistic decision trees is given and illustrated by using an example.

8.2 Rule Induction

The use of high-level knowledge representation in data modeling allows for enhanced transparency in the sense that the referred models can be understood by practioners who are not necessarily experts. Rule based systems inherently tend to be more transparent than other models such as neural networks and Bayesian classifiers. A set of concise and understandable rules can provide a better understanding of how the classification or prediction has been conducted. There are two general types of algorithms for rule induction, top down and bottom up algorithms. Top-down approaches start from the most general rule and specialize it gradually. Bottom-up methods start from a basic fact given in the training database and generalize it. In this chapter we will focus on a top-down model for generating linguistic rules based on Quinlan's First-Order Inductive Learning (FOIL) Algorithm[1].

The FOIL algorithm is based on classical binary logic where attributes are typically assumed to be discrete. Numerical variables are usually discretized by splitting the numerical domain into a finite number of intervals. However, because of the uncertainty involved in most real-world problems, sharp boundaries between intervals often lead to a loss of robustness and generality[2]. Fuzzy logic has been used to solve the problem of sharp transitions between two intervals. Fuzzy rule induction research has been popular in both fuzzy and machine learning communities as a means to learning robust transparent models. Many algorithms have been proposed including simple fuzzy logic rule induction[3], fuzzy association rule mining[4] and first-order fuzzy rule induction based on FOIL[2,5]. In this chapter, we will focus on an extension to the FOIL algorithm based on label semantics. A new type of FOIL model, linguistic FOIL (LFOIL), is proposed for generating a set of linguistic rules based on label semantics. The experimental results on a number of real-world problems show that LFOIL has comparable accuracy to C4.5[6] and other linguistic models while generating compact interpretable rules.

IF-THEN rule is a basic concept in fuzzy logic, it plays a central role in most of its applications especially in fuzzy control. IF-THEN rule knowledge base contains a number of fuzzy rules in the following form:

- IF x_1 is A and x_2 is B THEN y is C.

where A, B and C are general fuzzy sets of attribute x, consider a hypothetical example of "tipping" of a restaurant dinner. We want to give tips in proportion to the two input variables, service and food. Let us partition each of the two input variables into three regions: poor, good and excellent for service, and rancid, good and delicious for food. Without reducing the number of rules, either heuristically or otherwise, if we are to apply the conventional grid partitioning method to the input domain, we need $3^2 = 9$ fuzzy rules, e.g.:

- Rule 1: If service is poor and food is rancid then the tip is cheap.
- Rule 2: If service is poor and food is good then the tip is better-than-cheap.
- ...   ...
- Rule 9: If service is excellent and food is delicious then the tip is generous.

Fig. 8.1 illustrates the surface of "tipping" based on the IF-THEN rules given in the above hypothetical example. IF-THEN rules can be used to describe complex real-world problems using non-liner approximation.

One of the most expressive and humanly readable representations for learned hypotheses is a set of rules. There are two kinds of rules for learning from data: propositional rules and first-order rules[1]. In this section, we will briefly introduce

---

[1] The names are based on the property of the rule, whether it is in propositional logic or first-order logic.

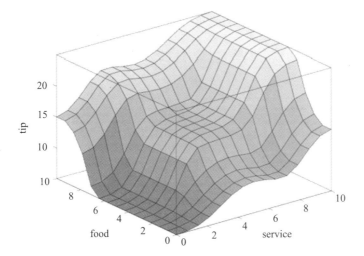

Fig. 8.1 An intuitive explanation of IF-THEN rules where a customer's tip is based on the quality of the food and service

some general ideas for rule learning and a particular algorithms for learning first-order rules, or Horn clauses, called FOIL. Let's consider a family of algorithms for learning rule sets based on the strategy of learning one rule, removing the data it covers, then iterating this process. Such algorithms are called sequential covering algorithms. Sequential covering algorithms learn one rule at a time, removing the covered examples and repeating the process on the remaining examples. In contrast, decision tree algorithms such as ID3 learn the entire set of disjuncts simultaneously as part of the single search for an acceptable decision tree. We might therefore, call algorithms such as ID3 simultaneous covering algorithms[7].

To generate candidate specializations of the current rule, FOIL generates a variety of new literals, each of which may be individually added to the rule body. More precisely, suppose the current rule being considered is

$$P(x_1,\ldots,x_k) \leftarrow L_1,\ldots,L_n$$

where $L_1,\ldots,L_n$ are literals forming the current rule and $P,x_1,\ldots,x_k$ is literals that form the rule head. The selection of the most promising liter from the candidates is guided by heuristic search. Given a rule θ and a candidate literal L that might be added to the body of θ, let φ be the rule created by adding literal L to θ (i.e., $\varphi \leftarrow \theta^L$). The information gain of adding L is defined as follows:

$$IG_{FOIL}(\theta,L) = t\left(\log_2 \frac{p_\varphi}{p_\varphi + n_\varphi} - \log_2 \frac{p_\theta}{p_\theta + n_\theta}\right)$$

where p_θ is the number of positives covered by rule θ and, n_θ is the number of negatives covered by θ, p_φ is the number of positives covered by φ, and n_φ is the number of negatives covered by φ. Finally, t is the number of positives covered by rule θ that are still covered after adding literal L to θ. This function IG_{FOIL} has a straightforward interpretation in terms of information theory, and it also considers the coverage of positives and negatives in order to avoid overspecialized rules (see Fig 8.2).

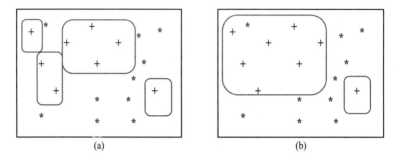

(a)   (b)

Fig. 8.2   Rule induction: what are good rules? A perfect rule is generated by adding term after term until the rule gives no error on the training set. This rule may be overspecialized (a). However, A rule may not perfect but covers a large number of examples, this rule has a good generation (b)

8.3 Multi-Dimensional Label Semantics

In previous chapters, we have introduced label semantics and shown how it can be used for data modeling. A few linguistic data mining models (e.g., linguistic decision trees and Bayesian estimation trees) have been proposed. In the following section, we will consider a linguistic rule induction model based on label semantics. We begin by attempting to clarify what we mean by a *linguistic rule*. Based on Definition 3.9, a linguistic rule is a rule that is represented in multi-dimensional logical expressions of labels.

Definition 8.1 (*Linguistic rule as multi-dimensional logical expressions of labels*)
    $MLE^{(n)}$ *is the set of all multi-dimensional label expressions that can be generated from the logical label expression* LE_j: $j = 1, \ldots, n$ *and is defined recursively by:*

(i)   If $\theta \in LE_j$ *for* $j = 1, \ldots, n$ *then* $\theta \in MLE^{(n)}$
(ii) If $\theta, \varphi \in MLE^{(n)}$ *then* $\neg\theta$, $\theta \wedge \varphi$, $\theta \vee \varphi$, $\theta \rightarrow \varphi \in MLE^{(n)}$

Any n-dimensional logical expression θ identifies a subset of $2^{\mathbb{L}_1} \times \ldots \times 2^{\mathbb{L}_n}$, denoted $\lambda^{(n)}(\theta)$, constraining the cross product of logical descriptions on each variable: $D_{x_1} \times \ldots \times D_{x_1}$. In such a way the imprecise constraint θ on n variables can be interpreted as the precise constraint $D_{x_1} \times \ldots \times D_{x_1} \in \lambda^{(n)}(\theta)$. We can easily extend λ-function to the multi-dimensional case, such that the set of n-dimensional label expressions $MLE^{(n)}$ is defined by:

Definition 8.2 (*Multi-dimensional λ-function*) $\lambda^{(n)}: MLE^{(n)} \rightarrow 2^{(2^{\mathbb{L}_1} \times \ldots \times 2^{\mathbb{L}_n})}$ *is defined recursively as follows: Let $\mathbb{F}_j$ denote the set of focal elements for $\mathbb{L}_j$: $j = 1, \ldots, n$ then $\forall \theta \in MLE^{(n)}$, $\lambda^{(n)} \subseteq \mathbb{F}_1 \times \ldots \times \mathbb{F}_n$.*

Given a particular data, how can we evaluate it if a linguistic rule is appropriate for describing it? Based on the one-dimensional case, we now extend the concept of appropriateness degrees to the multi-dimensional case as follows:

Definition 8.3 (*Multi-dimensional appropriateness degrees*) *Given a set of n-dimensional label expression $MLE^{(n)}$:*

$$\forall \theta \in MLE^{(n)}, \forall x_j \in \Omega_j : j = 1, \ldots, n$$

$$\mu_\theta^n(x) = \mu_\theta^n(x_1, \ldots, x_n) = \sum_{\langle F_1, \ldots, F_n \rangle \in \lambda^{(n)}(\theta)} m_x(F_1, \ldots, F_n)$$

$$= \sum_{\langle F_1, \ldots, F_n \rangle \in \lambda^{(n)}(\theta)} \prod_{j=1}^{n} m_{x_j}(F_j)$$

The appropriateness degrees in one-dimension are for evaluating the appropriateness of a single label for describing a single data element, while in multi-dimensional cases they are for evaluating the appropriateness of a linguistic rule for describing a multi-dimensional data. The following example illustrates the evaluation of multi-dimensional appropriateness degrees.

Example 8.1 *Consider a modellng problem with two variables x_1 and x_2 for which $\mathbb{L}_1 = \{small\ (s),\ medium\ (med),\ large(lg)\}$ and $\mathbb{L}_2 = \{low(lo),\ moderate\ (mod),\ high(h)\}$. Also suppose the focal elements for $\mathbb{L}_1$ and $\mathbb{L}_2$ are:*

$$\mathbb{F}_1 = \{\{s\}, \{s, med\}, \{med\}, \{med, lg\}, \{lg\}\}$$

$$\mathbb{F}_2 = \{\{lo\}, \{lo, mod\}, \{mod\}, \{mod, h\}, \{h\}\}$$

Given a logical expression (i.e., a linguistic rule):

$$\theta = (med \wedge \neg s) \wedge \neg lo$$

Then, according to the multi-dimensional generalization of Definition 3.10 we have that

$$\lambda^{(2)}((med \wedge \neg s) \wedge \neg lo) = \lambda^{(2)}(med \wedge \neg s) \cap \lambda^{(2)}(\neg lo)$$
$$= \lambda(med \wedge \neg s) \times \lambda(\neg lo)$$

Now, the set of possible label sets is obtained according to the λ-function in the one-dimensional case (Definition 3.10):

$$\lambda(med \wedge \neg s) = \{\{med\}, \{med, lg\}\}$$

$$\lambda(\neg lo) = \{\{mod\}, \{mod, h\}, \{h\}\}$$

Hence, based on Definition 8.2 we can obtain:

$$\lambda^{(2)}((med \wedge \neg s) \wedge \neg lo) = \{\langle\{med\},\{mod\}\rangle, \langle\{med\},\{mod,h\}\rangle,$$

$$\langle\{med\},\{h\}\rangle, \langle\{med,lg\},\{mod\}\rangle, \langle\{med,lg\},\{mod,h\}\rangle, \langle\{med,lg\},\{h\}\rangle\}$$

The above calculation based on a random set interpretation of label expressions and using the λ-function is illustrated in Fig. 8.3 : given focal set $\mathbb{F}_1$ and $\mathbb{F}_2$, we can construct a 2-dimensional space where the focal elements have corresponding focal cells. Representation of the multi-dimensional λ-function of the logical expression is represented by gray cells.

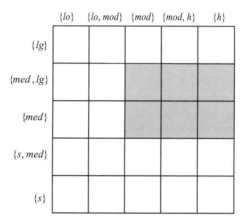

Fig. 8.3   Representation of the multi-dimensional λ-function (gray cells) of the logical expression $\theta = (med \wedge \neg s) \wedge \neg lo$ showing the focal cells $\mathbb{F}_1 \times \mathbb{F}_2$

Suppose we are given the following data element in the 2-dimensional case:

$$x = \langle x_1, x_2 \rangle = \langle x_1 = \{med\} : 0.6, \{med,lg\} : 0.4\rangle$$
$$= \langle x_2 = \{lo,mod\} : 0.8, \{mod\} : 0.2\rangle$$

According to Definition 8.3 we can obtain:

$$\mu_\theta(x) = (m(\{med\}) + m(\{med,lg\})) \times (m(\{mod\}) + m(\{mod,h\}) + m(\{h\}))$$

$$= (0.6 + 0.4) \times (0.2 + 0 + 0) = 0.2$$

and according to Definition 3.10 and 8.2:

$$\mu^n_{\neg\theta}(x) = 1 - \mu_\theta(x) = 0.8$$

In other words, we can say that the rule θ covers 20% of the data x. This interpretation of appropriateness for a rule is highlighted in the next section of linguistic rule induction.

8.4 Linguistic FOIL

In the last section, we have shown how to evaluate the appropriateness of a linguistic rule to describe a data vector. In this section, a new algorithm for learning a set of linguistic rules is proposed based on the FOIL algorithm [1] and is referred to as *Linguistic FOIL* (LFOIL). Essentially, the search heuristic for this rule learning model is an entropy measure for assessing the usefulness of a literal as the next component of the rule.

8.4.1 Information Heuristics for LFOIL

The heuristics used for LFOIL are a modified version of those of used in the FOIL algorithm to take account of labels semantics [1]. Consider a classification rule of the form:

$$R_i = \theta \rightarrow C_k \ \ where \ \ \theta \in MLE^{(n)}$$

Given a data set *DB* and a particular class C_k, the data belonging to class C_k are referred to as positive examples and the rest of the data negative examples. For a given rule R_i, the coverage of positive data is evaluated by

$$T_i^+ = \sum_{l \in DB_k} \mu_\theta(x_l) \tag{8.1}$$

and the coverage of negative examples is given by

$$T_i^- = \sum_{l \in (DB - DB_k)} \mu_\theta(x_l) \tag{8.2}$$

where DB_k is the subset of the database which consists of the data belonging to class C_k. The information for the original rule R_i can by evaluated[2] by

$$I(R_i) = -\log_2 \left(\frac{T_i^+}{T_i^+ + T_i^-} \right) \tag{8.3}$$

Suppose we then propose adding another label expression φ to the body of R_i generating a new rule

$$R_{i+1} = \varphi \wedge \theta \rightarrow C_k$$

where $\varphi, \theta \in MLE^{(n)}$. By adding the new literal φ, the positive and negative coverage becomes:

$$T_{i+1}^+ = \sum_{l \in DB_k} \mu_{\theta \wedge \varphi}(x_l) \tag{8.4}$$

$$T_{i+1}^- = \sum_{l \in (DB - DB_k)} \mu_{\theta \wedge \varphi}(x_l) \tag{8.5}$$

---

[2] In this chapter, we use two different notations of appropriateness degrees for the rule $R_i = \theta \rightarrow C_k$: μ_θ and μ_{R_i}. The former is used in logical expressions and the latter is used in the rule learning algorithm.

Therefore, the information becomes,

$$I(R_{i+1}) = -\log_2 \left(\frac{T_{i+1}^+}{T_{i+1}^+ + T_{i+1}^-} \right) \tag{8.6}$$

Then we can evaluate the information gain from adding expression φ according to:

$$G(\varphi) = T_{i+1}^+ (I(R_i) - I(R_{i+1})) \tag{8.7}$$

We can see that this measure of information gain consists of two components. T_{i+1}^+ is the coverage of positive data by the new rule R_{i+1} and $(I(R_i) - I(R_{i+1}))$ is the increase in information. The probability of C_k given a linguistic rule R_i is evaluated by:

$$P(C_k|R_i) = \frac{\sum_{l \in DB_k} \mu_\theta(x_l)}{\sum_{l \in DB} \mu_\theta(x_l)} = \frac{T_i^+}{T_i^+ + T_i^-} \tag{8.8}$$

When $P(C_k|R_{i+1}) \geq P(C_k|R_i)$ (i.e., by appending a new literal, more positive examples are covered), we can obtain that $(I(R_i) - I(R_{i+1})) \geq 0$. By choosing a literal φ with maximum G value, we can identify the new rule which covers the most extra positive examples and thus increase the accuracy of the rule.

8.4.2 Linguistic Rule Generation

We began by defining a prior knowledge base $KB \subseteq MLE^{(n)}$ and a probability threshold $PT \in [0,1]$. KB consists of fuzzy label expressions based on labels defined on each attribute. For example, given fuzzy labels $\{small_1 \ large_1\}$ to describe attribute 1 and $\{small_2 \ large_2\}$ to describe attribute 2, a possible knowledge base for the given two variables is: $KB = \{small_1, \neg small_1, large_1, \neg large_1, small_2, \neg small_2, large_2, \neg large_2\}$. In practice, it could become more general to include expressions like $small_1 \rightarrow small_2$. We are not discussing this kind of rules in this chapter.

The idea for FOIL is as follows: starting from a general rule, we make it more specific by adding new literals in order to cover more positive examples and less negative examples according to the heuristics introduced in the last section. After developing one rule, the positives are deleted from the original database. We then need to find a new rule based on this reduced database until all positives are covered. Here in this chapter, because of the new semantics we used, we can only partially cover data by some degrees. For a single rule, it is impossible to cover positives only for most cases. That is the reason why we need a probability threshold PT.

Figure 8.4 qualitatively illustrates the LFOIL algorithm. Each box represents a data in the left-hand figure, which in most cases cannot be fully covered. For example, see the left-hand figure of Fig. 8.4 , the data lying in the overlapping area of Rule A and B cannot be fully covered due to the limitations of the rule base. We need to find those rules with better generalization as well as good accuracy. For example, in the right-hand side of figure of Fig. 8.4 rule D is a rule that only covers positives, and therefore it may not be the best choice when with Rule C and Rule A. Although Rule A covers a negative example, it also covers the area of positives fairly well. Such a rule has a better generalization than Rule D. If we set PT too high, this may result in too many specific rules like Rule D, which may have perfect training accuracy but bad test accuracy because of the lack of generalization. The pseudo-code of LFOIL consists of two parts which are described as follows: (a) Generating a rule (Algorithm 5) and (b) generating a rule base (Algorithm 6).

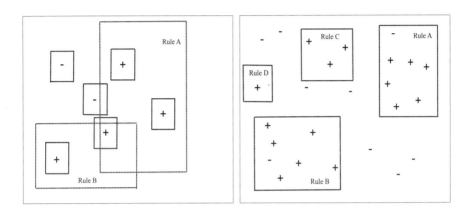

Fig. 8.4 Illustrations of the LFOIL algorithms. In the left-hand side figure each data has associated masses and it may not be fully covered. Consider that the positive data lies in the overlapping area of Rule A and Rule B, there is still a small square that cannot be covered due to the limitation of the rule base. Right-hand figure: in order to avoid generating too specified rules, we set a threshold to determine the purity in terms of a mixture of positives and negatives covered for a rule

---

Algorithm 5: Generating a Rule

- Given rule $R_i = \theta_1 \wedge \ldots \wedge \theta_d \to C_k$ be the rule at step i:
  Find the next literal $\theta_{d+1} \in KB - \{\theta_1, \ldots, \theta_d\}$ for which $G(\theta_{d+1})$ is maximal.
- Replace rule R_i with $R_{i+1} = \theta_1 \wedge \ldots \wedge \theta_d \wedge \theta_{d+1} \to C_k$
- If $P(C_k|\theta_1 \wedge \ldots \wedge \theta_{i+1}) \geq PT$
  Then: terminate
  Else: repeat the whole process.

Let $\Delta_i = \{R_1 \to C_k, \ldots, R_t \to C_k\}$ be the rule base at step i. We evaluate the coverage of Δ_i as follows:

$$CV(\Delta_i) = \frac{\sum_{l \in DB_k} \mu_{R_1 \vee \ldots \vee R_t}(x_l)}{|DB_k|} \quad (8.9)$$

We define a coverage function $\delta : \Omega_1 \times \ldots \times \Omega_n \to [0, 1]$ according to:

Algorithm 6: Generating a Rule Base

- Given a rule base $\Delta_i = \{R_1 \to C_k, \ldots, R_t \to C_k\}$ at time step i:
  Computing coverage of Δ_i which is denoted by $CV(\Delta_i)$
- if $CV(\Delta_i) < CT$
  Then: generate a new rule $R_{t+1} \to C_k$ and add R_j to form a new rule base Δ_{i+1}
- Else If: $CV(RB_{i+1}) \geq CT$ or $CV(RB_{i+1}) - CV(RB_i) < \varepsilon$
- Then: terminate the process

$$\delta(x|\Delta_i) = \mu_{\neg \Delta_i}(x) = \mu_{\neg(R_1 \vee \ldots \vee R_t)}(x) \tag{8.10}$$

$$= 1 - \mu_{(R_1 \vee \ldots \vee R_t)}(x) = 1 - \sum_{w=1}^{t} \mu_{R_w}(x)$$

where $\delta(x|\Delta_i)$ represents the degree to which x is *not* covered by a given rule base Δ_i. If CV is less than a predefined coverage threshold $CT \in [0,1]$:

$$CV(\Delta_i) < CT$$

then we generate a new rule for class C_k according to the above rule generation algorithm to form a new rule base Δ_{i+1} but where the entropy calculations are amended such that for a rule $R = \theta \to C_k$,

$$T^+ = \sum_{l \in DB_k} \mu_\theta(x_l) \times \delta(x_l|\Delta_i) \tag{8.11}$$

$$T^- = \sum_{l \in (DB - DB_k)} \mu_\theta(x_l) \tag{8.12}$$

The algorithm terminates when $CV(RB_{i+1}) \geq CT$ or $CV(RB_{i+1}) - CV(RB_i) < \varepsilon$ where $\varepsilon \in [0,1]$ is a very small value, i.e., if there are no improvements in covering positive data, we then terminate the algorithm in order to avoid an infinite loop.

8.4.3 Class Probabilities Given a Rule Base

Given a rule base $\Delta_i = \{R_1 \to C_k, \ldots, R_t \to C_k\}$ and an unclassified data x, we can estimate the probability of C_k, $P(C_k|x)$, as follows: Firstly, we determine the rule $R_{max} \to C_k$ for which $\mu_{R_j}(x)$ is maximal: i.e.,

$$R_{max} = \max_{j \in \Delta_i} \mu_{R_k} \tag{8.13}$$

Therefore, given the unclassified data x, rule R_{max} is the most appropriate rule from the rule base for describing and classifying x. For the rule $R_{max} \to C_j$ we evaluate two probabilities p_{max} and q_{max} where,

$$p_{max} = P(C_j | R_{max}) \qquad (8.14)$$

$$q_{max} = P(C_j | \neg R_{max}) \qquad (8.15)$$

We then use Jeffrey's rule [8] to evaluate the class probability of eac hclass given x according to,

$$P(C_j | x) = p_{max} \times \mu_{R_{max}}(x) + q_{max} \times (1 - \mu_{R_{max}}(x)) \qquad (8.16)$$

Here is the summary of this algorithm: we use the most appropriate rule for classification in this algorithm. Given a data element, we will select the most appropriate rule from the rule base. Using this rule we then obtain an estimate of class probabilities and subsequently identify the class with maximal probability.

8.5 Experimental Studies

In this section we first test the new algorithm with a toy problem which has been used in previous chapters. A figure of eight shape was generated according to the equation

$$x = 2^{(-0.5)}(sin(2t) - sin(t))$$

and

$$y = 2^{(-0.5)}(sin(2t) + sin(t))$$

where $t \in [0, 2\pi]$ (see Fig. 8.5). Points in $[-1.6, 1.6]^2$ are classified as legal if they lie within the 'eight' shape (marked with $\times$) and illegal if they lie outside (marked with points).

The database is consisted of 961 examples generated from a regular grid on $[-1.6, 1.6]^2$ for training, and 961 unseen examples from the same distribution as the test data set.

The following rules are generated by the LFOIL algorithm with $PT = 0.7$, $CV = 0.9$ and $\varepsilon = 0.005$:

$R_1 : x$ is $\neg$ very small $\wedge$ small $\wedge$ medium $\wedge \neg$ large and y is $\neg$ small $\wedge$ medium $\rightarrow$ legal
$R_2 : x$ is $\neg$ small $\wedge$ medium and y is $\neg$ very small $\wedge$ small $\wedge$ medium $\wedge \neg$ large $\rightarrow$ legal
$R_3 : x$ is medium $\wedge \neg$ large and y is large $\wedge$ very large $\rightarrow$ legal
$R_4 : x$ is large $\wedge$ very large and y is medium $\wedge \neg$ large $\rightarrow$ legal
$R_5 : x$ is very small $\wedge$ small $\wedge \neg$ medium and y is medium $\wedge \neg$ large $\rightarrow$ legal
$R_6 : x$ medium $\wedge \neg$ large and y is very small $\wedge$ small $\wedge \neg$ medium $\rightarrow$ legal

These rules are symmetric and as we can see from the Fig. 8.5 and capture the legal area very well. The area covered by R_1 is marked by a box shown in Fig. 8.5 .

We also test LFOIL on benchmark problems taken from the UCI machine learning repository [9]. The data descriptions are listed in the left-hand column of Table 8.1 . For each variable, we use of 3 fuzzy labels with percentile-based discretization (see Section 2.1). For each data set, we randomly split it into two

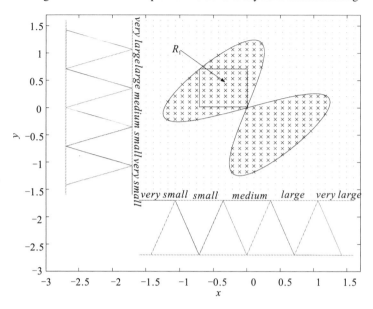

Fig. 8.5 The illustration of the 'eight' problem, where each attribute is uniformly discretized by 5 linguistic labels: *very small, small, medium, large* and *very large*, respectively

equal parts, one half for training and the other half for the test (i.e., 50-50 split experiments[10]. We ran 10 50-50 experiments on each data set and the average accuracy is listed in Table 8.1 together with the sizes of linguistic decision trees and the number of linguistic rules on the right. The parameter settings for LFOIL are $PT = 0.7$, $CV = 0.9$ and $\varepsilon = 0.005$. We also compare LFOIL with C4.5[3] and

Table 8.1 Experimental results on 7 numerical data sets from UCI repository [9]

Dataset	Descriptions		TestAccuracy(%)				Num. of Rules	
	Size	Attri	C4.5	FNB	LID3	LFOIL	LID3	LFOIL
BreastCancer	286	9	69.16	68.22	73.02	64.10	20	17
Breast-W	699	9	94.38	96.74	96.20	95.63	59	8
Heart-c	303	13	75.50	76.85	76.87	74.55	48	22
Heart-stalog	270	13	75.78	78.34	76.52	71.89	42	17
Heptitis	155	19	76.75	80.13	82.94	75.64	27	8
Liver	345	6	65.23	63.35	56.86	54.98	85	3
Pima	768	8	72.16	72.29	76.54	71.67	31	4

③ The results for C4.5 are obtained from a free machine learning toolkit Weka[11] with default settings. The parameter settings for LID3 are according to Reference[10].

Table 8.2 T-test on on experimental results with 90% confidence. '−' represents equivalence and '×' represents worse

Dataset	LFOIL vs. C4.5	LFOIL vs. FNB	LFOIL vs. LID3
BreastCancer	−	−	×
Breast-W	−	−	−
Heart-c	−	−	−
Heart-stalog	−	×	×
Heptitis	−	×	×
Liver	×	×	−
Pima	−	−	×

the other two linguistic models. Tthe results of the t-test with 90% confidence are shown in Table 8.2 .

As we can see from Tables 8.1 and 8.2 , though the predictive accuracy of LFOIL is worse than LID3 and FNB, it is fairly comparable to C4.5. More importantly in this context, we can extract a much smaller number of rules for classification from a large database than for either C4.5 or LID3. For example, let us consider the Pima Indian problem. The database contains the details of 768 females from the population of Pima Indians living near Phoenix Arizona, USA. The diagnostic binary-valued variable investigated is whether the patient shows signs of diabetes according to the World Health Organisation criteria. We use 3 fuzzy labels: low, medium and high for each of the 8 attributes. Using LFOIL we obtain the following rules to decide whether or not a patient has diabetes:

R_1: Plasma concentration (Attribute 2) is low $\wedge$ medium and the number of times pregnant (Attribute 1) is medium $\wedge \neg$ high $\rightarrow$ diabetes

R_2: Plasma concentration is medium and age (Attribute 8) is $\neg$ low $\rightarrow$ diabetes

R_3: Plasma concentration is low $\wedge$ medium and the number of times pregnant is high $\rightarrow$ diabetes

R_4: Plasma concentration is $\neg$ medium $\wedge$ high and *diabetes pedigree function* (Attribute 7) is medium $\rightarrow$ diabetes

Hence, although the accuracy is worse than LID3, the transparency is greatly improved by using only 4 rules (while the linguistic decision tree has 31 branches) that give a much better understanding of this problem. For some real-world situations, these rules could be much more useful than some probabilistic models for a clinical doctor.

8.6 Multiple Attribute Decision Making

In multiple-attribute decision making the underlying relationships between attributes and classification, decision or utility variable are often highly imprecise or uncertain. Recently, Van-Nam *et al.* proposed a methodology of aggregating evidence from different attributes on weighed combination rules in evidence theory[12]. This approach is a successful attempt to unify probability and fuzziness based on mass assignment.

8.6.1 Linguistic Attribute Hierarchies

The multiple-attribute decision making problem engages in the propagation of information that is often highly uncertain and imprecise. Fuzzy measures have played an important role in the fusion of multiple attributes. Recently, Van-Nam *et al.* have proposed to aggregate evidence from different attributes on the basis of weighted combination rules in evidence theory, where the underlying idea is to use mass assignment to provide a unified model of probability and fuzziness[12].

The process of aggregation of evidence in a multi-attribute decision problem based on a given set of attributes $x_1, \ldots, x_n$ can be viewed as a functional mapping $y = f(x_1, \ldots, x_n)$, where typically y corresponds to some measure of utility according to which different examples can be evaluated and ranked. Given the utility function f, attribute hierarchies break down the function into a hierarchy of sub-functions where each of them can represent a new intermediate attribute (see Fig. 8.6). For a example, the original set of attribute

$$\mathbb{X} = \{x_1, x_2, \ldots, x_n\}$$

can be partitioned into subsets of attributes $S_1, S_2, \ldots, S_m$ and the the new attribute z_i is defined as a function of S_i, where $i \in \{1, 2, \ldots, m\}$. Formally:

$$\forall i \in \{1, 2, \ldots, m\} \quad z_i = G_i(S_i) \tag{8.17}$$

The utility function $f()$ is defined by a new function $F()$ of the new attributes $z_1, z_2, \ldots, z_m$, so that:

$$y = f(x_1, \ldots, x_n) = F(z_1, \ldots, z_m) = F(G_1(S_1), \ldots, G_m(S_m)) \tag{8.18}$$

Definition 8.4 (Linguistic definitions) *A linguistic definition of label expressions* $\mathbb{L}_y$ *in terms of the logical expressions* $LE_k : k = 1, \ldots, m$ *is a set of linguistic probability rules of the following form:*

$$\Delta_i \rightarrow \alpha_F : P(\alpha_F | \Delta_i)$$

for every atom α_F *where* $F \in \mathbb{F}_y$ *for* $i = 1, \ldots T$, *and where* Δ_j *is a conjunction of expression from* $LE_k : k = 1, \ldots m$. $P(\alpha_F | \Delta_i)$ *denotes the conditional probability that* α_F *is appropriate to describe* y *given that* z_1, z_m *are described by* Δ_i.

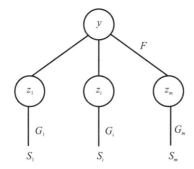

Fig. 8.6 Attribute hierarchy by partitioning the original set of attributes into m subsets. The new attribute z_i is a function G over attribute subset S_i

Given such a set definitions we can determine the mass assignment m_y for a given example with attribute values $z_1, \ldots, z_m$ according to Jeffrey's rule[8] by:

$$m_y(F) = \mu_{\alpha_F}(y) = \sum_{i=1}^{T} P(\Delta_i | z_1, \ldots, z_m) P(\alpha_F | \Delta_i) \qquad (8.19)$$

where if Δ_i is the conjunction $\theta_{i_1} \wedge \ldots \wedge \theta_{i_k}$ for $\theta_{i_j} \in LE_{i_j}$ then:

$$P(\Delta_i | z_1, \ldots z_m) = \prod_{j=1}^{k} \mu_{\theta_{i_j}}(z_{i_j}) \qquad (8.20)$$

Example 8.2 *Consider a decision problem with utility variable y depend on attributes z_1, z_2, z_3. Output y is labelled using just two overlapping labels*

$$\mathbb{L}_y = \{poor(p), good(g)\}$$

so that

$$\mathbb{F}_y = \{\{p\}, \{p, g\}, \{g\}\}$$

Attributes z_1, z_2, z_3 are each described using three labels as follows:

$$\mathbb{L}_1 = \{small(s), medium(m), large(l)\}$$
$$\mathbb{L}_2 = \{cold(c), warm(w), hot(ht)\}$$
$$\mathbb{L}_3 = \{low(lw), middle(md), high(h)\}$$

with focal sets:

$$\mathbb{F}_1 = \{\{s\}, \{s, m\}, \{m\}, \{m, l\}, \{l\}\}$$
$$\mathbb{F}_2 = \{\{c\}, \{c, w\}, \{w\}, \{w, ht\}, \{ht\}$$
$$\mathbb{F}_3 = \{\{lw\}, \{lw, md\}, \{md\}, \{md, h\}, \{h\}\}$$

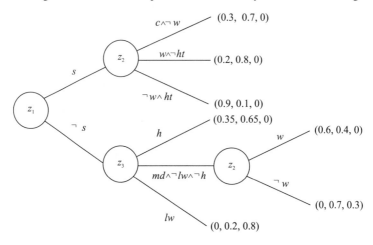

Fig. 8.7 Linguistic decision tree involving attributes z_1, z_2 and z_3

Consider the LDT shown in Fig. 8.7 involving all these three above attributes. In this case:

$$\mathbb{L}_{1,1} = \{\{small, \neg small\} \subseteq \mathbb{L}_1$$
$$\mathbb{L}_{1,2} = \{\{cold \wedge \neg warm, warm \wedge \neg hot, \neg warm \wedge hot\} \subseteq \mathbb{L}_2$$
$$\mathbb{L}_{1,3} = \{warm, \neg warm\} \subseteq \mathbb{L}_2$$
$$\mathbb{L}_{2,2} = \{low, middle \wedge \neg low \wedge \neg high, high\} \subseteq \mathbb{L}_3$$

Given a branch:

$$B = (z_1 \text{ is } \neg s) \wedge (z_3 \text{ is } md \wedge \neg lw \wedge \neg h) \wedge (z_2 \text{ is } w)$$

It encodes three rule with probabilistic weights and each with identical antecedents as the following:

$$B \rightarrow (y \text{ is } p \wedge \neg g) : 0.6$$
$$B \rightarrow (y \text{ is } p \wedge g) : 0.4$$
$$B \rightarrow (y \text{ is } \neg p \wedge g) : 0$$

Given the equivalence between focal elements and atoms then B identifies the mass assignment on $2^{\mathbb{L}_y}$ given by:

$$m_y = \{p\} : 0.6, \{p, g\} : 0.4$$

Hence, the rule can be summarized by:

$$(z_1 \text{ is } \neg s) \wedge (z_3 \text{ is } md \wedge \neg lw \wedge \neg h) \wedge (z_2 \text{ is } w) \rightarrow \{p\} : 0.6, \{p, g\} : 0.4$$

A particular example will then satisfy the antecedents of a number of rules with some probability. We can then generate a mass assignment describing the value of y for that example by taking a weighted combination of the mass assignments from those rules with non-zero probability. For instance, suppose for a given example we have the following appropriateness measure values for attributes z_1, z_2, z_3:

$$\mu_s(z_1) = 1, \ \mu_{md \wedge \neg lw \wedge \neg h}(z_3) = 1, \ \mu_w(z_2) = 0.6$$

Hence, we have non-zero probability values of 0.6 and 0.4 for the following two rules respectively:

$$(z_1 \ is \ \neg s) \wedge (z_3 \ is \ md \wedge \neg lw \neg h) \wedge (z_2 \ is \ w) \rightarrow \{p\} : 0.6, \{p, g\} : 0.4$$

$$(z_1 \ is \ \neg s) \wedge (z_3 \ is \ md \wedge \neg lw \neg h) \wedge (z_2 \ is \ \neg w) \rightarrow \{p, g\} : 0.7, \{g\} : 0.3$$

From this we can infer a mass assignment m_y:

$$
\begin{aligned}
m_y &= 0.6 \times (\{p\} : 0.6, \{p, g\} : 0.4) + 0.4 \times (\{p, g\} : 0.7, \{g\} : 0.3) \quad (8.21) \\
&= \{p\} : 0.36, \{p, g\} : 0.52, \{g\} : 0.12
\end{aligned}
$$

8.6.2 Information Propagation Using LDT

In order to have a better understanding of information propagation through a linguistic hierarchy, we will use an example to highlight the process.

Example 8.3 *Suppose we are given a random variable with 4 attributes x_1, x_2, x_3 and x_4 each with an underlying universe $[0, 1]$ and each the same set of basic labels:*

$$\mathbb{L} = \{very \ small(vs), small(s), medium(m), large(l), very \ large(vl)\}$$

These labels are defined by trapezoidal fuzzy labels shown in Fig. 8.8 , where the corresponding focal elements are also shown in the same figure:

$$\mathbb{F} = \{\{vs\}, \{vs, s\}, \{s\}, \{s, m\}, \{m\}, \{m, l\}, \{l\}, \{l, vl\}, \{vl\}\}$$

Given the attribute hierarchy shown in Fig. 8.9 , there are two intermediate attributes:

$$z_1 = G_1(x_1, x_2) \quad (8.22)$$

$$z_2 = G_2(x_3, x_4) \quad (8.23)$$

and utility function:

$$z_2 = F(z_1, z_2) \quad (8.24)$$

where the functions G_1, G_2 and F are defined by linguistic decision trees T_2, T_3 and T_1, respectively. If labels defined on y are:

$$\mathbb{L}_y = \{very \ bad(vb), bad(b), average(a), good(g), very \ good(vg)\}$$

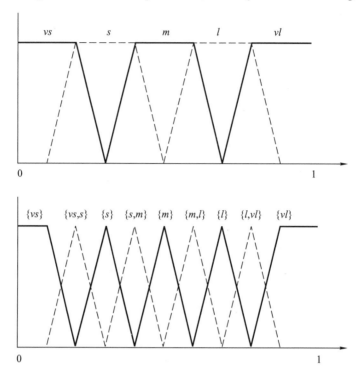

Fig. 8.8 Fuzzy labels defined in the universe of the given base attributes in Example 8.3. Each linguistic label is defined by a uniformly distributed trapezoidal fuzzy set while corresponding to focal elements in triangle shapes

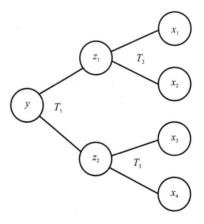

Fig. 8.9 Example of a simple linguistic attribute hierarchy using linguistic decision trees

then its corresponding focal set is:

$$\mathbb{F}_y = \{\{vb\}, \{vb, b\}, \{b\}, \{b, a\}, \{a\}, \{a, g\}, \{g\}, \{g, vg\}, \{vg\}\}$$

Suppose the linguistic decision trees T_1, T_2, and T_3 are defined at below, where $T_i \mapsto B_j$ denotes the jth branch in tree T_i.

$T_1 \mapsto B_1 \quad (z_1 \text{ is } vs \lor s) \to \{vb\} : 0.9, \{vb, b\} : 0.1$
$T_1 \mapsto B_2 \quad (z_1 \text{ is } \neg s \land m) \land (z_2 \text{ is } l) \to \{g\} : 0.4, \{g, vg\} : 0.6$
$T_1 \mapsto B_3 \quad (z_1 \text{ is } \neg s \land m) \land (z_2 \text{ is } \neg l) \to \{g, vg\} : 0.7, \{vg\} : 0.3$
$T_1 \mapsto B_4 \quad (z_1 \text{ is } \neg m \land l) \to \{a\} : 0.6, \{a, g\} : 0.2, \{g\} : 0.2$
$T_1 \mapsto B_5 \quad (z_1 \text{ is } \neg l \land vl) \to \{b, a\} : 0.7, \{a\} : 0.3$

$T_2 \mapsto B_1 \quad (x_1 \text{ is } vs \land s) \land (x_2 \text{ is } l) \to \{l\} : 0.8, \{l, vl\} : 0.2$
$T_2 \mapsto B_2 \quad (x_1 \text{ is } vs \land s) \land (x_2 \text{ is } \neg l) \to \{s, m\} : 0.5, \{m\} : 0.1, \{m, l\} : 0.4$
$T_1 \mapsto B_3 \quad (x_1 \text{ is } \neg s \land s) \land (x_2 \text{ is } m \lor l) \to \{l, vl\} : 0.1, \{vl\} : 0.9$
$T_2 \mapsto B_4 \quad (x_1 \text{ is } \neg vs \land s) \land (x_2 \text{ is } \neg l \land vl) \to \{s, m\} : 0.2, \{m\} : 0.6, \{m, l\} : 0.2$
$T_2 \mapsto B_5 \quad (x_1 \text{ is } \neg vs \land s) \land (x_2 \text{ is } (vs \lor s) \land \neg m) \to \{vs\} : 0.6, \{vs, s\} : 0.4$
$T_2 \mapsto B_6 \quad (z_1 \text{ is } \neg s) \to \{vs\} : 0.9, \{vs, s\} : 0.1$

$T_3 \mapsto B_1 \quad (x_4 \text{ is } vl) \to \{vs\} : 0.95, \{vs, s\} : 0.05$
$T_3 \mapsto B_2 \quad (x_3 \text{ is } m \lor l) \land (x_4 \text{ is } \neg vl) \to \{m, l\} : 0.1, \{l\} : 0.2, \{l, vl\} : 0.3, \{vl\} : 0.4$
$T_3 \mapsto B_3 \quad (x_3 \text{ is } \neg m \land \neg l) \land (x_4 \text{ is } \neg vl) \to \{s\} : 0.1, \{s, m\} : 0.6, \{m\} : 0.3$

Now consider an example

$$x = \langle x_1 = 0.18, x_2 = 0.44, x_3 = 0.57, x_4 = 0.85 \rangle$$

which has the following mass assignments based on the definitions of labels:

$\mu_{vs}(x_1) = 1, \mu_s(x_1) = 0.8 \Rightarrow \{vs\} : 0.2, \{vs, s\} : 0.8$
$\mu_s(x_2) = 0.6, \mu_m(x_2) = 1 \Rightarrow \{s, m\} : 0.6, \{m\} : 0.4$
$\mu_m(x_3) = 1, \mu_l(x_3) = 0.7 \Rightarrow \{m\} : 0.3, \{m, l\} : 0.7$
$\mu_l(x_4) = 0.5, \mu_{vl}(x_4) = 1 \Rightarrow \{l, vl\} : 0.5, \{vl\} : 0.5$

Based on linguistic decision tree T_2 we can have:

$\mu_{vs \land s}(x_1) = 0.8$
$\mu_{\neg vs \land s}(x_1) = 0$
$\mu_{\neg s}(x_1) = 0.2$
$\mu_l(x_2) = 0$
$\mu_{\neg l}(x_2) = 1$
$\mu_{\neg l \land vl}(x_2) = 0$
$\mu_{(l \lor vl) \land \neg m}(x_2) = 0$

Hence, we can calculate the branch probability of each branch in T_2:

$$P(T_2 \mapsto B_2|x) = \mu_{vs \wedge s}(x_1) \times \mu_{\neg l}(x_2) = 0.8 \times 1 = 0.8 \tag{8.25}$$

$$P(T_2 \mapsto B_6|x) = \mu_{\neg s}(x_1) = 0.2 \tag{8.26}$$

$$P(T_2 \mapsto B_1|x) = P(T_2 - B_3|x) = P(T_2 - B_4|x) = P(T_2 - B_5|x) = 0 \tag{8.27}$$

By considering the above equations we can obtain:

$$P(T_2|x) = \{T_2 \mapsto B_2 : 0.8, T_2 \mapsto B_6 : 0.2\} \tag{8.28}$$

The propagated mass assignment of variable z_1 given x is calculated by:

$$\begin{aligned}
m_{z_1}(x) &= \sum_{B \in T_2} P(z_1|B)P(B|x) \\
&= P(T_2 \mapsto B_2|x) \times P(T_2 \mapsto B_2) + P(T_2 \mapsto B_6|x) \times P(T_2 \mapsto B_6) \\
&= 0.8 \times (\{s,m\} : 0.5, \{m\} : 0.1, \{m,l\} : 0.4) + \\
&\quad 0.2 \times (\{vs\} : 0.9, \{vs,s\} : 0.1) \\
&= \{vs\} : 0.18, \{vs,s\} : 0.02, \{s,m\} : 0.4 \\
&\quad \{m\} : 0.08, \{m,l\} : 0.32
\end{aligned} \tag{8.29}$$

Similarly, from T_3 we can infer the following mass assignment m_{z_2} that:

$$\begin{aligned}
m_{z_2}(x) &= \sum_{B \in T_3} P(z_2|B)P(B|x) \\
&= \{m,l\} : 0.1, \{l\} : 0.2, \{l,vl\} : 0.3, \{vl\} : 0.4
\end{aligned} \tag{8.30}$$

Based on the mass assignment on z_1 and z_2 given x, we can calculate the branch probability of each branch in T_1.

$$P(T_1 \mapsto B_1|x) = 0.6, \ P(T_1 \mapsto B_2|x) = 0.24, \ P(T_1 \mapsto B_1|x) = 0.16$$

$$P(T_1 \mapsto B_4|x) = P(T_1 \mapsto B_5|x) = 0$$

Therefore, we can infer a mass assignment on utility, m_y according to:

$$\begin{aligned}
m_y &= 0.6 \times (\{vb\} : 0.9, \{vb,b\} : 0.1) + 0.24 \times (\{g\} : 0.4, \{g,vg\} : 0.6) \\
&\quad + 0.16 \times (\{g,vg\} : 0.7, \{vg\} : 0.3) \\
&= \{vb\} : 0.54, \{vb,b\} : 0.06, \{g\} : 0.096 \\
&\quad \{g,vg\} : 0.256, \{vg\} : 0.048
\end{aligned} \tag{8.31}$$

The propagation of mass assignment on labels up the hierarchy are in this example. Given m_y we can now evaluate the appropriateness of any expression from LE_y to describe the utility value example x. For example we have that,

$$\mu_{vb \vee b}(x) = \mu_{vb \vee b}(y) = 0.54 + 0.06 = 0.6$$

$$\mu_{g \vee vg}(x) = 0.4, \ \mu_{\neg a}(x) = 1$$

In this section, we discussed linguistic attribute hierarchies as a presentational tool for describing imprecise, uncertain and multi-dimensional functional relationships between basic attributes and high-level decision variables in multiple attribute decision problems. We gave an example using linguistic decision trees to define the functional relations between lower-level attributes and high-level vague concepts.

8.7 Summary

In this chapter, we have introduced another label semantics based data mining model. In particular, a new algorithm is proposed based on the FOIL algorithm and tested on a toy problem and some benchmark problems from the UCI repository. The results show that very compact linguistic rules can be learned that reflect the essence of the problem. Although the new algorithm is not better than the other two linguistic models in terms of accuracy, it has much better transparency and comparable accuracy to C4.5. In the second part of this chapter, we introduce the multiple attribute hierarchy for decision making. We used linguistic decision trees as the basic function. A detailed example was given to illustrate how to do decision making in this framework.

The main contribution of this chapter is to describe a method of evaluating linguistic rules through label semantics and to propose a new FOIL based algorithm for linguistic rule induction. In this new algorithm, we use a information based heuristics to guide the rule construction. This is not the only way of constructing good rules. Another approach is to search exhaustively through the knowledge base KB. Assuming that we do not use too many fuzzy labels for discretization, this approach may also be computationally tractable. The rules which covers less positive examples will be discarded according to a predefined threshold. Baldwin and Xie report a similar idea for generating simple fuzzy logic (IF-THEN) rules[3]. This approach could also be used in linguistic rule learning. Parameter setting of LFOIL is from trial and error experiments, and some further study is necessary to understand the influence of parameter settings.

References

[1] Quinlan J. R.:Learning logical definitions from relations, Machine Learning, 5: pp. 239-266. (1990).
[2] Drobics M., Bodenhofer U., Klement E. P.: FS-FOIL: an inductive learning method for extracting interpretable fuzzy descriptions, International Journal of Approximate Reasoning, 32: pp. 131-152. (2003).

[3] Baldwin J. F., Xie D.: Simple fuzzy logic rules based on fuzzy decision tree for classification and prediction problem, Intelligent Information Processing II, Z. Shi and Q. He (Ed.), Springer. (2004).

[4] Xie D.: Fuzzy associated rules discovered on effective reduced database algorithm, To appear in the Proceedings of IEEE-FUZZ, Reno, USA. (2005).

[5] Prade H., Richard G., Serrurier M.: Enriching relational learning with fuzzy predicates, N. Lavrac, et. al (Eds.): Proceedings of PKDD, LNAI 2838, pp. 399-410. (2003).

[6] Quinlan J. R.:C4.5: Programs for Machine Learning, San Mateo: Morgan Kaufmann. (1993).

[7] Mitchell T.: Machine Learning, McGraw-Hill, New York. (1997).

[8] Jeffrey R. C.: The Logic of Decision, Gordon & Breach Inc., New York. (1965).

[9] Blake C., Merz C. J.: UCI machine learning repository.

[10] Qin Z., Lawry J.: Decision tree learning with fuzzy labels, Information Sciences, 172/1-2: pp. 91-129. (2005).

[11] Witten I. H., Frank E.: Data Mining: Practical Machine Learning Tools and Techniques with Java Implementations, Morgan Kaufmann. (1999).

[12] Van-Nam H., Nakamori Y., Ho T., Murai T.: Multiple-attribute decision making under uncertainty: the evidential reasoning approach revisited, IEEE Transactions on Systems, Man and Cybernetics: Part A: Systems and Humans, 36(4), pp. 804-822. (2006).

9

A Prototype Theory Interpretation of Label Semantics

What the use of P implies, therefore, is that a hypothesis that may be true may be rejected because it has not predicted observable results that have not occured.

– Harold Jeffreys

9.1 Introduction

Using words rather than numbers to convey vague information as part of uncertain reasoning is a sophisticated human activity. The theory of fuzzy sets is now a popular tool for computing with words[1,2] which attempts to formally capture this human reasoning process[3−4]. Furthermore, linguistic modeling based on fuzzy IF-THEN rules [6−8] has achieved promising results in many application areas. However, the currently proposed interpretations of the membership function in fuzzy set theory are not consistent with the truth-functional calculus of fuzzy logic[9]. Alternatively, from the philosophical viewpoint of the epistemic stance, Lawry proposed a functional (but non-truth functional) calculus, label semantics, for computing with words[10,11]. In this framework, the meaning of linguistic labels is encoded by mass functions which represent the subjective probabilities that a given set of labels is appropriate to describe a given instance. Label semantics is a powerful new tool for modelling with vague concepts, the possible applications of which include knowledge fusion[12], decision tree learning[13], linguistic rule induction[14], and collective decision making[15,16].

Recently, Lawry and Tang have investigated the relationship between the theory of prototypes for vague concepts and the label semantics framework[17,18]. In this work, the meaning of linguistic labels can also be captured by the similarity between the underlying instances and the prototypes for linguistic labels. The calculus derived from this semantic interpretation results in the same calculus as label semantics. This chapter further explores the prototype theory interpretation of label semantics and introduces new methods for vague information coarsening and rule learning from data sets. We show that appropriateness measures of linguistic expressions for describing underlying instances can also be interpreted as probabilities that these instances are contained within uncertain neighborhoods as determined by the given linguistic expressions. Moreover, we show that in prototype theory vague information can be coarsened in a natural way. We then introduce linguistic inference systems in prototype theory, which have a similar structure to fuzzy inference systems, but which have a different way of modeling the vagueness of linguistic labels. Using the information coarsening process, we propose a linguistic rule induction method from data sets, where each linguistic IF-THEN rule has the following transparent structure: IF X is about DBX_i THEN Y is about DBY_i, where DBX_i and DBY_i are the prototype sets of the rule antecedent and consequence labels, respectively. More importantly, we show that the approximation and generalization capability of the rule base are controlled by the information granularity which is represented by the rule number and the size of prototype set associated with each linguistic label in the rule base.

The proposed approach to linguistic modeling and reasoning is distinct from that of fuzzy set theory. The fundamental difference lies in the semantic interpretation and uncertainty measurement of the linguistic expressions. Given an expression θ and element x, the membership $\mu_\theta(x)$ has no clear interpretation in the theory of fuzzy sets, although the intuitive idea is that $\mu_\theta(x)$ represents the membership degree of x belonging to the extensions of linguistic expression θ. In label semantics, $\mu_\theta(x)$ quantifies the appropriateness measure of linguistic expression θ for describing the instance x. In the prototype model this further reduces to the probability that x belongs to the uncertain neighborhood determined by θ. The second difference is the calculus for the combination of linguistic expressions. In the theory of fuzzy sets, the calculus is truth-functional, but in the theory of prototypes (label semantics), the calculus is not truth-functional, although it may be functional in a weaker sense[11,19].

Compared with fuzzy inference systems, the proposed linguistic inference systems have the following prominent advantages: The first is the high level of transparency of the proposed rule structure as discussed above. The second advantage is the efficiency of the rule induction algorithm. For each training data pair $(x, y) \in DB$, we can derive a linguistic IF-THEN rule of the form: IF X is about x then Y is about y. Our experiments shows that this induction method is very efficient and has very high accuracy. Another advantage is the adjustable generalization capability. We can improve the generalization capability of the rule base by firstly partitioning the training data set and then coarsening the rule base. Our experiments show that the balance between the prediction accuracy for the training data set and the generalization capability for the test data set can be easily achieved using clustering and the information coarsening method.

9.2 Prototype Semantics for Vague Concepts

In this section we review a new semantic interpretation for the vague concepts based on the theory of prototypes which has recently been proposed by Lawry and Tang[17,18]. This theory attempts to answer the following questions:

(1) How do we measure the vagueness of concept $L =$ about P where P is a set of prototypes for linguistic label L? In other words, to what extent can we say that x is similar to the prototypes for L?
(2) Moreover, how do we measure the vagueness of complex linguistic expression θ which is a logical combination of basic linguistic labels?

The proposed theory of prototypes attempts to answer these questions by quantifying the uncertain boundaries of similarity neighborhoods determined by basic labels. We firstly outline the calculus for evaluating the linguistic expressions within the prototype theory in Section 9.2.1, and then discuss the relationship between the prototype theory and label semantics. More detailed discussions on prototype theory are given in References [17] and [18]. For practical applications such as the linguistic modelling in Section 9.4 and Section 10.1 we then introduce a Gaussian-type density function $\delta_{(c,\sigma)}$ which describes the uncertainty of the word "about" in Section 9.2.3.

9.2.1 Uncertainty Measures about the Similarity Neighborhoods Determined by Vague Concepts

We assume that $\mathbb{L} = \{L_1, \ldots, L_n\}$ is the set of labels for elements from Ω, the underlying universe (in the sequel Ω will typically correspond to some convex subset of $\mathbb{R}^k$), and d is a mapping from $\Omega \times \Omega$ to $[0, +\infty)$ such that $d(x,x) = 0$ and $d(x,y) = d(y,x)$ for all $x,y \in \Omega$ (in this chapter, we take the Euclidean distance d). Moreover we define $d(x,P) = \inf_{y \in P} d(x,y)$ for any $x \in \Omega, P \subseteq \Omega$. For each label L_i we suppose that L_i can be described as "about P_i", where $P_i \subseteq \Omega$ is a set of prototypical cases of concept L_i. Then one natural question is: what elements are sufficiently similar to the prototypes of L_i for it to be appropriate to describe them using the label L_i? Suppose there exists a threshold $\varepsilon \geq 0$ such that $\{x : d(x,P_i) \leq \varepsilon\}$ can be considered as a neighborhood which includes all elements being sufficiently similar to the prototypes of L_i to be describable using the label L_i. So we have the following definition of the similarity neighborhood of the label.

Definition 9.1 *For any $L_i \in \mathbb{L}$ and $\varepsilon \geq 0$ the similarity neighborhood $\mathcal{N}_{L_i}^{\varepsilon}$ is defined as follows:*

$$\mathcal{N}_{L_i}^{\varepsilon} = \{x : d(x,P_i) \leq \varepsilon\} \tag{9.1}$$

We can further define the similarity neighborhood for any complex linguistic expression θ which is a combination of some basic linguistic labels and logical connectives. We firstly give the formal definition of linguistic expression.

Definition 9.2 *The set of linguistic expressions, LE, is defined recursively as follows:*

$$\mathbb{L} \subseteq LE;$$
$$\text{If } \theta \in LE, \varphi \in LE, \text{ then } \theta \wedge \varphi \in LE, \theta \vee \varphi \in LE, \neg\theta \in LE.$$

LE is actually a *T*-free algebra on $\mathbb{L}$ where $T = \{\wedge, \vee, \neg\}$. We now give the formal definition of the similarity neighborhood for any linguistic expression $\psi \in LE$.

Definition 9.3 $\forall \varepsilon \geq 0$ *and* $\psi \in LE$, *the similarity neighborhood* $\mathcal{N}_\psi^\varepsilon$ *is defined recursively as follows:*

$$\mathcal{N}_\psi^\varepsilon = \mathcal{N}_{L_i}^\varepsilon, \text{if } \psi = L_i \text{ where } L_i \in \mathbb{L}$$

$$\mathcal{N}_\psi^\varepsilon = \mathcal{N}_\theta^\varepsilon \cap \mathcal{N}_\varphi^\varepsilon, \text{if } \psi = \theta \wedge \varphi \text{ where } \theta, \varphi \in LE$$

$$\mathcal{N}_\psi^\varepsilon = \mathcal{N}_\theta^\varepsilon \cup \mathcal{N}_\varphi^\varepsilon, \text{if } \psi = \theta \vee \varphi \text{ where } \theta, \varphi \in LE$$

$$\mathcal{N}_\psi^\varepsilon = (\mathcal{N}_\theta^\varepsilon)^c, \text{if } \psi = \neg\theta \text{ where } \theta \in LE$$

The neighborhood size of the linguistic label "about *P*" is described by the word "about". Due to the vagueness of word "about" we assume ε is a random variable with a density function δ defined on $[0, \infty)$ such that $\delta(\varepsilon) \geq 0$ for any $\varepsilon \in [0, +\infty)$ and $\delta([0, +\infty)) = 1$ (for $I \subseteq \Omega$ we denote $\delta(I) = \int_I \delta(\varepsilon) d\varepsilon$). From this we can obtain the probability of any $x \in \Omega$ belonging to the similarity neighborhood determined by θ by integrating $\delta(\varepsilon)$ over $\{\varepsilon : x \in \mathcal{N}_\theta^\varepsilon\}$.

Definition 9.4 $\forall \theta \in LE$, $\forall x \in \Omega$, *the probability of x belonging to the similarity neighborhood with respect to* θ *is defined as:*

$$\mu_\theta(x) = \delta(\{\varepsilon : x \in \mathcal{N}_\theta^\varepsilon\}) \tag{9.2}$$

$\mu_\theta(x)$ also provides a measure of the typicality degree of x with respect to the linguistic expression θ. Notice that we do not have an explicit definition of the prototypes for complex linguistic expressions as we do for the linguistic labels in $\mathbb{L}$. However, we might view $x \in \Omega$ as a prototype for expression θ if $\mu_\theta(x) = 1$.

In fact the set $\{\varepsilon : x \in \mathcal{N}_\psi^\varepsilon\}$ for $x \in \Omega$ is given by a recursively defined measurable subset $I(\psi, x)$ of $[0, +\infty)$.

Definition 9.5 $\forall x \in \Omega$ *and* $\psi \in LE$, $I(\psi, x) \subseteq [0, \infty)$ *is defined recursively as follows:*

$$I(\psi, x) = [d(x, P_i), \infty), \text{if } \psi = L_i \text{ where } L_i \in \mathbb{L}$$

$$I(\psi, x) = I(\theta, x) \cap I(\varphi, x), \text{if } \psi = \theta \wedge \varphi \text{ where } \theta, \varphi \in LE$$

$$I(\psi, x) = I(\theta, x) \cup I(\varphi, x), \text{if } \psi = \theta \vee \varphi \text{ where } \theta, \varphi \in LE$$

$$I(\psi, x) = I(\theta, x)^c, \text{if } \psi = \neg\theta \text{ where } \theta \in LE$$

The following theorem shows that $I(\theta,x)$ is actually the set of all values ε for which the similarity neighborhood $\mathcal{N}_\theta^\varepsilon$ includes x.

Theorem 9.1 ([18]) $\forall x \in \Omega, \theta \in LE$,

$$\{\varepsilon : x \in \mathcal{N}_\theta^\varepsilon\} = I(\theta,x) \tag{9.3}$$

Proof Let $LE_0 = \mathbb{L}$, $LE_{m+1} = LE_m \cup \{\phi \wedge \varphi, \phi \vee \varphi : \phi, \varphi \in LE_m\}$ for $m > 0$, then $LE = \cup_{m=0}^{+\infty} LE_m$. Then it is easy to prove the above conclusion by carrying out the induction on m.

Corollary 9.1 ([18]) $\forall x \in \Omega, \theta \in LE$, *the probability of x belonging to the similarity neighborhood with respect to the linguistic expression θ is:*

$$\mu_\theta(x) = \delta(I(\theta,x)) \tag{9.4}$$

Proof According to Definition 9.4 and Theorem 9.1, the result is obtained immediately.

Notice that if we view $\mathcal{N}_\theta^\varepsilon$ as a random set from $[0,+\infty)$ into 2^Ω then $\mu_\theta(x)$ corresponds to the single point coverage function of $\mathcal{N}_\theta^\varepsilon$. This has a clear connection to the random set interpretation of fuzzy sets as proposed by Goodman and Nguyen [20,21].

Theorem 9.2 *For any $\theta, \varphi \in LE$ the following hold:*

$$\mu_{\theta \wedge \varphi}(x) \leq \min\{\mu_\theta(x), \mu_\varphi(x)\} \tag{9.5}$$

$$\mu_{\theta \vee \varphi}(x) \geq \max\{\mu_\theta(x), \mu_\varphi(x)\} \tag{9.6}$$

Proof Note that for any $\theta, \varphi \in LE$, according to Definition 9.5, we have

$$I(\theta \wedge \varphi, x) \subseteq I(\theta, x), I(\theta \wedge \varphi, x) \subseteq I(\varphi, x)$$

$$I(\theta \vee \varphi, x) \supseteq I(\theta, x), I(\theta \wedge \varphi, x) \supseteq I(\varphi, x)$$

Hence, according to Corollary 9.1, it is easy to prove the results.

In the following we will discuss a subset of linguistic expressions. Let $LE^{\wedge,\vee}$ be the set of linguistic expressions generated by applying connectives $\wedge$ and $\vee$ to linguistic labels in $\mathbb{L}$.

Definition 9.6 *For any $\theta \in LE^{\wedge,\vee}$ the real number $lb(\theta)$ is defined recursively as follows:*

$$lb(\theta) = d(x, P_i) \text{ if } \theta = L_i \tag{9.7}$$

$$lb(\theta) = \max(lb(\phi), lb(\varphi)) \text{ if } \theta = \phi \wedge \varphi \tag{9.8}$$

$$lb(\theta) = \min(lb(\phi), lb(\varphi)) \text{ if } \theta = \phi \vee \varphi \tag{9.9}$$

Theorem 9.3 *For any* $\theta \in LE^{\wedge,\vee}$ *the following hold:*

$$I(x,\theta) = [lb(\theta),+\infty\} \tag{9.10}$$

Proof Let

$$LE_0^{\wedge,\vee} = \mathbb{L}, \; LE_{m+1}^{\wedge,\vee} = LE_m^{\wedge,\vee} \cup \{\phi \wedge \varphi, \phi \vee \varphi : \phi, \varphi \in LE_m^{\wedge,\vee}\}$$

for $m > 0$, then

$$LE^{\wedge,\vee} = \cup_{m=0}^{+\infty} LE_m^{\wedge,\vee}.$$

We now carry out the induction on m. If $\theta = L_i$ then the results hold immediately. Assume that $\theta \in LE_m^{\wedge,\vee}$ the results hold. Then for any $\theta \in LE_{m+1}^{\wedge,\vee}$ either $\theta \in LE_m^{\wedge,\vee}$, for which case the results hold trivially, or

$$\theta \in \{\phi \wedge \varphi, \phi \vee \varphi : \phi, \varphi \in LE_m^{\wedge,\vee}\}$$

for which one of the following holds:

(1) If $\theta = \phi \wedge \varphi$ where $\phi, \varphi \in LE_m^{\wedge,\vee}$ then

$$I(x,\theta) = I(x,\phi \wedge \varphi) = I(x,\phi) \cap I(x,\varphi) = [lb(\phi),+\infty\} \cap [lb(\varphi),+\infty\} = [lb(\theta),+\infty\}$$

.

(2) If $\theta = \phi \vee \varphi$ where $\phi, \varphi \in LE_m^{\wedge,\vee}$ then

$$I(x,\theta) = I(x,\phi \vee \varphi) = I(x,\phi) \cup I(x,\varphi) = [lb(\phi),+\infty\} \cup [lb(\varphi),+\infty\} = [lb(\theta),+\infty\}$$

.

Theorem 9.4 *For any* $\theta \in LE^{\wedge,\vee}$ *the following hold:*

$$\mu_\theta(x) = \int_{lb(\theta)}^{+\infty} \delta(\varepsilon)d\varepsilon \tag{9.11}$$

Proof The result is from the Corollary 9.1 and Theorem 9.3.

9.2.2 Relating Prototype Theory and Label Semantics

As we have seen from the introduction to label semantics from previous chapters. It is a theory for modeling vague concepts which encodes the meaning of linguistic labels according to how they are used by a population of communicating agents to convey information. From this perspective, the focus is on the decision making process an intelligent agent must go through in order to identify which labels or expressions can actually be used to describe an object or value. In other words, in order to make an assertion describing an object in terms of some set of linguistic labels, an agent must first identify which of these labels are appropriate or assertable in this context. Given the way that individuals learn language through an ongoing process of interaction with the other communicating agents and with the environment, then we can expect there to be considerable uncertainty associated with any decisions of this kind. In label semantics we quantify this uncertainty in terms of appropriateness measures, linked to an associated mass function through a calculus which, while not truth-function, can be functional in a weaker sense[10].

The underlying philosophy of label semantics[11] is very close to the epistemic view of vagueness as expounded by Timothy Williamson[22]. Williamson assumes that for the extension of a vague concept there is a precise but unknown dividing boundary between it and the extension of the negation of that concept. However, while there are marked similarities between the epistemic theory and the label semantics view, there are also some important differences. For instance, the epistemic view would seem to assume the existence of some objectively correct, but unknown, definition of a vague concept. Instead of this we argue that individuals when faced with decision problems regarding assertions find it useful as part of a decision making strategy to assume that there is a clear dividing line between those labels which are and those which are not appropriate to describe a given instance. We refer to this strategic assumption across a population of communicating agents as the *epistemic stance*, a concise statement of which is as follows:

> *Each individual agent in the population assumes the existence of a set of labelling conventions, valid across the whole population, governing what linguistic labels and expressions can be appropriately used to describe particular instances.*

In practice these rules and conventions underlying the appropriate use of labels would not be imposed by some outside authority. In fact, they may not exist at all in a formal sense. Rather they are represented as a distributed body of knowledge concerning the assertability of predicates in various cases, shared across a population of agents, and emerging as the result of interactions and communications between individual agents all adopting the epistemic stance. The idea is that the learning processes of individual agents, all sharing the fundamental aim of understanding how words can be appropriately used to communicate information, will eventually converge to some degree on a set of shared conventions. The very process of convergence then to some extent vindicates the epistemic stance from the perspective of individual agents.

Hence, the epistemic stance requires that agents make decisions on what is or is not appropriate to assert, based on their past experience of language use and on the assumption that there are existing linguistic conventions that should be adhered to if they do not wish to be misunderstood or contradicted. This decision problem would naturally lead agents to consider their subjective beliefs concerning the appropriateness of the available description labels in a given context. Uncertainty about such beliefs could then be quantified by using subjective probabilities, as proposed originally by de Finetti[23] and Ramsey[24] for other types of epistemic uncertainty.

When applying label semantics to some practical applications such as linguistic modelling or linguistic information fusion, a basic problem is how to determine the mass function m_x. In order to solve this problem Lawry then introduced an ordering $\preceq_x$ on $\mathbb{L}$ where $L_i \preceq_x L_j$ means that the linguistic label L_j is more appropriate than the linguistic label L_i for describing the instance $x \in \Omega$. From this ordering assumption the mass function m_x is consonant (i.e., nested). In fact, from the theory of prototypes we can also derive a mass function m_x for each $x \in \Omega$, which validates the ordering $\preceq_x$ assumption in label semantics. In the following we show how to derive a mass function m_x according to the theory of prototypes.

Definition 9.7 *For $x \in \Omega$ and $\varepsilon \in [0, +\infty)$, define*

$$\mathscr{D}_x^\varepsilon = \{L_i \in \mathbb{L} : d(x, P_i) \le \varepsilon\} \tag{9.12}$$

$$m_x(S) = \delta(\{\varepsilon : \mathscr{D}_x^\varepsilon = S\}) \tag{9.13}$$

Intuitively speaking $\mathscr{D}_x^\varepsilon$ identifies the set of labels with prototypes lying within ε of x. Notice that the sequence $\mathscr{D}_x^\varepsilon$ as ε varies generates a nested hierarchy of label sets. Consequently m_x is a consonant mass function. Actually, the distance metric d naturally generates a total ordering $\preceq$ on the appropriateness of labels for any element $x \in \Omega$, where $L_i \preceq_x L_i$, $L_i \preceq_x L_j$ if $d(x, P_i) > d(x, P_j)$, and for $i \ne j$ the ordering between L_i and L_j can be arbitrary if $d(x, P_i) = d(x, P_j)$. A more important conclusion on the relationship between label semantic and prototype theory is as follows:

Theorem 9.5 [17,18] *For any $\theta \in LE$ and $x \in \Omega$ we have*

$$I(\theta, x) = \{\varepsilon : \mathscr{D}_x^\varepsilon \in \lambda(\theta)\} \tag{9.14}$$

Proof Let us carry out the induction on m of LE_m. If $\theta \in LE_0$ then the result holds trivially. Assume that it holds for $\theta \in LE_m$. Then for any $\theta \in LE_{m+1}$ either $\theta \in LE_m$, for which case the result holds trivially, or $\theta \in \{\phi \wedge \varphi, \phi \vee \varphi, \neg\phi : \phi, \varphi \in LE_m\}$ for which one of the following holds:

(1) $\theta = \phi \wedge \varphi$ where $\phi, \varphi \in LE_m$. Then

$$\begin{aligned} I(\theta, x) &= I(\phi \wedge \varphi, x) = I(\phi, x) \cap I(\varphi, x) = \{\varepsilon : \mathscr{D}_x^\varepsilon \in \lambda(\phi)\} \cap \{\varepsilon : \mathscr{D}_x^\varepsilon \in \lambda(\varphi)\} \\ &= \{\varepsilon : \mathscr{D}_x^\varepsilon \in \lambda(\phi) \cap \lambda(\varphi)\} = \{\varepsilon : \mathscr{D}_x^\varepsilon \in \lambda(\theta)\}. \end{aligned}$$

(2) $\theta = \phi \vee \varphi$ where $\phi, \varphi \in LE_m$. Then

$$\begin{aligned} I(\theta, x) &= I(\phi \vee \varphi, x) = I(\phi, x) \cup I(\varphi, x) = \{\varepsilon : \mathscr{D}_x^\varepsilon \in \lambda(\phi)\} \cup \{\varepsilon : \mathscr{D}_x^\varepsilon \in \lambda(\varphi)\} \\ &= \{\varepsilon : \mathscr{D}_x^\varepsilon \in \lambda(\phi) \cup \lambda(\varphi)\} = \{\varepsilon : \mathscr{D}_x^\varepsilon \in \lambda(\theta)\}. \end{aligned}$$

(3) $\theta = \neg\phi$ where $\phi \in LE_m$. Then

$$\begin{aligned} I(\theta, x) &= I(\neg\phi, x) = I(\phi, x)^c = (\{\varepsilon : \mathscr{D}_x^\varepsilon \in \lambda(\phi)\})^c \\ &= \{\varepsilon : \mathscr{D}_x^\varepsilon \in (\lambda(\phi))^c\} = \{\varepsilon : \mathscr{D}_x^\varepsilon \in \lambda(\theta)\}. \end{aligned}$$

From Eq. (9.14) in this theorem and the definition of appropriateness measures, we can see that the appropriateness measure $v_\theta(x)$ in label semantics and the probability of x belonging to $\mathscr{N}_\theta^\varepsilon$, $\mu_\theta(x)$, are equivalent.

Corollary 9.2 [17,18] *For any $\theta \in LE$ and $x \in \Omega$, we have*

$$\mu_\theta(x) = \nu_\theta(x) \tag{9.15}$$

where $\mu_\theta(x)$ and $\nu_\theta(x)$ are defined in Eqs. (9.4) and (3.7), respectively.

Proof

$$
\begin{aligned}
\mu_\theta(x) = \delta(I(\theta, x)) &= \delta(\{\varepsilon : \mathscr{D}_x^\varepsilon \in \lambda(\theta)\}) \\
&= \sum_{S \in \lambda(\theta)} \delta(\{\varepsilon : \mathscr{D}_x^\varepsilon = S\}) \tag{9.16} \\
&= \sum_{S \in \lambda(\theta)} m_x(S) = \nu_\theta(x).
\end{aligned}
$$

Although we can relate the theory of prototypes and label semantics through Definition 9.7 and Theorem 9.5, it may not always be necessary to derive the mass function m_x according to Definition 9.7 in some practical applications. Instead we can directly derive the appropriateness measure $\mu_\theta(x)$ for any $\theta \in LE$ and $x \in \Omega$ according to Definition 9.4 from the similarity neighborhood $\mathscr{N}_\theta^\varepsilon$. The main difference between the theory of prototypes and label semantics is that the mass functions m_x on labels for all $x \in \Omega$ are the starting points in label semantics, however, in the theory of prototypes the starting points are the prototypes for all basic labels and a density function δ on $[0, +\infty)$ which describes the uncertainty conveyed by the word "about".

9.2.3 Gaussian-Type Density Function

According to the prototype semantics for vague concepts, the meaning of linguistic expressions is determined by the prototypes of linguistic labels in $\mathbb{L}$ and the density function δ on the neighborhood size represented by the constraint "about". In practical applications the density function δ plays a very important role. In the following we propose a Gaussian-type density function $\delta_{(c,\sigma)}$ on $[0, +\infty)$ with the following form:

$$\delta_{(c,\sigma)}(\varepsilon) = \frac{1}{\sqrt{2\pi}\sigma} \exp\left(\frac{(\varepsilon - c)^2}{-2\sigma^2}\right) + \frac{1}{\sqrt{2\pi}\sigma} \exp\left(\frac{(\varepsilon + c)^2}{-2\sigma^2}\right), \varepsilon \geq 0 \tag{9.17}$$

where c and σ are the center and width of the Gaussian-type density function respectively.

Hence the linguistic label $L_i = $ about P_i has the following appropriateness measure:

$$\mu_{L_i}(x) = \delta([d(x, P_i), +\infty)) = 1 - F(d(x, P_i) \mid c, \sigma) + F(-d(x, P_i) \mid c, \sigma) \tag{9.18}$$

where

$$F(d \mid c, \sigma) = \frac{1}{\sqrt{2\pi}\sigma} \int_{-\infty}^{d} \exp((\varepsilon - c)^2/(-2\sigma^2))\mathrm{d}\varepsilon$$

is the normal cumulative distribution function with the mean c and standard deviation σ.

Fig. 9.1 shows a number of Gaussian-type density functions with different centers and widths. Fig. 9.2 shows the functions $\Delta(\varepsilon) \triangleq \delta_{(c,\sigma)}([\varepsilon, +\infty))$ derived from the Gaussian-type density functions illustrated in Fig. 9.1 .

We now give an example of the prototype interpretation of label semantics based on the Gaussian-type density function.

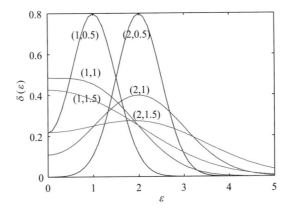

Fig. 9.1 The Gaussian-type density functions $\delta_{(c,\sigma)}(\varepsilon)$ with $(c, \sigma) = (1, 0.5), (1, 1), (1, 1.5), (2, 0.5), (2, 1)$ and $(2, 1.5)$ respectively

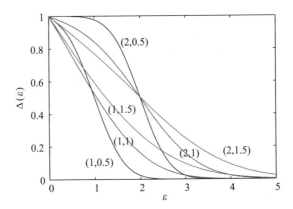

Fig. 9.2 The functions $\Delta(\varepsilon) \triangleq \delta_{(c,\sigma)}([\varepsilon, +\infty))$ with $(c, \sigma) = (1, 0.5), (1, 1), (1, 1.5), (2, 0.5), (2, 1)$ and $(2, 1.5)$ respectively

Example 9.1 *Assume that $\Omega = [0,1]$ and $L_1 =$ about 0.3, $L_2 =$ about 0.5 and $L_3 =$ about 0.7. We take the Gaussian-type density function $\delta_{(0,0.1)}$ and Euclidean distance d, and we assume that the prototypes of L_1, L_2 and L_3 are $P_1 = \{0.3\}$, $P_2 = \{0.5\}$ and $P_3 = \{0.7\}$, respectively. According to the Eq. (9.18), we have appropriateness measures*

$$\mu_{L_i}(x) = \delta_{(0,0.1)}([d(x,P_i),+\infty)) \ for \ i = 1,2,3$$

as shown in Fig. 9.3 . Alternatively, if we take the Gaussian-type density function $\delta_{(0.3,0.1)}$, then we obtain appropriateness measures as shown in Fig. 9.4 .

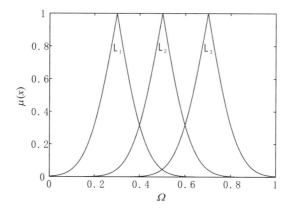

Fig. 9.3 The appropriateness measures for the linguistic labels about 0.3, about 0.5 and about 0.7, where the density function δ is a Gaussian-type density function $\delta_{(0,0.1)}$

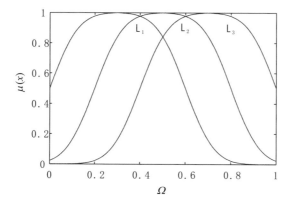

Fig. 9.4 The appropriateness measures for the linguistic labels about 0.3, about 0.5 and about 0.7, where the density function δ is a Gaussian-type density function $\delta_{(0.3,0.1)}$

If we take $\Omega = [0,1]^2$ with the following basic labels $L_1 = about\ (0.3,0.7), L_2 = about\ (0.5,0.5)$ and $L_3 = about\ (0.7,0.3)$ together with density function $\delta = \delta_{(0,0.1)}$, then the resulting appropriateness measures are shown in Fig. 9.5. If the Gaussian-type density function $\delta = \delta_{(0.3,0.1)}$ is used, then their appropriateness measures obtained are shown in Fig. 9.6. From these examples, we can see that the parameter c reflects the coverage sizes of basic labels and the parameter σ reflects the degree of coverage of basic labels.

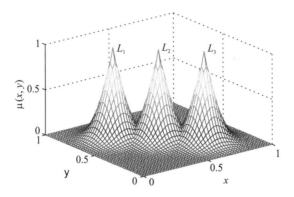

Fig. 9.5 The appropriateness measures for the linguistic labels about (0.3,0.7), about (0.5,0.5) and about (0.7,0.3), where the density function δ is a Gaussian-type density function $\delta_{(0,0.1)}$

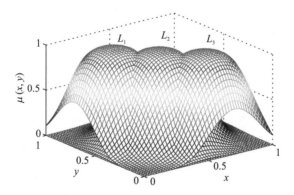

Fig. 9.6 The appropriateness measures for the linguistic labels about (0.3,0.7), about (0.5,0.5) and about (0.7,0.3), where the density function δ is a Gaussian-type density function $\delta_{(0.3,0.1)}$

9.3 Vague Information Coarsening in Theory of Prototypes

The theory of prototypes also provides a possible framework to represent vague information having different degrees of granularity. In this framework vague information can be transformed according to fine-to-coarse mapping. In this section we introduce a unified framework within the theory of prototypes to deal with information coarsening. The basic idea is to partition the underlying domain vaguely in such a way that the domain is covered by a set of vague concept labels which are represented by the prototypical elements and a density function on their neighborhood sizes. From the initial vague partitioning, the concepts can be coarsened using the logical operations defined in the sequel.

An important application of information coarsening is knowledge induction from data sets. Given a data set $DB = \{(x_i, y_i) : i = 1, \ldots, N\}$, we assume each pair of data (x_i, y_i) in the training data set determines a pair of concepts $(about\ x_i, about\ y_i)$. We then use the information coarsening process to derive more coarse concept pairs $(about\ DBX_i, about\ DBY_i)$, where DBX_i and DBY_i are the subsets of prototypes. In this way we can achieve a simplified and transparent knowledge base to reflect the correspondence relationship between input space and output space. This is in fact a mapping from a fine granular partition to a coarse partition. Further details of the application of information coarsening to data mining is given in Sections 9.4 and 10.1.

Definition 9.8 (Information Coarsening) *A coarsened label set $CLA = \{L_1^\vee, \ldots, L_m^\vee\}$ from $\mathbb{L}$ satisfies the the following two conditions: (a) $CLA \subseteq LE^\vee$ where $LE^\vee$ is the set of linguistic expressions generated by applying connective $\vee$ to the symbols in $\mathbb{L}$, (b) and each symbol $L \in \mathbb{L}$ is a component of some label in CLA. If the coarsened label $L^\vee = \vee_{j \in O} L_j$, where $O \subseteq \{1, \ldots, n\}$, then the prototype $P^\vee$ for $L^\vee$ is a subset of Ω*

$$P^\vee = \bigcup_{j \in O} P_j$$

where P_j is the set of prototypes of L_j, and the distance $d(x, P^\vee)$ is defined as

$$d(x, P^\vee) = \min_{j \in O} d(x, P_j).$$

Theorem 9.6 *For any $L^\vee \in CLA$ having the form $L^\vee = \vee_{j \in O} L_j$, we have*

$$\mu_{L^\vee}(x) = \max_{j \in O} \mu_{L_j}(x).$$

Proof According to the definition of appropriateness measure (see Eq. (9.2)), we have

$$\mu_{L^\vee}(x) = \delta(\varepsilon : x \in \mathcal{N}_{L^\vee, CLA}^\varepsilon) = \delta(\varepsilon : d(x, P^\vee) \leq \varepsilon) = \delta(\varepsilon : \min_{j \in O} d(x, P_j) \leq \varepsilon)$$

$$= \max_{j \in O} \delta(\varepsilon : d(x, P_j) \leq \varepsilon) = \max_{j \in O} \mu_{L_j}(x)$$

In the above proof, we use the notation $\mathscr{N}^\varepsilon_{L^\vee,CLA}$ but not $\mathscr{N}^\varepsilon_{L^\vee}$ to emphasize the symbol $L^\vee$ is a linguistic expression generated from *CLA*.

In fact, we have the following lemma on the similarity neighborhood determined by each $L^\vee \in CLA$.

Lemma 9.1 *For any $L^\vee = \vee_{j \in O} L_j \in CLA$, the following equation holds:*

$$\mathscr{N}^\varepsilon_{L^\vee,CLA} = \mathscr{N}^\varepsilon_{L^\vee,\mathbb{L}}$$

Proof For any $L^\vee = \vee_{j \in O} L_j \in CLA$,

$$\mathscr{N}^\varepsilon_{L^\vee,CLA} = \{x : d(x,P^\vee) \leq \varepsilon\} = \{x : \min_{j \in O} d(x,P_j) \leq \varepsilon\}$$

$$= \cup_{j \in O}\{x : d(x,P_j) \leq \varepsilon\} = \cup_{j \in O} \mathscr{N}^\varepsilon_{L_j,\mathbb{L}} = \mathscr{N}^\varepsilon_{L^\vee,\mathbb{L}}$$

So we can achieve the following more general conclusion from this lemma.

Theorem 9.7 *For any $\theta \in CLE$, the following equation holds:*

$$\mathscr{N}^\varepsilon_{\theta,CLA} = \mathscr{N}^\varepsilon_{\theta',\mathbb{L}}$$

where θ' is the expression resulting from replacing every occurrence of $L^\vee = \vee_{j \in O} L_j$ in θ by $\vee_{j \in O} L_j$.

Proof Let $CLE_0 = CLA$ and for $n > 0$, let

$$CLE_n = CLE_{n-1} \cup \{\theta \wedge \varphi, \theta \vee \varphi, \neg\theta \mid \theta, \varphi \in LE_{n-1}\}.$$

Hence $LE = \bigcup_n LE_n$. It is clear that for any $\theta \in CLE_0$ $\mathscr{N}^\varepsilon_{\theta,CLA} = \mathscr{N}^\varepsilon_{\theta',\mathbb{L}}$ according to Lemma 9.1. Assume that it is true for any $\psi \in CLE_k$. Then for $\psi \in LE_{k+1}$ either $\psi \in LE_k$, in which case the result holds trivially by the inductive hypothesis, or one of the following holds:

(1) $\psi = \theta \wedge \varphi \Longrightarrow \mathscr{N}^\varepsilon_\psi = \mathscr{N}^\varepsilon_{\theta \wedge \varphi} = \mathscr{N}^\varepsilon_\theta \cap \mathscr{N}^\varepsilon_\varphi = \mathscr{N}^\varepsilon_{\theta'} \cap \mathscr{N}^\varepsilon_{\varphi'} = \mathscr{N}^\varepsilon_{\theta' \wedge \varphi'} = \mathscr{N}^\varepsilon_{\psi'}$.

(2) $\psi = \theta \vee \varphi \Longrightarrow \mathscr{N}^\varepsilon_\psi = \mathscr{N}^\varepsilon_{\theta \vee \varphi} = \mathscr{N}^\varepsilon_\theta \cup \mathscr{N}^\varepsilon_\varphi = \mathscr{N}^\varepsilon_{\theta'} \cup \mathscr{N}^\varepsilon_{\varphi'} = \mathscr{N}^\varepsilon_{\theta' \vee \varphi'} = \mathscr{N}^\varepsilon_{\psi'}$.

(3) $\psi = \neg\theta \Longrightarrow \mathscr{N}^\varepsilon_\psi = \mathscr{N}^\varepsilon_{\neg\theta} = (\mathscr{N}^\varepsilon_\theta)^c = (\mathscr{N}^\varepsilon_{\theta'})^c = \mathscr{N}^\varepsilon_{\psi'}$.

Based on the coarsened label set *CLA*, we then have a more coarse knowledge representation framework *CLE* than *LE* allowing us to process linguistic information at different granularity. In particular, for any $x \in \Omega$ we can derive a mass function $m_{x,CLA}$ on *CLA* from the appropriateness measures $\mu_{L^\vee}(x)$ for all $L^\vee \in CLA$. From this we can then derive the appropriateness measure

$$\mu_\theta(x) = \delta(\varepsilon : x \in \mathscr{N}^\varepsilon_{\theta,CLA}) = \sum_{F \in \lambda_{CLA}(\theta)} m_{x,CLA}(F),$$

where

$$m_{x,CLA}(F) = \delta(\varepsilon : \mathscr{D}^\varepsilon_{x,CLA} = F).$$

The following theorem shows that appropriateness measure are invariant to translation from *CLE* to *LE*.

Theorem 9.8 *For any* $\theta \in CLE$,

$$\sum_{F \in \lambda_{CLA}(\theta)} m_{x,CLA}(F) = \sum_{F \in \lambda_{\mathbb{L}}(\theta')} m_{x,\mathbb{L}}(F),$$

where θ' *is the expression resulting from replacing every occurrence of* $L^\vee = \vee_{j \in oL_j}$ *in* θ *by* $\vee_{j \in oL_j}$.

Proof Notice that according to Theorem 9.7 for any $\theta \in CLE$,

$$\sum_{F \in \lambda_{CLA}(\theta)} m_{x,CLA}(F) = \mu_\theta(x) = \delta(\varepsilon : x \in \mathcal{N}^\varepsilon_{\theta,CLA}) = \delta(\varepsilon : x \in \mathcal{N}^\varepsilon_{\theta',CLA})$$

$$= \mu_{\theta'}(x) = \sum_{F \in \lambda_{\mathbb{L}}(\theta')} m_{x,\mathbb{L}}(F).$$

The above discussion on information coarsening within the theory of prototypes shows that we can process information based on a coarsened label set CLA, so as to preserve the information contained in the label set $\mathbb{L}$. More importantly, the coarsened label $L^\vee$ also has the form "about $P^\vee$", where $P^\vee$ is a prototype subset. This kind of coarsened linguistic label will be applied to our proposed linguistic modelling and rule induction method in Sections 9.4 and 10.1.

9.4 Linguistic Inference Systems

Given two variables X and Y into universes Ω_X and $\Omega_Y (\subseteq \mathbb{R})$ respectively, where the uncertain relationship between these two variables is described by a set of IF-THEN rules which involve linguistic labels and vague concepts, we now consider to formally model the mapping between X and Y. In particular, in the following two sections we will focus on the following three issues:

(1) How to interpret linguistic IF-THEN rules within the theory of prototypes?
(2) What is the inference process given such a set of IF-THEN rules?
(3) How can we learn a rule base of linguistic IF-THEN rules from a training data set?

Assume that the basic label sets on Ω_X and Ω_Y are $LX = \{L_1, \ldots, L_m\}$ and $LY = \{H_1, \ldots, H_m\}$, respectively. The knowledge base consists of the following m rules:

$$\text{IF } X \text{ is } L_i \text{ THEN } Y \text{ is } H_i, i = 1, \ldots, m \tag{9.19}$$

These rules provide an approximation to the underlying mapping $y = f(x)$ from Ω_X to Ω_Y. This approximation mapping can be obtained as follows.

From these IF-THEN rules we have

$$H_i = f(L_i) \text{ for } i = 1, \ldots, m,$$

this means that for any $x \in \Omega_X$ we have

$$\mu_{H_i}(f(x)) = \mu_{L_i}(x) \text{ for } i = 1,\ldots,m.$$

Moreover, from the appropriateness measures

$$\mu_{H_i}(f(x)) \text{ for } i = 1,\ldots,m$$

We can derive a mass function $m_{f(x)}$ on LY (see Definition 9.7). We then convert the mass function $m_{f(x)}$ into a probability distribution $p(\cdot \mid m_{f(x)})$ from which we can estimate the output $\bar{y} \approx f(x)$. In this section we introduce two conversion mechanisms from the mass function $m_{f(x)}$. Initially however we give the following definition.

Definition 9.9 [10] *The conditional probability distribution* $p(\cdot \mid \theta)$ *given a linguistic expression* θ *on* Ω_Y *is defined as follows:*

$$p(y \mid \theta) = \frac{\mu_\theta(y)p(y)}{\int_{\Omega_Y} \mu_\theta(y)p(y)dy} \tag{9.20}$$

where $p(\cdot)$ *is a prior probability distribution on* Ω_Y.

We now consider possible conversion mechanisms which can convert the mass function $m_{f(x)}$ into a probability distribution on Ω_Y. One conversion method is based on the pignistic probability derived from the mass function $m_{f(x)}$ [25].

Definition 9.10 *The conditional probability distribution* $p_1(\cdot \mid m_{f(x)})$ *given a mass function* $m_{f(x)}$ *is defined as follows:*

$$p_1(y \mid m_{f(x)}) = \sum_{H \in LY} BetP(H)p(y \mid H) \tag{9.21}$$

where $p(y \mid H)$ *is defined in Definition 9.9 and* $BetP(H)$ *is the Pignistic probability derived from* $m_{f(x)}$ [25]:

$$BetP(H) = \sum_{H \in T, T \subseteq LY} \frac{m_{f(x)}(T)}{(1 - m_{f(x)}(\emptyset))|T|}.$$

Another conversion method is based on the single point coverage function derived from the mass function $m_{f(x)}$.

Definition 9.11 *The conditional probability distribution* $p_2(\cdot \mid m_{f(x)})$ *given a mass function* $m_{f(x)}$ *is defined as follows:*

$$p_2(y \mid m_{f(x)}) = \frac{\sum_{H \in LY} spc(H)p(y \mid H)}{\sum_{H \in LY} spc(H)} \tag{9.22}$$

where $spc(H)$ *is the single point coverage of* H *derived from* $m_{f(x)}$:

$$spc(H) = \sum_{H \in T, T \subseteq LY} m_{f(x)}(T) = \mu_H(f(x)) = \mu_L(x).$$

In general the reasoning process in the linguistic inference systems having a rule base of the form given in Eq. (9.19) is outlined as follows:

(1) Given input $X = x$, compute the appropriateness degrees

$$\mu_{L_i}(x) \text{ for } i = 1, \ldots, m$$

(2) Compute the mass function $m_{f(x)}$ on LY from

$$\mu_{H_i}(f(x)) = \mu_{L_i}(x) \text{ for } i = 1, \ldots, m$$

(3) Compute the conditional probability distribution $p(\cdot \mid m_{f(x)})$ on Ω_Y according to Eqs. (9.21) or Eq. (9.22) (Note the computation of mass function $m_{f(x)}$ can be omitted if Eq. (9.22) is applied).
(4) Estimate the value $f(x)$ on Ω_Y according to the following equation:

$$f(x) = \int_{\Omega_Y} y p(y \mid m_{f(x)}) dy. \tag{9.23}$$

For the practical applications considered in Section 10.2 we use Eq. (9.22) to estimate output $f(x)$ because the computation of Eq. (9.22) is simpler than the Eq. (9.21) and the performances of these two methods are almost identical in our experiments. In summary, according to Eq. (9.22) the mapping $f(x)$ is then approximated by:

$$f(x) = \frac{\sum_{i=1}^{m} \mu_{L_i}(x) c_i}{\sum_{i=1}^{m} \mu_{L_i}(x)} \tag{9.24}$$

where

$$c_i = \int_{\Omega_Y} y p(y \mid H_i) dy = \frac{\int_{\Omega_Y} y p(y) \mu_{H_i}(y) dy}{\int_{\Omega_Y} p(y) \mu_{H_i}(y) dy} = \frac{\int_{\Omega_Y} y \mu_{H_i}(y) dy}{\int_{\Omega_Y} \mu_{H_i}(y) dy} \tag{9.25}$$

and where we assume that the prior probability distribution $p(\cdot)$ is a uniform distribution.

Notice that the proposed linguistic inference systems have the same reasoning steps as the inference systems based on the theory of fuzzy sets[6–8,26]. In the fuzzy inference systems each of the linguistic labels involved is interpreted as a fuzzy set which has its own independent membership function. However, in our proposed linguistic inference systems, each linguistic label while having its own prototypes, shares the density function δ with all other linguistic labels. Consequently the parameters involved in the linguistic rule base are reduced significantly. More importantly, the following section that the linguistic rule induction from the training data set is comparatively straightforward.

9.5 Summary

In this chapter we have proposed a basic linguistic label of the form about $; P$ where P is the prototype set of the underlying vague concept. The neighborhood size of the underlying concept is described by the word "about" which represents a density function on $[0, +\infty)$. We have then described a theory of prototypes for representing this kind of vague concept. In particularly we have focused on linguistic modellng and information coarsening in the theory of prototypes.

References

[1] Zadeh L. A.: Fuzzy logic = computing with words, IEEE Transaction on Fuzzy Systems. 4(2): pp. 103-111. (1996).

[2] Zadeh L. A.: From computing with numbers to computing with words - from manipulation of measurements to manipulation of perceptions, IEEE Trans. Circuits Systems I 45(1), pp. 105-119. (1999).

[3] Zadeh L. A.: The concept of linguistic variable and its application to approximate reasoning, part I, Information Sciences 8(3), pp. 199-249. (1975).

[4] Zadeh L. A.: The concept of linguistic variable and its application to approximate reasoning, part II, Information Sciences 8(4), pp. 301-357. (1975).

[5] Zadeh L. A.: The concept of linguistic variable and its application to approximate reasoning, part III, Information Sciences 9(1), pp. 43-80. (1975).

[6] Takagi T., Sugeno M.: Fuzzy identification of systems and its applications to modeling and control, IEEE Trans. Syst., Man, Cybernetics, 15, pp. 116–132. (1985).

[7] Lee C.: Fuzzy logic in control systems: part I, IEEE Trans. Syst., Man, Cybernetics, 20(2), pp. 404-419. (1990).

[8] Lee C.: Fuzzy logic in control systems: part II, IEEE Trans. Syst., Man, Cybernetics, 20(2), pp. 419-435. (1990).

[9] Dubois D., Prade H.£ºThe three semantics of fuzzy sets, Fuzzy Sets and Systems, 90, pp. 141-150. (1997).

[10] Lawry J.: Modelling and Reasoning with Vague Concepts, Springer. (2006).

[11] Lawry J.: Appropriateness measures: an uncertainty model for vague concepts. Synthese, 161(2), pp. 255-269. (2008).

[12] Lawry J., Hall J. W., Bovey R.: Fusion of expert and learnt knowledge in a framework of fuzzy labels, Journal of Approximate Reasoning, 36: pp. 151-198. (2004).

[13] Qin Z., Lawry J.: Decision tree learning with fuzzy labels, Information Sciences, 172/1-2: pp. 91-129. (2005).

[14] Qin Z., Lawry J.: LFOIL: Linguistic rule induction in the label semantics framework. Fuzzy Sets and Systems 159(4): pp. 435-448. (2008).

[15] Tang Y., Zheng J.: Linguistic modelling based on semantic similarity relation among linguistic labels, Fuzzy Sets and Systems 157(12), pp. 1662-1673. (2006).

[16] Tang Y.: A collective decision model involving vague concepts and linguistic expressions, IEEE Trans. Syst., Man, Cybernetics B, 38(2), pp. 421-428. (2008).

[17] Lawry J., Tang Y.: Relating prototype theory and label semantics, in: Dubois D., Lubiano M. A., Prade H., Gil M. A., Grzegorzewski P., Hryniewicz O.(Eds.), Soft Methods for Handling Variability and Imprecision, pp. 35-42. (2008).

[18] Lawry J., Tang Y.: Uncertainty modeling for vague concepts: A prototype theory approach. Artificial Intelligence, 173, pp.1539-1558. (2009).

[19] Lawry J.: A framework for linguistic modelling, Artificial Intelligence, 155: pp. 1-39. (2004).

[20] Goodman I., Nguyen H.: Uncertainty Model for Knowledge Based Systems, North Holland. (1985).

[21] Nguyen H.: On modeling of linguistic information using random sets, Information Sciences 34, pp. 265-274. (1984).

[22] Williamson T.: Vagueness, Routledge. (1994).

[23] de Finetti B.: Fondamenti logici del ragionamento probabilistico, Bollettino dell' Unione Matemztica Italiana 9, pp. 258-261. (1930).

[24] Ramsey F. P.: The Foundations of Mathematics, and other Logical Essays, Kegan Paul, Trench, Trubner and Company Ltd, London. (1931).

[25] Smets P., Kennes R.: The transferable belief model, Artificial Intelligence, 66, pp. 191-234. (1994).

[26] Mamdani E., Assilian S.: An experiment in linguistic synthesis with a fuzzy logic controller, International Journal of Man-Machine Studies 7(1), pp. 1-13. (1975).

10

Prototype Theory for Learning

10.1 Introduction

Assume that X is the input variable defined on the domain $\mathbb{R}^k$, and Y is the output variable defined on the domain $\mathbb{R}$. Now assume that we have a training data set $DB = \{(x_j^1, \ldots, x_j^k, y_j) : j = 1, \ldots, N\}$. We now consider how to derive a linguistic rule base from this training data set, which can fit this training data set accurately and at the same time has a high generalization capability. In the following we firstly propose a rule induction method which is very simple and natural. Then in order to improve the generalization capability of the rule base we present a clustering based method to coarsen the rule base.

10.1.1 General Rule Induction Process

According to the proposed prototype theory for labels, it is natural to derive the following rule base from the training data set DB of the form

$$DB = \{(x_j^1, \ldots, x_j^k, y_j) : j = 1, \ldots, N\}$$

IF X is about x_i THEN Y is about $y_i, i = 1, \ldots, N$,

where $x_i = (x_i^1, \ldots, x_i^k)$.

So we can define the label sets $LX = \{L_1, \ldots, L_N\}$ on $\mathbb{R}^k$ and $LY = \{H_1, \ldots, H_N\}$ on $\mathbb{R}$, where L_i is the label having the prototype $(x_i^1, \ldots, x_i^k)$ and density function δ_X and H_i is the label having the prototype y_i and density function δ_Y. The density functions δ_X and δ_Y can take the forms of Gaussian-type functions (see Eq. (9.18)).

In general, the value N may be very large in which case computation costs are high when reasoning based on this rule set. Also, a large number of rules may result in over-fitting of the training data set and consequently poor generalization. Hence, it is necessary to coarsen the rule base using the information coarsening method proposed in the previous section.

The basic idea of our rule coarsening algorithm is to firstly partition the data set DB based on some clustering algorithm, and then to coarsen the knowledge base based on the clustering result.

More specifically, assume that the data set is partitioned into $M (M \ll N)$ subsets such that $DB = \bigcup_{i=1}^{M} DB_i$ and $DB_i \cap DB_j = \emptyset$ for any $i \neq j$. Then each subset DB_i determines a coarsened label pair $\langle L_i^{\vee}, H_i^{\vee} \rangle$, where $L_i^{\vee}$ has the prototype set

$$DBX_i = \{(x_j^1, \ldots, x_j^k) : (x_j^1, \ldots, x_j^k, y_j) \in DB_i\}$$

such that $d(x, DBX_i) = \min_{p \in DBX_i} d(x, p)$ for any $x \in \mathbb{R}^k$, and $H_i^{\vee}$ has the prototype set $DBY_i = \{y_j : (x_j^1, \ldots, x_j^k, y_j) \in DB_i\}$ such that

$$d(y, DBY_i) = \min_{p \in DBY_i} d(y, p), \quad \forall y \in \mathbb{R}$$

From these partitions we obtain a coarsened label set $CLX = \{L_1^{\vee}, \ldots, L_M^{\vee}\}$ on $\mathbb{R}^k$ and a coarsened label set $CLY = \{H_1^{\vee}, \ldots, H_M^{\vee}\}$ on $\mathbb{R}$. Hence we have the following coarsened knowledge base:

$$\text{IF } X \text{ is } L_i^{\vee} \text{ THEN } Y \text{ is } H_i^{\vee}, i = 1, \ldots, M.$$

Notice that according to the prototype semantics for the vague concepts, each coarsened label is determined by its prototype set and the corresponding density function δ on its neighborhood size. So the coarsened linguistic IF-THEN rules can be rewritten as the following transparent forms:

$$\text{IF } X \text{ is about } DBX_i \text{ THEN } Y \text{ is } about\ DBY_i, i = 1, \ldots, M$$

where the coarsened labels about DBX_i and about DBY_i are equivalent to the linguistic expressions $\vee_{p \in DBX_i}$ about p and $\vee_{p \in DBY_i}$ about p, respectively.

In fact, according to the estimation method defined in the Eq. (9.24) and Eq. (9.25) the coarsened rules are equivalent to the following more transparent rules:

$$\text{IF } X \text{ is about } DBX_i \text{ THEN } Y \text{ is about } c_i, i = 1, \ldots, M (M \ll N)$$

where

$$c_i = \frac{\int_{-\infty}^{+\infty} y \mu_{about\ DBY_i}(y)}{\int_{-\infty}^{+\infty} \mu_{about\ DBY_i}(y)} \approx \frac{\sum_{j=1}^{N} \mu_{about\ DBY_i}(y_j) y_j}{\sum_{j=1}^{N} \mu_{about\ DBY_i}(y_j)} \tag{10.1}$$

10.1.2 A Clustering Based Rule Coarsening

It is clear that the coarsened knowledge base depends on the partitioning of the training data set DB. Different partitioning results in a different knowledge base since each cluster determines a linguistic rule. In the following we give a simple and effective partitioning method for linguistic rule coarsening. In this partitioning method, we minimize the following objective function:

$$J = \sum_{j=1}^{N} \sum_{i=1}^{M} \mu_{\text{about } DBY_i}(y_j)(c_i - y_j)^2 \tag{10.2}$$

where c_i is the cluster center of sub-data set DBY_i and $\bigcup_{i=1}^{M} DBY_i = DBY$ and $DBY_i \cap DBY_j = \emptyset \ (i \neq j)$.

Clearly it is only when $\dfrac{\partial J}{\partial c_i} = 0$ that the objective function J is minimal. Hence, by letting $\dfrac{\partial J}{\partial c_i} = 0$ we have

$$c_i = \frac{\sum_{j=1}^{N} \mu_{\text{about } DBY_i}(y_j) y_j}{\sum_{j=1}^{N} \mu_{\text{about } DBY_i}(y_j)} \tag{10.3}$$

which is consistent with the Eq. (10.1). This suggests that J is a reasonable objective function in the context of our proposed inference method.

On the other hand, by fixing the cluster centers c_i for $i = 1, \ldots, M$, for a given element y_j we can derive the distances $d(y_j, c_i)$ for all cluster centers c_i. W.l.o.g. assume that $(d(y_j, c_1))^2 \geq \ldots \geq (d(y_j, c_M))^2$. Then, only when the following equation hold

$$\mu_{\text{about } DBY_1}(y_j) \leq \ldots \leq \mu_{\text{about } DBY_M}(y_j) = 1 \tag{10.4}$$

The function

$$\sum_{i=1}^{M} \mu_{\text{about } DBY_i}(y_j)(d(y_j, c_i))^2 \tag{10.5}$$

is minimal. From this we can derive $y_j \in DBY_M$. So for each $y_j \in DBY$, $y_j \in DBY_i$ only if $(d(y_j, c_i))^2 = \min_{1 \leq h \leq M}(d(y_j, c_h))^2$, that is

$$d(y_j, c_i) = \min_{1 \leq h \leq M} d(y_j, c_h)$$

So we have a new clustering algorithm (see Fig. 10.1 for a brief description) which is appropriate for linguistic rule coarsening. This algorithm is similar to the fuzzy c-means clustering algorithm[1], but is more concise and has a clear operational interpretation. In addition, the above clustering algorithm can be directly generalized to multi-dimensional data clustering.

Overall, an outline of the proposed linguistic rule induction process is as follows:

(1) Firstly partition the data set DBY on $\mathbb{R}$ into M clusters DBY_i for $i = 1, \ldots, M$.
(2) For each data point (p, y) in DB, if $y \in DBY_i$ then p is a member of subset DBX_i for $i = 1, \ldots, M$.
(3) According to the Eq. (10.1) compute c_i for each subset DBY_i, $i = 1, \ldots, M$.
(4) For simplicity set the density function $\delta_X = \delta_Y$ on $[0, +\infty)$ (Such as the Gaussian-type density function $\delta_{(c,\sigma)}$).

Using the above partitioning algorithm, the rule base can be simplified by specifying a small rule number M and computing the rule consequences c_i off-line. However, the prototype set DBX_i in the rule antecedents may still be very large. In this situation, we generate new elements to represent the prototype set of the coarsened label in each rule antecedent. Assume that DBX_i is the original prototype set for the coarsened label $L_i^\vee$, we then may determine $M_i(\ll |DBX_i|)$ cluster centers as the new prototypical elements for the coarsened label $L_i^\vee$ by using the proposed clustering algorithm (multi-dimensional partitioning). The first advantage of this further clustering for the prototype sets of the coarsened labels in the rule antecedents is that it may avoid over-fitting and hence improve the generalization capability of the rule base. The second advantage is that it can simplify the reasoning process of the rule base. In the following section we will test our proposed linguistic modeling and rule induction method on two benchmark time series prediction problems.

Given data set $DBY = \{y_j : j = 1, \ldots, N\}$ and cluster number M,

Partition data set DBY randomly, such that $\bigcup_{i=1}^{M} DBY_i = DBY$, $DBY_i \cap DBY_j = \emptyset$ $(i \neq j)$ and $DBY_i \neq \emptyset$.

For $l = 1, 2, \ldots$
Step 1: Determine the partition matrix:
$\mu_{ij}^{(l-1)} = \delta\{\varepsilon : d(y_j, DBY_i) \leq \varepsilon\}$, where $d(y_j, DBY_i) = \min_{y_{j'} \in DBY_i} |y_j - y_{j'}|$

Step 2: Compute the cluster centers:
$$c_i^{(l)} = \frac{\sum_{j=1}^{N} (\mu_{ij}^{(l-1)}) y_j}{\sum_{j=1}^{N} (\mu_{ij}^{(l-1)})}, 1 \leq i \leq M.$$

Step 3: Update prototype set DBY_i associated with each cluster i:
$DBY_i = \{y_j : d(y_j, c_i^{(l)}) = \min_{1 \leq h \leq M} d(y_j, c_h^{(l)})\}$ for $i = 1, \ldots, M$.

Until $|c^{(l)} - c^{(l-1)}| < \varepsilon$.

Fig. 10.1   The description of prototype-based c-means algorithm for rule coarsening in prototype theory.

10.2 Linguistic Modeling of Time Series Predictions

In this section we apply the proposed linguistic inference system to the Mackey-Glass time series prediction problem and sunspots prediction problem. In these applications, we take d to be Euclidean distance. The experiments on the first example show that the linguistic inference system and its corresponding rule induction method are very efficient for linguistic modeling. The performance is superior to other learning methods applied to this example. The experiments on the second example show that our information coarsening method is very effective at improving the generalization capability of the knowledge base.

10.2.1 Mackey-Glass Time Series Prediction

We construct a linguistic inference system to predict a time series that is generated by the following Mackey-Glass (MG) time-delay differential equation:

$$\dot{x}(t) = \frac{0.2x(t - \tau)}{1 + x^{10}(t - \tau)} - 0.1x(t)$$

This time-series is chaotic, and so there is no clearly defined period. The series will not converge or diverge, and the trajectory is highly sensitive to initial conditions. This is a benchmark problem in the neural network and fuzzy modeling research communities[2-4].

To obtain the time series value at integer points, we applied the fourth-order Runge-Kutta method to find the numerical solution to the above MG equation. Here we assume $x(0) = 1.2$, $\tau = 17$, and $x(t) = 0$ for $t < 0$.

In this time-series prediction the objective is to use known values of the time series up to the point in time t, in order to predict the future time point $t + 6$. For each t, the input training data for the linguistic model is a four dimensional vector of the form

$$X(t) = [x(t - 18), x(t - 12), x(t - 6), x(t)]$$

The output training data corresponds to the trajectory prediction, $y(t) = x(t + 6)$. With t ranging from 118 to 1117, we obtain 1000 input/output data values. We use the first 500 data values for the linguistic model training (these become the training data set DB), while the remaining values are used as test data.

Firstly we consider the extreme situation where each training data point determines one IF-THEN rule, so we can derive a knowledge base having 500 IF-THEN rules:

$$\text{IF } X \text{ is about } X(t) \text{ THEN } Y \text{ is about } y(t), t = 118, \ldots, 617$$

where $(X(t), y(t))$ is a training data point. The neighborhood size of the underlying vague concept is described by the word "about" which represents a Gaussian-type density function $\delta_{(c,\sigma)}$ (see Eq. (9.17)). We run this linguistic model with the fixed center $c = 0$ and varying width σ from 0.001 to 0.06. Of course, we can also vary the center c of the density function to optimize the performance of our linguistic model, but for simplicity we fix the center $c = 0$. We plot the RMSE of the training and test data against the width σ of the density function $\delta_{(0,\sigma)}$ in Fig. 10.2 . The best prediction result RMSE = 0.0059 for the test data is achieved when $c = 0$ and $\sigma = 0.026$. Table 10.1 shows a comparison of the prediction performance on this problem across various learning algorithms. The previous results were taken from References [2] and [3]. As is apparent from Table 10.1 our approach outperforms all the other algorithms on this problem. The best result reported in the literature derived from a genetic fuzzy learning, which requires 50,000 iterations and 100 individuals in the genetic learning. Hence, our proposed linguistic inference system improves on both the prediction performance and the computational cost of the learning process.

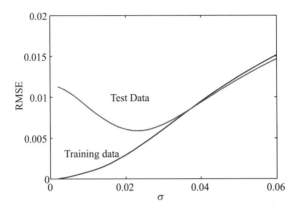

Fig. 10.2 The RMSE of Mackey-Glass training and test data vs the width σ of the Gaussian-type density function δ with the fixed center $c = 0$, where each training data determines one rule

Table 10.1 Comparison of results for different learning algorithms

Learning algorithm	RMSE
Kim & Kim	0.026
Wang (product operator)	0.091
Min operator	0.090
ANFIS	0.007
Auto Regressive Model	0.19
Cascade Correlation NN	0.06
Back. Pro. NN	0.02
6th order polynomial	0.04
Linear Predictive model	0.55
GEFREX	0.0061
Linguistic Model With 500 Rules	0.0059

One interesting phenomenon is that RMSE of the training data approaches 0 when $\sigma \to 0$. That is, we can get any high prediction accuracy for the training data set when each training data determines one linguistic rule. Denote the tth rule determined by $(X(t), y(t))$ as R_t. Then, given training data $X(t)$, the activation degree of rule R_s $(s \neq t)$ will tend to zero, and the activation degree of rule R_t, as given by the appropriateness measure of the antecedent label for $X(t)$, will tend to one, as the width σ of the Gaussian-type density function δ tends to zero. However, for the test data or any data which is different from the training data the activation degrees of all rules tends to zero when the width σ of the Gaussian-type density function δ tends to zero, resulting in low prediction accuracy for the test data. Hence, appropriately increasing the width σ of the Gaussian-type density function can improve the generalization capability of the linguistic model. Although the generalization capability can be improved by increasing the width σ, the complexity of the linguistic model is not reduced. The information coarsening presented in the previous section provides a way to reduce the complexity of the linguistic model, while at the same time improving the generalization capability of the reduced linguistic model.

We now apply the information coarsening process to the knowledge base derived from the Mackey-Glass training data. We know that the key to information coarsening is to partition the training data set appropriately and determine the prototypical elements for the coarsened concepts. In this example, we partition the training data $\{y(t) : t = 118,\ldots,617\}$ into 20 clusters DBY_i for $i = 1,\ldots,20$ using the clustering algorithm proposed in the previous section, where DBY_i is a subset including all elements belonging to the ith cluster (in clustering we assume $c = 0$ and $\sigma = 0.1$). From this we derive a linguistic model with the following rules:

IF X is *about DBX_i* THEN Y is *about DBY_i$: $i = 1,\ldots,20$

where DBX_i is a subset of input vectors corresponding to the output values in DBY_i.

We ran this linguistic model with the fixed center $c = 0$ and varying width σ from 0.02 to 0.21 for the training data and test data respectively. Fig. 10.3 and Fig. 10.4 show the RMSE of the training data and test data against the width σ of the Gaussian-type density function $\delta_{(0,\sigma)}$. The RMSE curves labelled "$|DB_i|$ Clusters" show that the best prediction results for the test data is RMSE = 0.0104 when $c = 0$ and $\sigma = 0.03$. Note from Table 10.1 that only GEFRESX and ANFIS have better performance than this coarsened rule-base. When $c = 0$ and $\sigma = 0.03$ we plot the prediction results of the linguistic inference system for the training data and test data as time series in Figs. 10.5 and 10.6 , respectively. Figs. 10.7 and 10.8 show the results as scatter plots of actual against predicted values.

As pointed out in Section 10.1, this linguistic inference system is equivalent to the following rule base:

IF X is about DBX_i THEN Y is about c_i : $i = 1,\ldots,20$

where DBX_i is a subset of input vectors corresponding to the output values in DBY_i, and c_i is as follows (see Eq. (10.1)):

$$c_i = \frac{\int_{-\infty}^{+\infty} y\mu_{about\ DBY_i}(y)}{\int_{-\infty}^{+\infty} \mu_{about\ DBY_i}(y)} \approx \frac{\sum_{y \in DBY_i} y}{|DBY_i|} = \tilde{c}_i$$

Hence, for any training data $(X(t), y(t))$ if $X(t) \in DBX_i$ then $f(X(t)) \to \tilde{c}_i$ as the width σ of the Gaussian-type density function tends to 0. This means that the RMSE

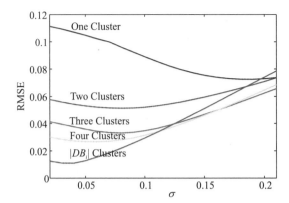

Fig. 10.3 The RMSE of Mackey-Glass training data vs the width σ of the Gaussian-type density function δ with the fixed center $c = 0$, where the rule number is 20

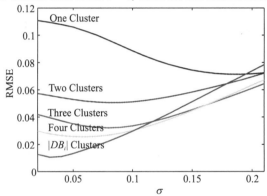

Fig. 10.4 The RMSE of Mackey-Glass test data vs the width σ of the Gaussian-type density function δ with the fixed center $c = 0$, where the rule number is 20

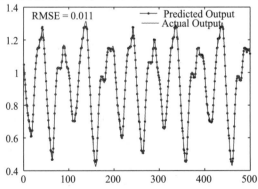

Fig. 10.5 Mackey-Glass prediction result of the training data using 20 rules ($c = 0, \sigma = 0.01$): solid line is the actual output, dotted line is the predicted output

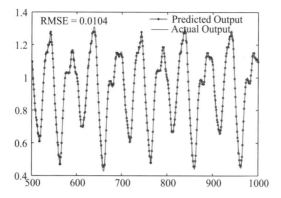

Fig. 10.6 Mackey-Glass prediction result of the testing data using 20 rules ($c = 0, \sigma = 0.03$): solid line is the actual output, dotted line is the predicted output

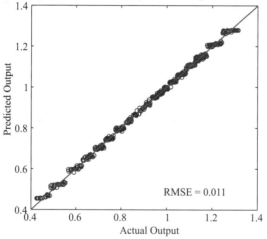

Fig. 10.7 Scatter plot showing the actual output vs the predicted output of Mackey-Glass training data using 20 rules ($c = 0, \sigma = 0.03$)

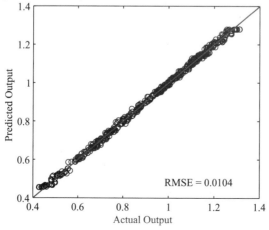

Fig. 10.8 Scatter plot showing the actual output vs the predicted output of Mackey-Glass test data using 20 rules ($c = 0, \sigma = 0.03$)

of the training data tends to a fixed value when $\sigma \to 0$. However, for any other test data it is possible that no rule is activated which may result in poor generalization capability. Consequently, we would expect a non-zero value of σ to result in the best generalization from training to the test data.

We can now further coarsen the previous knowledge base by clustering DBX_i, the prototypical elements associated with the antecedent of the ith rule for $i = 1, \ldots, 20$. Here, we partition each DBX_i into 1, 2, 3, and 4 clusters, and take the cluster centers of DBX_i as the prototypical elements of the antecedent in the ith rule. The coarsened knowledge base then has the following rules:

IF X is about cluster centers $of\ DBX_i$ THEN Y is about $c_i : i = 1, \ldots, 20$.

We also plot the RMSE of the training data and test data with the different cluster numbers against the width σ of the Gaussian-type density function $\delta_{(0,\sigma)}$ in Figs. 10.3 and 10.4 . The results in Table 10.2 show that even a very coarsened knowledge base can predict MG time series with very high accuracy, which is comparable with some well-known prediction algorithms in Table 10.1 .

Table 10.2 Learning Results for the Linguistic Models

Linguistic Model	RMSE
500 Rules with $(c, \sigma) = (0, 0.026)$	0.0059
20 Rules with $(c, \sigma) = (0, 0.03)$ and $|DB_i|$ Clusters	0.0104
20 Rules with $(c, \sigma) = (0, 0.06)$ and 4 Clusters	0.0256
20 Rules with $(c, \sigma) = (0, 0.08)$ and 3 Clusters	0.0321
20 Rules with $(c, \sigma) = (0, 0.08)$ and 2 Clusters	0.0506
20 Rules with $(c, \sigma) = (0, 0.19)$ and 1 Cluster	0.0714

This example shows that information coarsening can reduce the complexity of the linguistic model and improve the transparency of the linguistic model, however it may also decrease the prediction performance of the linguistic model. In this example, the best prediction result for the test data is achieved when each training data determines one rule. However, when the training data is noisy, information coarsening may help overcome the over-fitting problem, and hence improve generalization capability. In the following, we apply our proposed linguistic model and information coarsening process to the sunspots prediction problem which is a noisy and a high-dimensional prediction problem.

10.2.2 Prediction of Sunspots

This problem is taken from the Time Series Data Library [5]. Sunspots, which are often considerably larger than the earth, were first discovered in about 1610 shortly after the invention of the telescope, and have an average life time of about 11 years, although this can vary between 7 to 15 years. Sunspot numbers have been recorded since 1700 but no method has been found to accurately predict or determine when or why these events occur. It is known however, that sunspot numbers are related to solar activity such as the magnetic field of the sun changing, which occurs about every 22 years. In this experiment we use sunspot relative numbers between the years 1700–1979 which was organized as described in Reference [6]. We use 209 examples (1712–1920) as the training data, and 59 examples (1921–1979) as the test data. The input attributes were x_{t-12} to x_{t-1} and the output attribute was x_t (i.e., one-year-ahead).

In this experiment, we still use Gaussian-type density function $\delta_{(c,\sigma)}$ to determine the appropriateness functions of all labels. Initially, we ran the prediction model which is directly derived from the training data. This generates 209 rules where each training data point determines one rule. For the density function $\delta_{(c,\sigma)}$, we select the center $c = 0$ and vary the width σ from 18 to 60. From Fig. 10.9 , we can see that the RMSE for the sunspot training data increases as the width σ of the density function increases from 18 to 60. In the previous sub-section we have pointed out that RMSE for the training data will tend to 0 as the width σ of the Gaussian-type density function δ tends to 0. Fig. 10.9 is consistent with this analysis. On the other hand, from Fig. 10.10 we can see that the minimal RMSE for the sunspot test data is achieved when $\sigma = 36$. By comparing Fig. 10.9 and Fig. 10.10 , we can say that the prediction results over fit the training data when the width σ of the density function is less than 38. Hence, from the viewpoint of the generalization capability of the linguistic model, the results suggest that the rule base with density function $\delta_{(0,36)}$ is optimal. The prediction results for the sunspot training data and test data under the situation $(c,\sigma) = (0,36)$ are plotted in Fig. 10.11 and Fig. 10.12 , respectively. The comparisons show that our linguistic model can effectively predict the trend of the sunspot time series. Moreover, in Figs. 10.13 and 10.14 we give the scatter plots showing the predicted results against the actual results of sunspot training data and test data, respectively. These scatter plots show that for low sunspot numbers the prediction results are overestimated, and for high sunspot numbers the prediction results are underestimated. One possible reason for this phenomenon is that the labels in the input space concentrate on some local area and are consequently too fine. Hence, it may be necessary to coarsen the rule base. Coarsening may overcome the phenomena of underestimation and overestimation.

We now use our proposed c-means clustering to partition the 209 examples (1712–1920) into 5 clusters. This results in 5 linguistic IF-THEN rules. Each cluster i determines a sub-training data set DB_i where DBX_i and DBY_i are the prototype set of the antecedent and consequence in the ith rule. In this situation, we have the rule base:

IF X is about DBX_i THEN Y is about $DBY_i, i = 1,\ldots,5$.

Here, the neighborhood size of the underlying vague concept is described by the word "about" which represents a Gaussian-type density function $\delta_{(c,\sigma)}$. We run this rule base with the fixed center $c = 0$ and varying width σ from 18 to 60. From Figs. 10.15 and 10.16 we can see that the RMSE for the test data in this coarsened linguistic model (the curve labelled "$|DB_i|$ Clusters") is less than RMSE

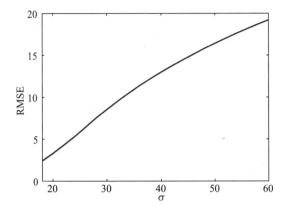

Fig. 10.9 The RMSE of sunspot training data vs the width σ of the Gaussian-type density function δ with the fixed center $c = 0$, where each training data determines one rule

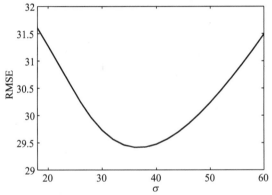

Fig. 10.10 The RMSE of sunspot test data vs the width σ of the Gaussian density function δ with the fixed center $c = 0$, where each training data determines one rule

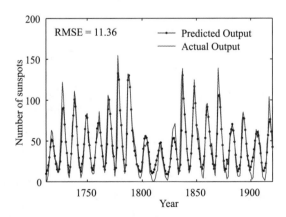

Fig. 10.11 Sunspot prediction result of the training data using 209 rules ($c = 0, \sigma = 36$), where each training data determines one rule

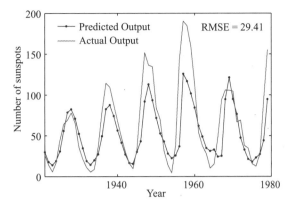

Fig. 10.12 Sunspot prediction result of the test data using 209 rules ($c = 0, \sigma = 36$), where each training data determines one rule

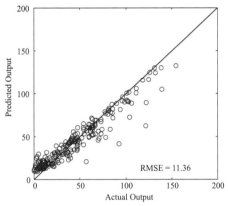

Fig. 10.13 Scatter plot showing the actual output vs the predicted output of sunspot training data using 209 rules ($c = 0, \sigma = 36$), where each training data determines one rule

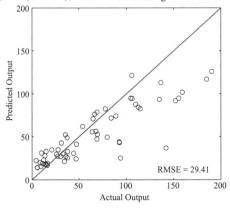

Fig. 10.14 Scatter plot showing the actual output vs the predicted output of sunspot test data using 209 rules ($c = 0, \sigma = 36$), where each training data determines one rule

derived from the linguistic model having 209 rules. This means that the prediction performance of the coarsened linguistic model is improved. As mentioned in the previous sub-section, RMSE for the training data would attend to a fixed value when $\sigma \to 0$.

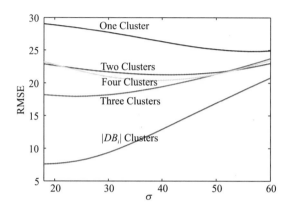

Fig. 10.15 The RMSE of sunspot training data vs the width σ of the Gaussian-type density function δ with the fixed center $c = 0$, where the rule number is 5

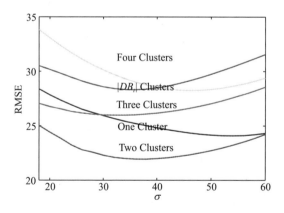

Fig. 10.16 The RMSE of sunspot test data vs the width σ of the Gaussian-type density function δ with the fixed center $c = 0$, where the rule number is 5

We further partition DBX_i into 1, 2, 3, and 4 clusters, and take the cluster centers as the prototypical elements of the antecedent in the ith rule for $i = 1, \ldots, 5$. That is, the rule base has the form:

IF X is about Cluster Centers of DBX_i THEN Y is about $DBY_i, i = 1, \ldots, 5$.

In Figs. 10.15 and 10.16 we also show the prediction performances of these 4 coarsened linguistic models with different cluster numbers. Roughly speaking, the RMSE for the test data decreases as the cluster number of DBX_i decreases from $|DB_i|$ to 2. Table 10.3 shows the RMSE for the test data for the different linguistic models with different granularity. The optimal performance of the rule base is obtained when the cluster number is reduced to 2.

Table 10.3 Learning results for the linguistic models

Linguistic Model	RMSE
209 Rules with $(c, \sigma) = (0, 36)$	29.4139
5 Rules with $(c, \sigma) = (0, 36)$ and $|DB_i|$ Clusters	28.3229
5 Rules with $(c, \sigma) = (0, 46)$ and 4 Clusters	28.2590
5 Rules with $(c, \sigma) = (0, 32)$ and 3 Clusters	25.9793
5 Rules with $(c, \sigma) = (0, 38)$ and 2 Clusters	21.9113
5 Rules with $(c, \sigma) = (0, 54)$ and 1 Cluster	24.0986

When the cluster number of DBX_i is 2, we obtain the best performance (RMSE = 21.91) for the test data. Figs. 10.17 and 10.18 show the prediction results of this coarsened linguistic model with $(c, \sigma) = (0, 38)$ for the training data and test data, respectively. We also show the scatter plots of the predicted results of this coarsened linguistic model with $(c, \sigma) = (0, 38)$ against the actual results for the sunspot data in Figs. 10.19 and 10.20 . Table 10.4 shows the comparison results of the prediction performance among various learning algorithms. The first three results were taken from Reference [6]. The performance of our proposed linguistic inference system is comparable with the best of these algorithms.

Table 10.4 Comparison of results for the different learning algorithms

Learning algorithm	RMSE
Fuzzy Naive Bayes	28.4735
ε−Support Vector Regression System	20.4481
Best Fuzzy Semi-Naive Bayes	22.3530
Back. Pro. NN	32.0341
ANFIS	25.8950
Linguistic Model with 5 Rules	21.9113

In Table 10.4 we also list the results we derive from a backpropagation neural network[7] and ANFIS (an adaptive network-based fuzzy inference system[8]). With the backpropagation neural network for this example, we obtain the best prediction

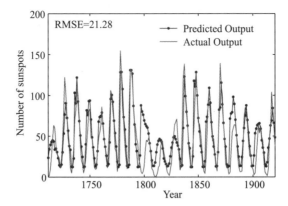

Fig. 10.17 Sunspot prediction result of the training data using 5 rules ($c = 0, \sigma = 38$), where the antecedent of each rule has two prototypical elements. Solid line is the actual output, dotted line is the predicted output

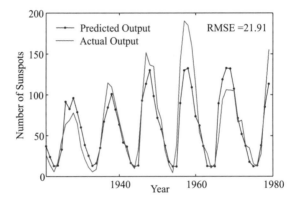

Fig. 10.18 Sunspot prediction result of the test data using 5 rules ($c = 0, \sigma = 38$), where the antecedent of each rule has two prototypical elements. Solid line is the actual output, dotted line is the predicted output

performance for the test data RMSE = 32.452 (its corresponding RMSE of the training data is 3.6820) when the number of hidden nodes is 3. In our experiments, neural networks where the number of hidden nodes is greater than 3 tend to overfit the training data. With ANFIS for this example, the rule number is 5 which is the same as that of our linguistic model. In this case, the performance of ANFIS is not better than that of our linguistic inference system.

10.3 Summary

In this chapter we proposed a new rule learning algorithm based on the prototype theory based label semantics. Our proposed linguistic model has a simple and

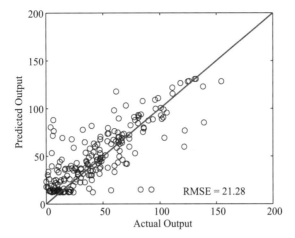

Fig. 10.19 Scatter plot showing the actual output vs the predicted output of sunspot training data using 5 rules ($c = 0, \sigma = 38$), where the antecedent of each rule has two prototypical elements

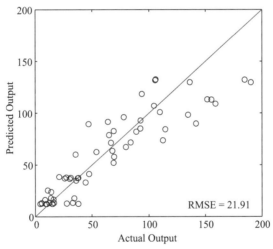

Fig. 10.20 Scatter plot showing the actual output vs the predicted output of sunspot test data using 5 rules ($c = 0, \sigma = 38$), where the antecedent of each rule has two prototypical elements

transparent structure, and rule induction from training data is relatively easy and direct. The general characteristics of the proposed algorithm can be summarized as follows:

(1) The linguistic IF-THEN rule has a transparent and simple form:

$$\text{IF } X \text{ is about } P \text{ THEN } Y \text{ is about } p$$

where P is the prototype set of the rule antecedent, and p is the prototype of the rule consequence.

(2) Compared with fuzzy inference systems, there are a relatively small number of parameters making the process of parameter estimation more straightforward.

(3) Other learning algorithms such as ANN, GAs or statistical learning methods could be easily incorporated into the linguistic inference system to improve the performance of the linguistic model further.

References

[1] Bezdek J. C., Keller J. M., Krishnapuram R., Pal N.: Fuzzy models and algorithms for pattern recognition and image processing. The Handbooks on Fuzzy Sets, Netherlands, (1999).

[2] Kim D., Kim C.: Forecasting time series with genetic fuzzy predictor ensemble, IEEE Trans. Fuzzy Syst. 5, pp. 523-535. (1997).

[3] Russo M.: Genetic fuzzy learning, IEEE Trans. Evol. Comput., 4(3), pp. 259-273. (2000).

[4] Tang Y., Xu Y.: Application of fuzzy naive bayes and a real-valued genetic algorithm in identification of fuzzy model, Information Sciences, 169(3-4), pp. 205-226. (2005).

[5] Hyndman R., Akram M.: Time series Data Library. Monash University. http://www-personal.buseco.monash.edu.au/~hyndman/TSDL/index.htm.

[6] Randon N. J.: Fuzzy and Random Set Based Induction Algorithms, PhD Thesis, Department of Engineering Mathematics, University of Bristol. (2004).

[7] Rumelhart D. E., Hinton G. E., Williams R. J.: Learning internal representations by error propagation, in D. E. Rumelhart and J. L. McClelland, eds. Parallel Data Processing, 1, Cambridge, MA: The M.I.T. Press, pp. 318-362. (1986).

[8] Jang J. S. R., Sun C. T., Mizutani E.: Neuro-Fuzzy and Soft Computing, Prentice-Hall, Inc. Simon & Schuster. (1997).

11

Prototype-Based Rule Systems

11.1 Introduction

Chapter 9 introduced a prototype-based interpretation for label semantics[1−3]. According to this interpretation, each basic label L has the form of "about P"[3], where P is a set of prototypes of L and the constraint "about" is represented by a random threshold ε with associated probability distribution δ. ε is interpreted as the uncertain upper bound on the distance an element x can be from the prototypes P for L to be appropriate to describe x. Moreover, using a prototyped-based interpretation, the appropriateness measure $\mu_L(x)$ of a basic label L for describing a instance x can also be expressed as the probability of the underlying instance x lying within ε of the associated set of prototypes P. Using this new interpretation and the associated representation framework, Tang and Lawry proposed a prototype-based IF-THEN rule of the form "IF X is about P THEN Y is about Q", this type of rule has a very transparent structure with a natural semantic interpretation[3]. The induction of prototype-based rules is then shown to be relatively straightforward and computationally efficient[3].

This chapter further explores prototype-based linguistic inference systems by proposing a more general prototype-based IF-THEN rule of the form "IF X is about P THEN Y is about $f(X)$", where $f(X)$ is a linear function of the input variables X. This type of rule has a similar structure to T-S fuzzy IF-THEN rules[4], but has a different interpretation and consequently requires a new type of rule induction algorithm. A fundamental difference between prototype-based rules and T-S fuzzy rules lies in the interpretation of the linguistic expressions. Fuzzy set theory uses membership functions to define linguistic expressions, while in label semantics meanings are determined using appropriateness measures. Furthermore, the calculus for the combination of linguistic expressions differs between fuzzy sets and appropriateness measures. For instance, in fuzzy set theory, the calculus is truth-functional, but in label semantics the calculus is not truth-functional, although it may be functional in a weaker sense[5,6].

A rule learning algorithm is proposed to infer general prototype-based IF-THEN rules from a data set. This rule learning algorithm has two steps. The first step is to identify the rule structure using a new clustering algorithm combined with least-square regression. The second step is to optimize the probability density function δ associated with the constraint "about" as well as the coefficients of linear functions involved in the rules by using a conjugate gradient algorithm. Experiments on a number of benchmark problems show that the proposed prototype-based linguistic inference system is very robust. In particular it performs well on high-dimensional and noisy data.

11.2 Prototype-Based IF-THEN Rules

In this section we propose a prototype-based IF-THEN rule for linguistic modeling. The proposed rule has a similar structure to T-S fuzzy rules [4], but has a different underlying uncertainty model. The reasoning process for this prototype-based linguistic inference system is based on the prototype theory for vague concepts presented in the previous section.

The proposed prototype-based IF-THEN rule base has the following form: for $i = 1, \ldots, M$,

$$\text{IF } X \text{ is about } P_i \text{ THEN } Y \text{ is about } f_i(X) \tag{11.1}$$

where P_i is a subset of $\mathbb{R}^n$ and $f_i(X)$ is a mapping from $\mathbb{R}^n$ to $\mathbb{R}$. For simplicity we assume that

$$f_i(X) = A_i[1, X]^{\mathrm{T}} = a_0^i + a_1^i x_1 + \ldots + a_n^i x_n \tag{11.2}$$

where $X = (x_1, \ldots, x_n)^{\mathrm{T}}$ and $A_i = (a_1^i, \ldots, a_n^i)$, a linear combination of input variables in the rule antecedents. In the following we assume that the constraint "about" is represented by a Gaussian additive probability density function $\delta_{(c,\sigma)}$ on $[0, +\infty)$ with the following form:

$$\delta_{(c,\sigma)}(\varepsilon) = \frac{1}{\sqrt{2\pi}\sigma}\left[\exp\frac{(\varepsilon - c)^2}{-2\sigma^2} + \exp\frac{(\varepsilon + c)^2}{-2\sigma^2}\right] \tag{11.3}$$

where c and σ are the center and width of the Gaussian additive probability density function respectively.

This type of probability density function for δ was first proposed in Reference [3]. Using the Gaussian additive probability density function the linguistic label $L_i = $ about P_i has the following appropriateness measure:

$$\begin{aligned}\mu_{L_i}(x) &= \delta([d(x, P_i), +\infty)) \\ &= 1 - F(d(x, P_i) \mid c, \sigma) + F(-d(x, P_i) \mid c, \sigma)\end{aligned} \tag{11.4}$$

where

$$F(d \mid c, \sigma) = \frac{1}{\sqrt{2\pi}\sigma}\int_{-\infty}^{d} \exp((\varepsilon - c)^2/(-2\sigma^2))\mathrm{d}\varepsilon \tag{11.5}$$

It is the normal cumulative distribution function with mean c and standard deviation σ.

We assume that output variable Y is a random variable which has a prior probability distribution $p(\cdot)$ on $\mathbb{R}$. Given any $X \in \mathbb{R}^n$, then how do we update the probability distribution $p(\cdot)$ on $\mathbb{R}$ based on the linguistic rule base? That is, what is the posterior probability distribution $p_{RB}(\cdot \mid X)$, where RB denotes the linguistic rule base. Note that for any $X \in \mathbb{R}$, we can obtain the appropriateness measures $\mu_{about\, P_i}(X)$ for $i = 1, \ldots, M$. It is natural to assume that

$$\mu_{about\, f_i(X)}(y) = \mu_{about\, P_i}(X) \qquad (11.6)$$

for $i = 1, \ldots, M$, where $y \in \mathbb{R}$ is the unknown value corresponding to the input X. By normalizing the appropriateness measures $\mu_{about\, f_i(X)}(y)$ we obtain a weight for each linguistic label about $f_i(X)$. So we have the following definition:

Definition 11.1 Given $X \in \mathbb{R}^n$ the posterior probability distribution $p_{RB}(\cdot \mid X)$ on $\mathbb{R}$ is defined as follows: for any $y \in \mathbb{R}$

$$p_{RB}(y \mid X) = \sum_{i=1}^{M} \left[\frac{\mu_{about\, P_i}(X)}{\sum_{i=1}^{M} \mu_{about\, P_i}(X)} p(y \mid about\, f_i(X)) \right] \qquad (11.7)$$

In the above definition the conditional probability $p(y \mid about\, f_i(X))$ is given in Reference [7] as follows:

Definition 11.2 [7] The conditional probability distribution $p(\cdot \mid \theta)$ given a linguistic expression θ on $\mathbb{R}$ is defined as follows: for any $y \in \mathbb{R}$

$$p(y \mid \theta) = \frac{\mu_{\theta}(y) p(y)}{\int_{\mathbb{R}} \mu_{\theta}(y) p(y) dy} \qquad (11.8)$$

where $p(\cdot)$ is a prior probability distribution on $\mathbb{R}$.

After we obtain the posterior probability distribution $p_{RB}(\cdot \mid X)$ on $\mathbb{R}$, we take the expectation $E(y \mid X)$ as the estimate of $f(X)$:

Definition 11.3 Given input $X \in \mathbb{R}$, the output $f(X)$ of the linguistic rule base RB is defined as follows:

$$f(X) = \int_{\mathbb{R}} y p_{RB}(y \mid X) dy$$

$$= \sum_{i=1}^{M} \left[\frac{\mu_{about\, P_i}(X)}{\sum_{j=1}^{M} \mu_{about\, P_j}(X)} \int_{\mathbb{R}} y p(y \mid about\, f_i(X)) dy \right]$$

Assume that the prior probability distribution $p(\cdot)$ on $\mathbb{R}$ is a uniform distribution, then the output $f(X)$ of the linguistic rule base can be simplified further.

Theorem 11.1 Given M rules having the form as in Eq. (11.1), then for any input $X \in \mathbb{R}^n$ the estimated $f(X)$ from the rule-base is as follows:

$$f(X) = \frac{\sum_{i=1}^{M} \mu_{about\, P_i}(X) f_i(X)}{\sum_{i=1}^{M} \mu_{about\, P_i}(X)} \qquad (11.9)$$

Proof Since the prior probability distribution $p(\cdot)$ on $\mathbb{R}$ is a uniform distribution, then according to Eq. (11.8), we have:

$$\int_{\mathbb{R}} y p(y \mid \text{about } f_i(X)) dy = \frac{\int_{\mathbb{R}} y \mu_{\text{about } f_i(X)}(y) dy}{\int_{\mathbb{R}} \mu_{\text{about } f_i(X)}(y) dy} \tag{11.10}$$

Moreover,

$$\int_{\mathbb{R}} y \mu_{\text{about } f_i(X)}(y) dy$$

$$= \int_{-\infty}^{f_i(X)} y \mu_{\text{about } f_i(X)}(y) dy + \int_{f_i(X)}^{+\infty} y \mu_{\text{about } f_i(X)}(y) dy$$

$$= \int_{-\infty}^{0} (f_i(X) + y) \delta(|y|, +\infty)) dy + \int_{-\infty}^{0} (f_i(X) - y) \delta(|y|, +\infty) dy$$

$$= f_i(X) \int_{-\infty}^{+\infty} \delta(|y|, +\infty) dy$$

On the other hand, we have

$$\int_{\mathbb{R}} \mu_{\text{about } f_i(X)}(y) dy = \int_{-\infty}^{+\infty} \delta(|y - f_i(X)|, +\infty)) dy$$

$$= \int_{-\infty}^{+\infty} \delta(|y|, +\infty) dy \tag{11.11}$$

So we can derive the following formula

$$\int_{\mathbb{R}} y \mu_{\text{about } f_i(X)}(y) dy = f_i(X) \int_{\mathbb{R}} \mu_{\text{about } f_i(X)}(y) dy \tag{11.12}$$

Hence, according to Definition 11.2, the result follows immediately.

If functions $f_i(X)$ involved in the rule base are single constants $f_i(X) = a_i$, then we obtain rules of the form:

$$\text{IF } X \text{ is about } P_i \text{ THEN } y \text{ is about } a_i, i = 1, \dots, M, \tag{11.13}$$

where P_i is a subset of $\mathbb{R}^n$ and a_i is a real number for $i = 1, \dots, M$. And for any input $X \in \mathbb{R}^n$ the output of this linguistic inference system is as follows:

$$\frac{\sum_{i=1}^{M} \mu_{\text{about } P_i}(X) a_i}{\sum_{i=1}^{M} \mu_{\text{about } P_i}(X)} \tag{11.14}$$

We can see that this linguistic inference system with constant consequences is actually the one proposed in Reference [3]. In this case, all input values $X \in \mathbb{R}^n$ share the same linguistic rule base denoted by $RB(a_1, \dots, a_M)$. On the contrary, for rules with the functional consequences different inputs have different rule bases. For input $X \in \mathbb{R}^n$ the corresponding rule base is $RB(f_1(X), \dots, f_M(X))$. So the current rule base can be considered as a dynamic rule base which is potentially more flexible for modelling uncertain phenomena.

11.3 Rule Induction Based on Data Clustering and Least-Square Regression

Given a training data set DB which includes N data pairs (X_i, y_i) where $X_i = (x_1^i, \ldots, x_n^i)$ is an n-dimensional vector in $\mathbb{R}^n$, we now consider how to induce rules of the form given in Eq. (11.1)?

For rules of the form in Eq. (11.14) a rule induction method based on the clustering and information coarsening was proposed in[3]. This early work motivates us to propose a rule induction method based on a clustering algorithm for the general rule base given in Eq. (11.1).

In the following, we take the linear combination functions $f_i(X)$ as the consequences of rules. Notice that we can derive a linear combination function $f_i(X)$ which is best fitting a given sub-data set $DB_i = \{(X_j, y_j) : j = 1, \ldots, N_i\}$ by applying least squares regression

$$O_i = \sum_{(X_j, y_j) \in DB_i} (y_j - f_i(X_j))^2. \tag{11.15}$$

This can be done by letting the gradient information $\frac{\partial O_i}{\partial A_i} = 0$:

$$B_i A_i = C_i$$

where

$$B_i = \begin{pmatrix} N_i & \sum_{j=1}^{N_i} x_1^j & \cdots & \sum_{j=1}^{N_i} x_n^j \\ \sum_{j=1}^{N_i} x_1^j & \sum_{j=1}^{N_i} x_1^j x_1^j & \cdots & \sum_{j=1}^{N_i} x_1^j x_n^j \\ \vdots & \vdots & \cdots & \vdots \\ \sum_{j=1}^{N_i} x_n^j & \sum_{j=1}^{N_i} x_n^j x_1^j & \cdots & \sum_{j=1}^{N_i} x_n^j x_n^j \end{pmatrix} \tag{11.16}$$

$$C_i = \left(\sum_{j=1}^{N_i} y_j \quad \sum_{j=1}^{N_i} x_1^j y_j \quad \cdots \quad \sum_{j=1}^{N_i} x_n^j y_j \right)^T \tag{11.17}$$

So we have $f_i(X) = A_i[1, X]^T$, where

$$A_i = B_i^{-1} C_i \tag{11.18}$$

Eq. (11.18) is concise in notation. However, it is expensive in computation when dealing with matrix inversion and, moreover, it becomes ill-defined if B_i is singular. As a result, we can employ sequential formulas to compute A_i for $i = 1, \ldots, M$. Assume that $DB_i = \{[X_j, y_j] : j = 1, \ldots, N_i\}$ then A_i can be iteratively calculated using the sequential formulas adopted in the following learning algorithm[8]:

$$A_i(j+1) = A_i(j) + S(j+1)[1, X_{j+1}]^T (y_{j+1} - [1, X_{j+1}] A_i(j))$$

$$S(j+1) = S(j) - \frac{S(j)[1,X_{j+1}]^T[1,X_{j+1}]S(j)}{1+[1,X_{j+1}]S(j)[1,X_{j+1}]^T}, j = 0,\ldots,N_i$$

where $S(j)$ is often called the covariance matrix and the least squares estimate A_i is equal to $A_i(N_i)$. The initial conditions are $A_i(0) = 0$ and $S(0) = \gamma I$, where γ is a large positive number and I is the $(n+1) \times (n+1)$ identity matrix.

The above discussions on the estimations of linear functions $f_i(X)$ motivate us to propose a rule induction method based on the clustering of the training data set DB and least square criterion. Initially we apply a clustering algorithm to obtain M clusters DB_i of the training data set DB, and then we apply linear regression to determine a functional mapping $Y = f_i(X)$ for each cluster DB_i. For each $(X_j, y_j) \in DB_i$ the rule base effectively captures the data provided that $d(y_j, f_i(X_j))$ is small. This is formalized by the following condition:

$$(X_j, y_j) \in DB_i \Leftrightarrow d(y_j, f_i(X_j)) = \min_{1 \le k \le M} d(y_j, f_k(X_j)) \tag{11.19}$$

for $i = 1, \ldots, M$.

However, classical clustering algorithms such as c-means and FCM[9] do not generally result in clusters having this requirement. Hence, we propose a new clustering algorithm for linguistic rule induction. Eq. (11.19) naturally generates a partition updating criterion for clustering as follows:

$$\text{Minimize } J = \sum_{i=1}^{M} \sum_{(X_j, y_j) \in DB_i} d(y_j, f_i(X_j)) \tag{11.20}$$

Hence, the basic procedures for this clustering algorithm can be outlined as follows: Given an initial partition $\{DB_i : i = 1, \ldots, M\}$ of the training data set DB, estimate the linear combination function $f_i(X)$ for each cluster DB_i using Eq. (11.18), then using Eq. (11.19) to update the partition by computing the distances $d(y_j, f_i(X_j))$ for all training data and linear combination functions $f_i(X)$. Continue this iteration until the objective function J converges to a minima. Fig. 11.1 gives a brief description of our proposed clustering algorithm for linguistic rule induction.

After obtaining the clusters $\{DB_i : i = 1, \ldots, M\}$ for the training data set DB, we can immediately derive a rule base of the form in Eq. (11.1):

IF X is about DBX_i THEN Y is about $f_i(X), i = 1, \ldots, M$

where $DBX_i = \{X_j : (X_j, y_j) \in DB_i\}$. The Gaussian additive probability density function $\delta_{(c,\sigma)}$ can be estimated using the following formulas:

$$c = \bar{\varepsilon}/(2M) \tag{11.21}$$

$$\sigma = \frac{2}{M}\left(\frac{1}{N}\sum_{j=1}^{N}(d(X_j, \bar{X}) - \bar{\varepsilon})^2\right)^{1/2} \tag{11.22}$$

Given data set $DB = \{(X_j, y_j) : j = 1, \ldots, N\}$ and cluster number M, partition data set DB
randomly, such that $\bigcup_{i=1}^{M} DB_i = DB$, $DB_i \cap DB_k = \emptyset$ and $DB_i \neq \emptyset$.
For $l = 1, 2, \ldots$
Step 1: Determine the linear combination functions for the clusters DB_i:

$$f_i(X) = A_i[1, X]^T,$$

where A_i is derived from Eq. (11.18) for $i = 1, \ldots, M$.
Step 2: Compute the objective function $J^{(l)}$:

$$J^{(l)} = \sum_{i=1}^{M} \sum_{(X_j, y_j) \in DB_i} d^2(x_j, f_i(X_j))$$

Step 3: Update the clusters DB_i:
$DB_i = \{(X_j, y_j) : d(y_j, f_i(X_j)) = \min_{1 \leq k \leq M} d(y_j, f_k(X_j))\}$ for $i = 1, \ldots, M$

Until $|J^{(l)} - J^{(l-1)}| < \varepsilon$.

Fig. 11.1 The description of clustering algorithm for the linguistic rule induction.

where

$$\overline{X} = \frac{1}{N} \sum_{j=1}^{N} X_j \qquad (11.23)$$

$$\overline{\varepsilon} = \frac{1}{N} \sum_{j=1}^{N} d(X_j, \overline{X}) \qquad (11.24)$$

Moreover, we can further coarsen the rule base using the cluster centers of DBX_i
to represent the prototypes of the ith rule antecedent label. In general we use crisp
c-means to obtain the cluster centers P_i of DBX_i for $i = 1, \ldots, M$. In this way we can
simplify the rule base and improve the transparency. The key to this rule coarsening
is to determine the prototype numbers $|P_i|$ for $i = 1, \ldots, M$. In the following we
present a method to estimate the prototype number of DBX_i. Assume that P_i is the
set of cluster centers (or prototypes) of DBX_i, then it is required that

$$\frac{\sum_{X_j \in DBX_i} \mu_{\text{about } P_i}(X_j)}{|DBX_i|} \geq \beta \qquad (11.25)$$

where β is a threshold ($\in (0, 1]$) representation the lowest degree of representative.
Notice that the threshold β depends on the probability density function δ. By
increasing the value of β we can obtain a more precise model for the training data.
On the contrary, by decreasing the value of β we can obtain a more coarse and
transparent model. The motivation here is that the left hand side of Eq. (11.25) is
the probability that an element picked up at random from DBX_i will lie within ε
of P_i.

11.4 Rule Learning Using a Conjugate Gradient Algorithm

For the induction method proposed in the previous section the identification of linear functions does not take into account the influence of the probability density function δ. Furthermore, the induced rule base is only optimal in the sense of objective function J (Eq. 11.20) and least square criterion (Eq. 11.19). This may suggest that we can further fine tune the induced rules by adjusting the linear functions and probability density function δ. In this section an algorithm based on a conjugate gradient method is proposed to optimize the parameters of the prototype-based IF-THEN rules generated by the induction method proposed in the previous section.

In the following we only consider rules in the form:

$$\text{IF } X \text{ is } L_i \text{ THEN } Y \text{ is about } f_i(X), i = 1, 2, \ldots, M \qquad (11.26)$$

where $L_i = $ about DBX_i or $L_i = $ about P_i (where $P_i \subseteq \mathbb{R}^n$ is the set of cluster centers of DBX_i), and $f_i(X)$ is a linear function from $\mathbb{R}^n$ to $\mathbb{R}$ such that $f_i(X) = A_i[1, X]^{\mathrm{T}} = a_0^i + a_1^i x_1 + \cdots + a_n^i x_n$.

Given a training data set $DB = \{(X_i, y_i) : X_i \in \mathbb{R}^n, y_i \in \mathbb{R}, i = 1, \ldots, N\}$, we assume that a rule base is learnt from DB by using the clustering algorithm proposed in the previous section. In order to fine tune this rule base we take the MSE of the training data set as a measure of performance of the linguistic model, defined as follows:

$$O = \frac{1}{N} \sum_{j=1}^{N} (f(X_j) - y_j)^2 \qquad (11.27)$$

where $f(X_j)$ is the output of the linguistic inference system for the input X_j given by:

$$f(X_j) = \frac{\sum_{k=1}^{M} \mu_{L_k}(X_j) f_k(X_j)}{\sum_{k=1}^{M} \mu_{L_k}(X_j)} \qquad (11.28)$$

The parameters involved in this linguistic inference system consist of the prototypes DBX_i (or its cluster centers P_i), the coefficients A_i for $i = 1, \ldots, M$, and the center c and width σ of the Gaussian additive probability density function. These parameters can be initially estimated from the clustering algorithm proposed in the previous section. Here we propose a gradient-based learning algorithm to tune these parameters further. In order to simplify the learning process we only learn the parameters A_i for $i = 1, \ldots, M$ and the Gaussian additive probability density function. The prototypes DBX_i or P_i for $i = 1, \ldots, M$ are determined by the clustering algorithm.

The total number of parameters for optimization is $(n + 1)M + 2$. Let $\mathbf{v} = [A_1, \ldots, A_M, c, \sigma]$ denote the vector of parameter values, and let O denote the objective function. Let $\mathbf{g}$ be defined by:

$$\mathbf{g} = \left[\frac{\partial O}{\partial A_1}, \ldots, \frac{\partial O}{\partial A_M}, \frac{\partial O}{\partial c}, \frac{\partial O}{\partial \sigma} \right] \qquad (11.29)$$

We now use the conjugate gradient algorithm to optimize these parameters based on the following updating rules:

$$\mathbf{v}_{k+1} = \mathbf{v}_k + \alpha_k \mathbf{d}_k, \mathbf{d}_k = -\mathbf{g}_k + \beta_k \mathbf{d}_{k-1}$$

$$\mathbf{d}_0 = -\mathbf{g}_0, \beta_k = \frac{\mathbf{g}_k \mathbf{g}_k^T}{\mathbf{g}_{k-1} \mathbf{g}_{k-1}^T}$$

where $\mathbf{v}_0$ is determined by the clustering algorithm proposed in the previous section, and the search distance α_k along the direction $\mathbf{d}_k$ is determined by a line search algorithm such as a golden section search[10].

All the gradient information involved in Eq. (11.29) is determined as follows:

$$\frac{\partial O}{\partial A_i} = \frac{2}{N} \sum_{j=1}^{N} (f(X_j) - y_j) \frac{\partial f(X_j)}{\partial A_i} \tag{11.30}$$

$$\frac{\partial O}{\partial c} = \frac{2}{N} \sum_{j=1}^{N} (f(X_j) - y_j) \frac{\partial f(X_j)}{\partial c} \tag{11.31}$$

$$\frac{\partial O}{\partial \sigma} = \frac{2}{N} \sum_{j=1}^{N} (f(X_j) - y_j) \frac{\partial f(X_j)}{\partial \sigma} \tag{11.32}$$

where

$$\frac{\partial f(X_j)}{\partial A_i} = \frac{\mu_{L_i}(X_j)}{\sum_{k=1}^{M} \mu_{L_k}(X_j)} [1, X_j]$$

$$\frac{\partial f(X_j)}{\partial c} = \frac{\sum_{i=1}^{M} f_i(X_j) \frac{\partial \mu_{L_i}(X_j)}{\partial c} \sum_{i=1}^{M} \mu_{L_i}(X_j)}{\left(\sum_{i=1}^{M} \mu_{L_i}(X_j)\right)^2} - \frac{\sum_{i=1}^{M} \mu_{L_i}(X_j) f_i(X_j) \sum_{i=1}^{M} \frac{\partial \mu_{L_i}(X_j)}{\partial c}}{\left(\sum_{i=1}^{M} \mu_{L_i}(X_j)\right)^2}$$

$$\frac{\partial \mu_{L_i}(X_j)}{\partial c} = \frac{1}{\sqrt{2\pi}\sigma} \left[\exp \frac{(d(X_j, P_i) - c)^2}{-2\sigma^2} - \exp \frac{(d(X_j, P_i) + c)^2}{-2\sigma^2} \right]$$

$$\frac{\partial f(X_j)}{\partial \sigma} = \frac{\sum_{i=1}^{M} f_i(X_j) \frac{\partial \mu_{L_i}(X_j)}{\partial \sigma} \sum_{i=1}^{M} \mu_{L_i}(X_j)}{\left(\sum_{i=1}^{M} \mu_{L_i}(X_j)\right)^2} - \frac{\sum_{i=1}^{M} \mu_{L_i}(X_j) f_i(X_j) \sum_{i=1}^{M} \frac{\partial \mu_{L_i}(X_j)}{\partial \sigma}}{\left(\sum_{i=1}^{M} \mu_{L_i}(X_j)\right)^2}$$

and

$$\frac{\partial \mu_{L_i}(X_j)}{\partial \sigma} = \frac{(d(X_j, P_i) - c)}{\sqrt{2\pi\sigma^2}} \exp\left(\frac{(d(X_j, P_i) - c)^2}{-2\sigma^2}\right)$$
$$+ \frac{(d(X_j, P_i) + c)}{\sqrt{2\pi\sigma^2}} \exp\left(\frac{(d(X_j, P_i) + c)^2}{-2\sigma^2}\right)$$

If the prototype in the ith rule is DBX_i, then the distance $d(X_j, P_i)$ in the above formulas should be replaced by $d(X_j, DBX_i)$.

According to the above discussion we can see that the proposed identification of prototype-based rules consists of two steps. The first step is to use the proposed clustering algorithm together with least squares regression to determine the prototype sets for the linguistic labels in rule antecedents and linear functions in the rule consequences, and also to estimate the initial Gaussian additive probability density function parameters using Eqs. (11.21) and (11.22). In this step we can also use cluster centers determined from the training data as prototypes for linguistic labels in the rule antecedents, so as to improve generalization. The second step is to fine tune the parameters of the rule base using the conjugate gradient algorithm proposed in this section. These two steps are then iterated until a user defined maximum iteration number is reached.

11.5 Applications in Prediction Problems

In this section we apply the prototype-based linguistic inference system to three prediction problems. In these applications we take d to be the Euclidean distance. The first example is a 2-dimensional nonlinear function estimation problem. This simple example illustrates that the proposed induction algorithm can generate effective rules based on multi-modal clusters. The second prediction problem is the Mackey-Glass time series which is often used as a benchmark problem in artificial neural networks and fuzzy modeling. Our results are comparable with the best algorithms in the literatures. The final example is the sunspots time series which is not only high dimensional, but also a noisy prediction problem. A linguistic inference system with only 2 prototype-based rules works very well for this difficult problem, suggesting that our linguistic inference system can generate robust, effective and simple models.

11.5.1 Surface Predication

In this example a training data set based on a grid of 23×23 points and a test data set based on a grid of 45×45 points were generated to describe the surface defined by equation $z = \sin(x \times y)$ where $x, y \in [0, 3]$.

By fixing the prototype sets P_i of rule antecedent labels, we then used the conjugate gradient algorithm presented in Section 11.4 to adjust the coefficients

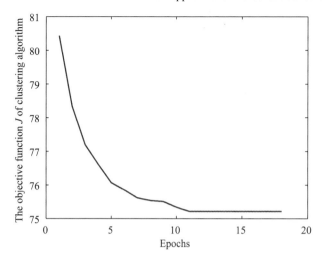

Fig. 11.2 The objective function J with 3 clusters for the training data set generated from equation $z = \sin(x \times y)$

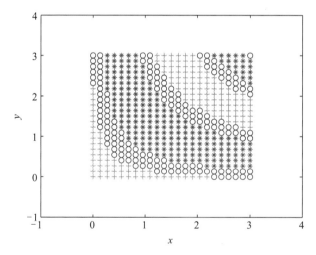

Fig. 11.3 The prototype sets P_i of L_i for $i = 1, 2, 3$, where points marked "o" represent the elements of P_1, points marked "*" represent the elements of P_2, and points marked "+" represent the elements of P_3

of linear functions $f_i(x,y)$ for $i = 1,2,3$ in the rule consequences and the parameters of Gaussian additive probability density function $\delta_{(c,\sigma)}$ (the initial values of c and σ were estimated using Eqs. (11.21) and (11.22)). Fig. 11.4 shows the RMSE for the training data set and test data set against the epoch number. From this figure we can see that the clustering algorithm results in a rule base with a relatively low RMSE, which is then significantly improved by the conjugate gradient algorithm. Fig. 11.4 also shows that convergence of the conjugate gradient algorithm is very quick in this example.

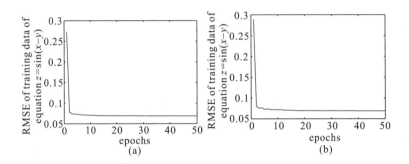

Fig. 11.4   (a) RMSE against epoch for the training data generated from equation $z = \sin(x \times y)$ for the linguistic model with 3 prototype-based rules. (b) RMSE against epoch for the test data generated from equation $z = \sin(x \times y)$ for the linguistic model with 3 prototype-based rules

The final estimates obtained for the linear functions were as follows:

$$f_1(x,y) = 0.4513 - 0.0886x - 0.0886y$$

$$f_2(x,y) = 0.7503 + 0.0793x + 0.0793y$$

$$f_3(x,y) = 0.1730 - 0.2576x - 0.2576y$$

The resulting parameters for the Gaussian additive probability density function were $c = 0.158$ and $\sigma = 0.1136$. Hence the final prototype-based rules were as follows: for $i = 1,2,3$

$$\text{IF } (x,y) \text{ is } L_i = \text{about } P_i \text{ THEN } z \text{ is about } f_i(x,y) \qquad (11.33)$$

where for $i = 1,2,3$ P_i is the prototype set of L_i, which is the ith cluster derived from the training data set using the clustering algorithm outlined in Fig. 11.1 . The appropriateness measures for the learnt labels $L_i = \text{about } P_i$ and the associated linear functions $z = f_i(x,y)$ for $i = 1,2,3$ are shown in Figs. 11.5 , 11.6 , and 11.7 respectively, where about is described by a Gaussian additive probability density function $\delta_{(0.158,0.1136)}$. Figs. 11.8 and 11.9 show comparisons between the predicted surface derived from the rule base and original surface for the training and test data sets respectively.

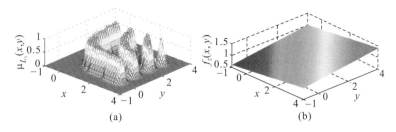

Fig. 11.5 The prototype-based rule: $L_1 \rightarrow$ *about* $f_1(x,y)$. (a) The appropriateness measures $\mu_{L_1}(x,y)$. (b) The linear function $f_1(x,y) = 0.4513 - 0.0886x - 0.0886y$

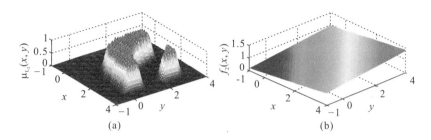

Fig. 11.6 The prototype-based rule: $L_2 \rightarrow$ *about* $f_2(x,y)$. (a) The appropriateness measures $\mu_{L_2}(x,y)$. (b) The linear function $f_2(x,y) = 0.7503 + 0.0793x + 0.0793y$

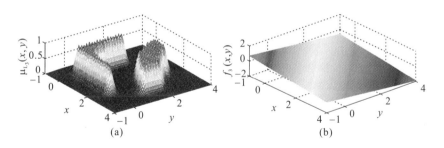

Fig. 11.7 The prototype-based rule: $L_3 \rightarrow$ *about* $f_3(x,y)$. (a) The appropriateness measures $\mu_{L_3}(x,y)$. (b) The linear function $f_3(x,y) = 0.1730 - 0.2576x - 0.2576y$

11.5.2 Mackey-Glass Time Series Prediction

In this subsection we investigated the construction of a linguistic inference system to predict the time series generated by the following Mackey-Glass (MG) time-delay differential equation:

$$\dot{x}(t) = \frac{0.2x(t-\tau)}{1+x^{10}(t-\tau)} - 0.1x(t)$$

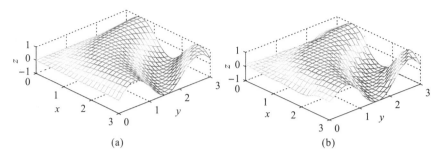

Fig. 11.8 (a) The original surface of equation $z = \sin(x \times y)$ for the training data set. (b) The prediction surface generated from linguistic model for the training data set

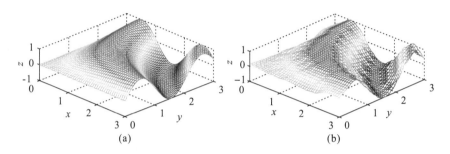

Fig. 11.9 (a) The original surface of equation $z = \sin(x \times y)$ for the test data set. (b) The prediction surface generated from linguistic model for the test data set

This time-series is chaotic with no clearly defined period. The series does not converge or diverge, and the trajectory is highly sensitive to initial conditions. This is a benchmark problem in the neural network and fuzzy modeling research communities[11–13]. To obtain the time-series values at integer points, we applied the fourth-order Runge-Kutta method to find the numerical solution to the above MG equation. Here we assumed $x(0) = 1.2$, $\tau = 17$, and $x(t) = 0$ for $t < 0$.

In this time-series prediction, the objective is to use known values up to time t, in order to predict future values at time point $t + 6$. For each t, the input training data for the linguistic model is a four dimensional vector of the form, $X(t) = [x(t - 18), x(t - 12), x(t - 6), x(t)]$. The output training data corresponds to the trajectory prediction, $y(t) = x(t + 6)$. With t ranging from 118 to 1117, we obtained 1000 input/output data values of which the first 500 formed the training set DB and the second 500 the test set.

We assumed that the rule number was $M = 16$. By running the clustering algorithm proposed in Section 11.3 we obtained an initial set of clusters DB_i. Using Eqs. (11.21) and (11.22) we obtained $c = 0.0137$ and $\sigma = 0.0150$ for Gaussian additive probability density function δ. Fig. 11.10 shows that the convergence of

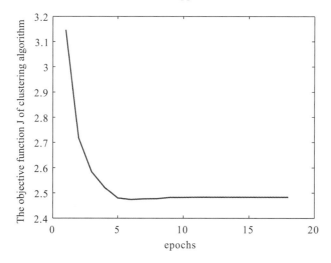

Fig. 11.10 The objective function J with 16 clusters for the MG training data set

the objective function J (see Eq. (11.20)). Applying the clustering algorithm we obtained the following rule base:

$$\text{IF } X \text{ is } L_i \text{ THEN } Y \text{ is about } f_i(X), i = 1, \ldots, 16 \qquad (11.34)$$

where $L_i =$ about DBX_i and $f_i(X) = A_i[1, X]^T$.

In this rule base we took the cluster DBX_i as the prototypes of the label in the ith rule antecedent. We then used the conjugate gradient algorithm to train this linguistic model by tuning the linear combination functions $f_i(X)$ for $i = 1, \ldots, 16$ and the Gaussian additive probability density function $\delta_{(c,\sigma)}$. Fig. 11.11 shows the RMSE curves of the training data set and test data set plotted against the epoch for this linguistic model. We can see that the clustering algorithm gives a good estimate for the parameters of the linguistic model, which is subsequently improved by applying the conjugate gradient algorithm. This indicates that our proposed clustering algorithm can give a good initial estimation for the linguistic model. In order to see the impact of the probability density function on the performance of the linguistic model, we also plot the center and width curves for the Gaussian additive probability density function in Fig. 11.12 . During the learning process, the center c of the Gaussian additive probability density function varies in an unusual way, while the width σ converges in an almost monotonic manner. The value of center c finally converged to $c = 0.0132$ and the value of width σ converged to $\sigma = 0.0255$. Given these parameter values, the RMSE of the training data set and test data are 0.0059 and 0.007, respectively. Table 11.1 gives the performance of a number of well-known learning algorithms on the MG data (results are taken from [3,8,11]). From this we can see that our linguistic model has the same performance as ANFIS which also has 16 fuzzy IF-THEN rules. Notice that the best performance on this data set is from the prototype-based linguistic inference system with constant consequences [3], in which each rule has the form as in Eq. (11.13). However that linguistic inference system has a huge rule base where each training data (X_i, y_i) determines a prototype-based rule about $X_i \rightarrow$ about y_i for $i = 1, \ldots, 500$. The current prototype-based linguistic inference system with linear functions as consequences, only has 16 rules and hence is considerably more concise. GEFRES in Table 11.1 also has better accuracy than our model. However, GEFRES is a genetic fuzzy learning algorithm with 20 fuzzy IF-THEN rules, which requires 50,000 iterations and a population of 100 individuals.

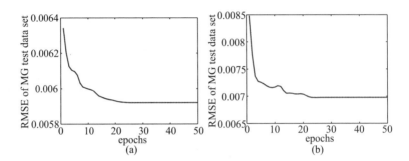

Fig. 11.11 The performance of linguistic model with 16 prototype-based rules. (a) RMSE against epoch for MG training data. (b) RMSE against epoch for MG test data

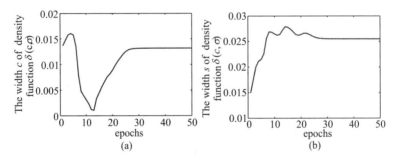

Fig. 11.12 The Gaussian additive probability density function $\delta_{(c,\sigma)}$ for the linguistic model with 16 prototype-based rules. (a) The curve of center c against epochs. (b) The curve of width σ against epochs

We now consider the coarsened rule base consisting of the following prototype-based rules: for $i = 1, \ldots, 16$

$$\text{IF } X \text{ is about } P_i \text{ THEN } Y \text{ is about } f_i(X) \tag{11.35}$$

where P_i is the set of crisp means of DBX_i and $f_i(X) = A_i[1, X]^T$ for $i = 1, \ldots, 16$. Here we used Eq. (11.25) to determine the prototype number $|P_i|$ for DBX_i by setting

Table 11.1 Comparison results for different learning algorithms

Learning algorithm	RMSE
Kim & Kim	0.026
Wang (product operator)	0.091
Min operator	0.090
ANFIS with 16 Rules	0.007
Auto Regressive Model	0.19
Cascade Correlation NN	0.06
Back. Pro. NN	0.02
6th order polynomial	0.04
Linear Predictive model	0.55
GEFREX	0.0061
500 Prototype-based Rules (Constants)	0.0059
16 Prototype-based Rules (linear functions)	0.007

$\beta = 0.04$. This rule base had the same parameters as the rule base shown in Eq. (11.34) except for the rule antecedents. We then used conjugate gradient algorithm to train the model by fixing the prototypes P_i in the rule antecedent labels. The RMSE curves of the training data set and test data set for this linguistic model are shown in Fig. 11.13 . The RMSE of the test data for this coarsened linguistic model is 0.0176, which is worse than that of linguistic model given in Eq. (11.34). We also plot the curves for the center c and width σ of Gaussian additive density function against epochs in Fig. 11.14 . The final values of c and σ for this coarsened linguistic model are $c = 0.0415$ and $\sigma = 0.0628$, respectively. By comparing Figs. 11.12 and 11.14 , we can see that the curves for the parameters c and σ are similar for both rule bases.

11.5.3 Prediction of Sunspots

The sunspot time-series is a well known high-dimensional prediction problem with a noisy and sparse data set. Hence, we use this problem to investigate the robustness of our proposed prototype-based linguistic inference system.

The sunspot database is taken from the Time Series Data Library[14]. In this experiment we used sunspot relative numbers between the years 1700–1979 which was organized as described in Reference [3] and [15]. We use 209 examples (1712–1920) as the training data, and 59 examples (1921–1979) as the test data. The input attributes were x_{t-12} to x_{t-1} and the output attribute was x_t (i.e., one-year-ahead).

By setting the rule number $M = 2$ and running the clustering algorithm proposed in Section 11.3 only four epochs were required (See Fig. 11.15) to obtain two clusters DB_1 and DB_2 of the sunspot training data set. We also obtained two linear functions $f_1(X)$ and $f_2(X)$ associated with the clusters DB_1 and DB_2 respectively,

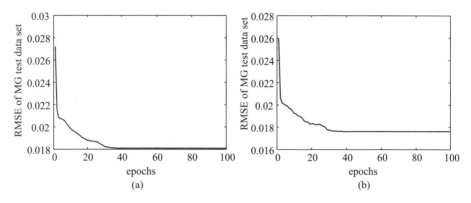

Fig. 11.13 The performance of linguistic model with 16 coarsened rules. (a) The RMSE against epochs curve for the MG training data. (b) The RMSE against epochs curve for the MG test data

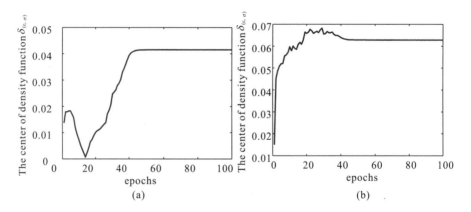

Fig. 11.14 The Gaussian additive probability density function $\delta_{(c,\sigma)}$ for the linguistic model with 16 coarsened rules. (a) The curve of center c against epochs. (b) The curve of width σ against epochs

where $X = (x_{t-12}, \ldots, x_{t-1})$. From these clustering results, we then obtained two linguistic IF-THEN rules:

$$\text{IF } X \text{ is about } DB_1 \text{ THEN } Y \text{ is about } f_1(X)$$

$$\text{IF } X \text{ is about } DB_2 \text{ THEN } Y \text{ is about } f_2(X)$$

where the Gaussian additive probability density function $\delta_{(c,\sigma)}$ associated with the constraint about was estimated using Eqs. (11.21) and (11.22).

We then used the conjugate gradient algorithm to adjust the coefficients of the linear functions $f_1(X)$ and $f_2(X)$ as well as the Gaussian additive density function

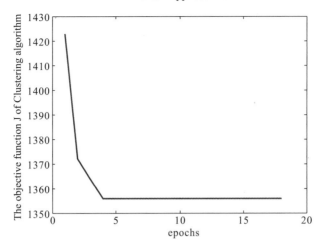

Fig. 11.15 The objective function J of clustering algorithm for the sunspot training data

parameters c and σ. Fig. 11.16 shows the RMSE curves of sunspot training and test data. From this figure, we can see that the performance of the linguistic model for the sunspot test data set is not improved when the conjugate gradient algorithm is applied. The RMSE of sunspot test data set oscillates through the iteration process which may indicate the following:

(1) The sunspot data set is noisy and the behavior of the sunspot training data set and test data set is dissimilar.
(2) The sunspot training data set is sparse with respect to its high dimensionality. In this example the dimension number is 12. However there are only 209 training examples.
(3) The learnt linguistic model over-fits the training data set and has a poor generalization capability for the test data set.

Hence, we need a more robust and coarsened linguistic model for the sunspot prediction problem. There are two ways to coarsen the linguistic rule base. One is to reduce the rule number, the other is to reduce the number of prototypes in each rule antecedent. Note that in this linguistic model the rule number $M = 2$ can not realistically be reduced further. We can only coarsen the rule base by reducing the number of prototypes of the rule antecedents. Using the method suggested in Eq. (11.25) where $\beta = 0.08$ we obtained two reduced prototype sets $P_1 = \{p_1^1, p_2^1, p_3^1\}$ and $P_2 = \{p_1^2, p_2^2, p_3^2\}$ from two clusters DB_1 and DB_2 of sunspot training data set. That is, P_i is the set of cluster centers of DB_i for $i = 1, 2$.

We then used the conjugate gradient algorithm to adjust this coarsened rule base by fixing the prototype sets P_1 and P_2. After 100 learning epochs and optimizing $f_1(X)$, $f_2(X)$, c and σ we obtained the following two rules:

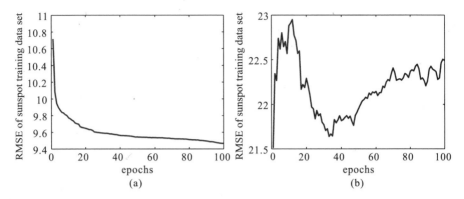

Fig. 11.16 (a) The RMSE of sunspot training data against epochs. (b) The RMSE of sunspot test data against epochs. Here, the prototype sets DB_1 and DB_2 are the clusters of training data set DB, such that $DB_1 \cup DB_2 = DB$ and $DB_1 \cap DB_2 = \emptyset$

$$\text{IF } X \text{ is about } P_1 \text{ THEN } Y \text{ is about } f_1(X)$$
$$\text{IF } X \text{ is about } P_2 \text{ THEN } Y \text{ is about } f_2(X)$$

where the center and width of the Gaussian additive density function $\delta_{(c,\sigma)}$ are $c = 28.8854$ and $\sigma = 29.6356$.

Fig. 11.17 shows the RMSE of the sunspot training data set and test data set. From this figure we can see that the generalization capability of the rule base is improved by reducing the number of prototypical elements in the rule antecedents. As a result of the learning process performance of both the sunspot training data and test data set was improved. Both the RMSE for the training data set and test data

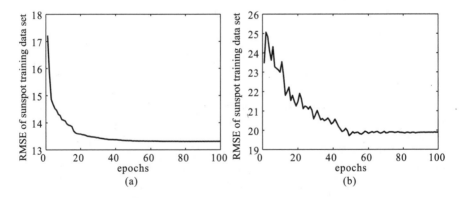

Fig. 11.17 (a) The RMSE of sunspot training data against epochs. (b) The RMSE of sunspot test data against epochs. Here, the prototype sets P_1 and P_2 are the sets of cluster centers of DB_1 and DB_2, respectively

set converged to local minima. The best RMSE for the test data set was 19.715. Fig. 11.18 shows the prediction results for the training data set and test data set using the learnt rule base. Fig. 11.19 shows a scatter plots of predicted against actual values. A comparison of results for different learning algorithms for this prediction problem is shown in Table 11.2 where the prediction results of the other learning algorithms are taken from References [3] and [16]. Note that the prediction accuracy of our prototype-based linguistic inference system is superior to the other learning algorithms applied to this example.

Table 11.2   Comparison results for different learning algorithms applied to the sunspot problem

Learning algorithm	RMSE
Fuzzy Naive Bayes	28.4735
ε−Support Vector Regression System	20.4481
Best Fuzzy Semi-Naive Bayes	22.3530
Back. Pro. NN	32.0341
ANFIS	25.895
5 prototype-based rules (Constants)	21.9113
2 prototype-based rules (Linear functions)	19.715

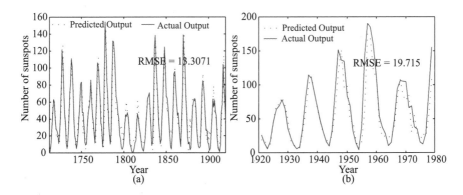

Fig. 11.18   (a) Sunspot prediction result for the training data using 2 rules ($c = 35.9125, \sigma = 29.6356$). (b) Sunspot prediction result for the test data using 2 rules ($c = 35.9125, \sigma = 29.6356$). Here the antecedent of each rule has 3 prototypical elements. The solid line is the actual output, the dotted line is the predicted output

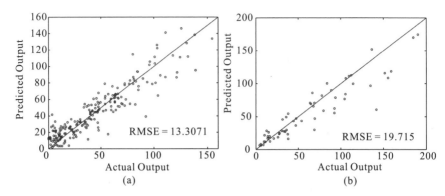

Fig. 11.19 (a) Scatter plot showing the desired output vs the predicted output of sunspot training data using 2 rules ($c = 35.9125, \sigma = 29.6356$). (b) Scatter plot showing the desired output vs the predicted output of sunspot test data using 2 rules ($c = 35.9125, \sigma = 29.6356$). Here the antecedent of each rule has 2 prototypical elements

11.6 Summary

In this chapter we have proposed a prototype-based linguistic inference system which is a generalization of the linguistic inference system proposed in Reference [3]. The rule form adopted by this more general linguistic inference system is as follows:

IF X is about P THEN Y is about $f(X)$

where P is a prototype set of the rule antecedent label, $f(X)$ is a linear function of the input variables, and "about" is represented by a probability density function δ on $[0, +\infty)$.

These prototype-based linguistic rules have a similar form to T-S fuzzy rules[4], but have a different calculus for modelling uncertainty. The reasoning method in the proposed inference system is based on the prototype model for label semantics[1,2] which has a clear operational interpretation for uncertainty measures on linguistic labels. In this chapter we also developed a clustering-based rule induction method to identify the prototype-based IF-THEN rules from data. Our experiments on a number of benchmark prediction problems show that the proposed prototype-based linguistic inference system is very effective and robust. In particular, it is appropriate for high-dimensional modelling with sparse and noisy data, in that it is able to reach a trade-off between the prediction accuracy and generalization capability.

References

[1] Lawry J., Tang Y.: Relating prototype theory and label semantics, in: Dubois D., Lubiano M. A., Prade H., Gil M. A., Grzegorzewski P., Hryniewicz

O.(Eds.), Soft Methods for Handling Variability and Imprecision, pp. 35-42. (2008).

[2] Lawry J., Tang Y.: Uncertainty modeling for vague concepts: A prototype theory approach. Artificial Intelligence, 173, pp.1539-1558. (2009).

[3] Tang Y., Lawry J.: Linguistic modeling and information coarsening based on prototype theory and label semantics. International Journal of Approximate Reasoning, 50(8), pp. 1177-1198. (2009).

[4] Takagi T., Sugeno M.: Fuzzy identification of systems and its applications to modeling and control, IEEE Trans. Syst., Man, Cybernetics , 15, pp. 116–132. (1985).

[5] Lawry J.: A framework for linguistic modelling, Artificial Intelligence, 155: pp. 1-39. (2004).

[6] Lawry J.: Modelling and Reasoning with Vague Concepts, Springer. (2006).

[7] Lawry J.: A methodology for computing with words, International Journal of Approximate Reasoning, 28, pp. 51-89. (2001).

[8] Jang J. S. R., Sun C. T. and Mizutani E.: Neuro-Fuzzy and Soft Computing, Prentice-Hall, Inc. Simon & Schuster. (1997).

[9] Bezdek J. C., Keller J. M., Krishnapuram R., and Pal N.: Fuzzy models and algorithms for pattern recognition and image processing. The Handbooks on Fuzzy Sets, Netherlands, (1999).

[10] Hagan M., Demuth H., Beale M.: Neural Network Design, MA: PWS Publishing, Boston. (1996).

[11] Kim D., Kim C.: Forecasting time series with genetic fuzzy predictor ensemble, IEEE Trans. Fuzzy Syst. 5, pp. 523-535. (1997).

[12] Russo M.: Genetic fuzzy learning, IEEE Trans. Evol. Comput., 4(3), pp. 259-273. (2000).

[13] Tang Y., Xu Y.: Application of fuzzy naive bayes and a real-valued genetic algorithm in identification of fuzzy model, Information Sciences, 169(3-4), pp. 205-226. (2005).

[14] Hyndman R., Akram M.: Time series Data Library. Monash University. http://www-personal.buseco.monash.edu.au/~hyndman/TSDL/index.htm.

[15] Randon N. J.: Fuzzy and Random Set Based Induction Algorithms, PhD Thesis, Department of Engineering Mathematics, University of Bristol. (2004).

[16] Nguyen H.: On modeling of linguistic information using random sets, Information Sciences 34, pp. 265-274. (1984).

12

Information Cells and Information Cell Mixture Models

12.1 Introduction

Based on the prototype theory interpretation[1,2], this chapter develops a new framework for concept modeling and learning: the framework of information cell mixture models. We firstly introduce an information cell model to represent a vague concept having the form "$L_i = about\ P_i$". An information "cell" has a transparent structure and operational semantics derived from the prototype theory interpretation of label semantics[1–4]. We then develop the information cell mixture model for modellng a complex concept having form "about P", where P has n possible states P_i with probability $Pr(L_i)$. In other words, an information cell mixture model is actually a set of weighted information cells. This type of knowledge representation can model the behavior of disjunction of basic concepts. Based on this new knowledge representation, we further develop an information cellularization algorithm for concept learning. The basic aim is to learn a set of most appropriate concepts $\mathbb{L} = \{L_1, \ldots, L_n\}$ with a probability distribution $\{Pr(L_1), \ldots, Pr(L_n)\}$ from a data set DB. Finally we illustrate the basic idea and efficiency of the information cell mixture models by some examples.

12.2 Information Cell for Cognitive Representation of Vague Concept Semantics

We assume that $\mathbb{L} = \{L_1, \ldots, L_n\}$ is a set of labels for elements from domain $\Omega = \mathbb{R}^m$. For each label L_i we assume that L_i is a linguistic expression having a form as "about P", where $P_i \subseteq \mathbb{R}^m$ is a set of prototypical cases of concept L_i. Clearly this type of concept is very common in the human natural language to make communication and convey information. In some sense, it is the smallest unit for concept description. Appropriately modeling this type of concept unit has a fundamental importance in knowledge representation and machine learning. Due to the vague constraint "about" involved in the concept unit L_i the semantics of concept are obviously vague. In the following, a transparent cognitive structure referred to as an information cell is proposed to model the concept semantics.

Definition 12.1 (Information cell) *An information cell (or a semantic cell) for vague concept L_i = about P_i on the domain Ω is a 3-tuple representation $\langle P_i, d_i, \delta_i \rangle$, where P_i is a set of prototypes for concept L_i, d_i is a distance function on Ω where for any $X, Y \in \Omega$ $d_i(X,Y) = d_i(Y,X)$ and $d_i(X,X) = 0$, and δ_i is a density function on $[0, +\infty)$ (For $I \subseteq [0, +\infty)$ we denote $\delta_i(I) = \int_I \delta_i(\varepsilon)d\varepsilon$).*

In this definition P_i we use the term information nucleus to refer to the set of all prototypical cases of L_i, and we implicitly introduces an information membrane which bounds the positive neighborhood for L_i softly. The distance function d_i is used to measure the size ε of the positive neighborhood, and due to the vagueness of "about" the density function δ_i reflects the distribution of size ε of the positive neighborhood. For simplicity, P_i is assumed to be a single element in Ω, for any $X, Y \in \Omega$ the distance

$$d_i(X,Y) \triangleq \|X - Y\| \text{(Euclidean distance)}$$

and the density function $\delta_i(\varepsilon)$ is a normalized normal density function

$$\delta(\varepsilon \mid c_i, \sigma_i) = \frac{f(\varepsilon \mid c_i, \sigma_i)}{F_{c_i}^{\sigma_i}}$$

where $f(\varepsilon \mid c_i, \sigma_i)$ is a normal density function

$$\frac{1}{\sqrt{2\pi}\sigma_i} \exp \frac{(\varepsilon - c_i)^2}{-2\sigma_i^2}$$

and $F_{c_i}^{\sigma_i}$ is the normalization factor

$$\int_0^{+\infty} f(\varepsilon \mid c_i, \sigma_i)d\varepsilon.$$

Based on this transparent cognitive structure, information cell $L_i = \langle P_i, d_i, \delta_i \rangle$, we can define a positive density function $\delta_{L_i}(X)$ on Ω.

Definition 12.2 (Positive density function)
The positive density function associated with the information cell $L_i = \langle P_i, d_i, \delta_i \rangle$, δ_{L_i}, is defined as follows: for any $X \in \Omega$,

$$\delta_{L_i}(X) = \delta_i(d_i(X, P_i)) \tag{12.1}$$

where $d_i(X, P_i) = \inf_{Y \in P_i} d_i(X, Y)$.

Notice that the positive density function and density function associated with the same information cell have the similar notation, but they have different domains. Their meanings can be easily distinguished in the context.

Definition 12.3 (Positive neighborhood) *For any $L_i \in \mathbb{L}$ and $\varepsilon \geq 0$ the positive neighborhood $\mathscr{PN}_{L_i}^{\varepsilon}$ for information cell L_i is defined as follows:*

$$\mathscr{PN}_{L_i}^{\varepsilon} = \{X : d_i(X, P_i) \leq \varepsilon\} \tag{12.2}$$

where $d_i(X, P_i) = \inf_{Y \in P_i} d_i(X, Y)$.

Intuitively speaking $\mathscr{PN}_{L_i}^{\varepsilon}$ identifies the set of positive neighbors lying within ε of prototypes P_i for label L_i. Here the neighborhood radius of $\mathscr{PN}_{L_i}^{\varepsilon}$ is measured by the threshold ε, and ε is a random variable with a density function δ_i. From this we can obtain the belief (degree) of each point X in Ω being a positive neighbor for L_i by integrating $\delta_i(\varepsilon)$ over $\{\varepsilon : X \in \mathscr{PN}_{L_i}^{\varepsilon}\}$.

Definition 12.4 (Positive neighborhood function) $\forall L_i \in \mathbb{L}$, $\forall X \in \Omega$, *the belief (degree) of X being a positive neighbor for information cell L_i is given by:*

$$\mu_{L_i}(X) = \delta_i(\{\varepsilon : X \in \mathscr{PN}_{L_i}^{\varepsilon}\}) = \delta_i([d_i(X, P_i), +\infty)) \tag{12.3}$$

We also use notation $\Delta(\varepsilon)$ to represent the integration $\delta([\varepsilon, +\infty))$. Sometimes we use notation $\Delta_{L_i}(X)$ or $\Delta_i(X)$ to represent the positive neighborhood function

$$\mu_{L_i}(X) \triangleq \delta_i([d_i(X, P_i), +\infty)).$$

Therefore, for each information cell L_i there are two functions, positive density function $\delta_i(X)$ and positive neighborhood function $\Delta_i(X)$, defined on the domain Ω. Clearly the positive neighborhood function of information cell L_i is similar to the membership function of a fuzzy set. Hence we can use information cells to represent vague concepts in many uncertain situations such as group decision making[5] and information aggregation[6].

Given a data set $DB = \{X_1, \ldots, X_N\}$ and an information cell $L_i = \langle P_i, d_i, \delta_i \rangle$, we may want to know how many elements in DB are covered by information cell L_i. The following definition gives one possible answer to this question.

Definition 12.5 *The number of elements in DB covered by information cell $L_i = \langle P_i, d_i, \delta_i \rangle$, $|L_i|_{DB}$, is defined as follows,*

$$|L_i|_{DB} = \int_0^{+\infty} |\mathscr{PN}_{L_i}^{\varepsilon} \cap DB| \delta_i(\varepsilon) \mathrm{d}\varepsilon. \tag{12.4}$$

Intuitively speaking, the set of elements in DB covered by the positive neighborhood $\mathscr{PN}_{L_i}^{\varepsilon}$ of information cell L_i is $\mathscr{PN}_{L_i}^{\varepsilon} \cap DB$. In other words, with the probability $\delta_i(\varepsilon)$, the number of elements in DB covered by information cell L_i is

$$|\mathscr{PN}_{L_i}^{\varepsilon} \cap DB|,$$

so the number of elements in DB covered by information cell L_i is the integration of

$$|\mathscr{PN}_{L_i}^{\varepsilon} \cap DB| \delta_i(\varepsilon) \text{ over } [0, +\infty).$$

Clearly, $|L_i|_{DB}$ can also be calculated from the positive neighborhood degrees $\mu_{L_i}(X_i)$ for $X_i \in DB$.

Proposition 12.1 *The number of elements in DB covered by information cell* $L_i = \langle P_i, d_i, \delta_i \rangle$, $|L_i|_{DB}$, *is as follows,*

$$|L_i|_{DB} = \sum_{k=1}^{N} \mu_{L_i}(X_k).$$ (12.5)

Clearly, if *DB* has only one element X then $|L_i|_{\{X\}} = \mu_{L_i}(X)$.

12.3 Information Cell Mixture Model (ICMM) for Semantic Representation of Complex Concept

We can see that the positive neighborhood functions $\mu_{L_i}(X)$ or $\Delta_i(X)$ of information cells $L_i = \langle P_i, d_i, \delta_i \rangle$ are all uni-modal, which may not represent more complex concepts having multi-modal neighborhood functions, if we assume that P_i is a single prototype. In this section we introduce a new tool to represent complex concepts.

Definition 12.6 (Information cell mixture model) *An information cell mixture model is formally represented as* $\mathscr{LP} = \langle \mathbb{L}, Pr \rangle$, *where* $\mathbb{L}$ *is a set of information cells* $L_i = \langle P_i, d_i, \delta_i \rangle$ *for* $i = 1, \dots, n$
and Pr is a probability distribution on $\mathbb{L}$ *such that* $\sum_{i=1}^{n} Pr(L_i) = 1$.

The information cell mixture model $\mathscr{LP}$ uses a set of information cells to represent a complex concept, where each information cell L_i is assigned a probability $Pr(L_i)$. In this definition, the information cells can be considered as the basic blocks for knowledge representation, and more complex knowledge can be constructed using mixture models of information cells. In general, for simplicity we assume that each information cell has a single prototype. This assumption may limit the knowledge representation capability of information cells. However, the information cell mixture model provides a way to represent the complex concept with multiple prototypes. Hence, the mixture model of information cells still has a transparent structure and operational semantics. In other words, the information cell mixture model $\mathscr{LP} = \langle \mathbb{L}, Pr \rangle$ represents a complex concept *about P* where *P* has *n* crisp but uncertain states P_i for $i = 1, \dots, n$. In the following section, we will develop a reliable learning algorithm to create an information cell mixture model from data set.

For the information cell mixture model we can also define the positive density function and the positive neighborhood function in the domain Ω.

Definition 12.7 (Positive density function $\delta_{\mathscr{LP}}$) *The positive density function of a mixture model of information cells* $\mathscr{LP}$, $\delta_{\mathscr{LP}}$, *is defined as follows: for any* $X \in \Omega$

$$\delta_{\mathscr{LP}}(X) = \sum_{i=1}^{n} \delta_i(X) Pr(L_i)$$ (12.6)

where $\delta_i(X)$ *are the positive density functions of information cells* L_i *for* $i = 1, \dots, n$ *(see definition 12.2).*

Definition 12.8 (Positive neighborhood function $\Delta_{\mathscr{L}\mathscr{P}}$) *The positive neighborhood function of an information cell mixture model $\mathscr{L}\mathscr{P}$, $\mu_{\mathscr{L}\mathscr{P}}$ (or $\Delta_{\mathscr{L}\mathscr{P}}$), is defined as follows: for any $X \in \Omega$*

$$\mu_{\mathscr{L}\mathscr{P}}(X) = \sum_{i=1}^{n} \mu_{L_i}(X)Pr(L_i) \tag{12.7}$$

For the information cell mixture model $\mathscr{L}\mathscr{P}$ we can not consider that the elements P_i for $i = 1,\ldots,n$ are the prototypes of the underlying concept. The prototypes of $\mathscr{L}\mathscr{P}$ are uncertain and can take value P_i with probability $Pr(L_i)$. Actually, in general $\mu_{\mathscr{L}\mathscr{P}}(X) \neq 1$ for $X \in P_i$.

Definition 12.9 *The number of elements in DB covered by an information cell mixture model $\mathscr{L}\mathscr{P}$, $|\mathscr{L}\mathscr{P}|_{DB}$, is defined as follows,*

$$|\mathscr{L}\mathscr{P}|_{DB} = \sum_{i=1}^{n} |L_i|_{DB}Pr(L_i). \tag{12.8}$$

A direct application of information cell mixture models is classification, since each mixture model of information cells represents a concept which in general corresponds to a class on the domain Ω. Note that the positive neighborhood function $\Delta(X)$ reflects the degree of element X being a positive case of the underlying concept. This indicates that we can adopt $\Delta(X)$ to make a classification decision.

Definition 12.10 (Δ Decision rule for classification) *Given two information cell mixture models $\mathscr{L}\mathscr{P}_1$ and $\mathscr{L}\mathscr{P}_2$, $X \in \Omega$ belongs to the concept $\mathscr{L}\mathscr{P}_1$ if*

$$\mu_{\mathscr{L}\mathscr{P}_1}(X) > \mu_{\mathscr{L}\mathscr{P}_2}(X) \tag{12.9}$$

In order to represent a concept using an information cell mixture model, we only need $(m+3)n$ parameters in which there are n m-dimensional prototypes P_i, n probability values assigned to the prototypes, and n normalized normal density functions. This type of representation for a complex concept is still very simple, and has a very transparent cognitive structure and operational semantics.

12.4 Learning Information Cell Mixture Model from Data Set

This section presents a method for learning an information cell mixture model $\mathscr{L}\mathscr{P}$ from a data set DB. We assume that the basic concept L_i involved in $\mathscr{L}\mathscr{P}$ is represented by an information cell having a single prototype $P_i \in \Omega$ and a density function $\delta(\varepsilon \mid c_i, \sigma_i)$ on $[0, +\infty)$. In the proposed learning algorithm we use k-means algorithm to determine all prototypes P_i involved in $\mathscr{L}\mathscr{P}$ and learn the density functions and probabilities associated with information cells by optimizing an objective function $J(\mathscr{L}\mathscr{P})$ from a data set DB. The learning algorithm for optimizing the objective function $J(\mathscr{L}\mathscr{P})$ is analyzed in detail, which involves the updating of density functions and probabilities of information cells.

12.4.1 Objective Function Based on Positive Density Function

Given a data set $DB = \{X_1, \ldots, X_N\}$, our objective is to derive an information cell mixture model $\mathscr{LP} = \langle \mathbb{L}, Pr \rangle$ where $\mathbb{L} = \{L_1, \ldots, L_n\}$ are the most appropriate information cells for describing the underlying data set DB. We call this induction process the information cellularization or conceptualization driven by the data set. Notice that the prototypes involved in the information cell mixture model have clear and operational semantics: they are the typical cases or average cases of the underlying concepts. This means we can take the k-mean algorithm to determine the prototypes P_i of information cell mixture model $\mathscr{LP}$. Once the prototypes P_i are given, we should learn the density functions δ_i of information cells L_i and the probability distribution Pr of information cells. They can be learnt by maximizing the positive density function $\delta_{\mathscr{LP}}(X)$ on the data from the training data set DB, since $\delta_{\mathscr{LP}}(X)$ reflects the likelihood of X 'generated' from the information mixture model $\mathscr{LP}$. The log likelihood function of $\mathscr{LP}$ given the data set DB is defined as follows:

$$\text{maximize} J(\mathscr{LP}) = \ln \delta_{\mathscr{LP}}(DB) \triangleq \ln \prod_{k=1}^{N} \delta_{\mathscr{LP}}(X_k) = \sum_{k=1}^{N} \ln \delta_{\mathscr{LP}}(X_k)$$

$$= \sum_{k=1}^{N} \ln \left(\sum_{i=1}^{n} \delta(\varepsilon_{ik} \mid c_i, \sigma_i) Pr(L_i) \right) \tag{12.10}$$

where for $i = 1, \ldots, n$ and $k = 1, \ldots, N$:

$$\varepsilon_{ik} = d_i(X_k, P_i) = \|X_k - P_i\|, \delta(\varepsilon_{ik} \mid c_i, \sigma_i) = \frac{f(\varepsilon_{ik} \mid c_i, \sigma_i)}{F_{c_i}^{\sigma_i}}$$

The above log likelihood function is very difficult to optimize because it contains the log of the sum. But if we assume the existence of unobserved data whose values inform us which information cell "generated" each data, then we can define the complete log likelihood function as follows:

$$J_c(\mathscr{LP}) = \sum_{k=1}^{N} \sum_{i=1}^{n} z_{ik} \ln \left(\delta(\varepsilon_{ik} \mid c_i, \sigma_i) Pr(L_i) \right) \tag{12.11}$$

where $z_{ik} \in \{0, 1\}$ and $\sum_{i=1}^{n} z_{ik} = 1$.

12.4.2 Updating Probability Distribution of Information Cells

Then we may use the Expectation-Maximization (EM) algorithm to optimize the above complete log likelihood function, which comprises two steps: the computation of conditional expectation of complete log likelihood function given the current estimate $\hat{\mathscr{LP}}$, and its maximization.

According to the EM algorithm we firstly compute the following conditional expectation of the complete log likelihood function:

$$Q\left(\mathscr{LP},\hat{\mathscr{LP}}\right) = E(J_c(\mathscr{LP}) \mid \hat{\mathscr{LP}}) = \sum_{k=1}^{N}\sum_{i=1}^{n}\hat{q}_{ik}\ln\left(\delta(\varepsilon_{ik} \mid c_i,\sigma_i)Pr(L_i)\right)$$

$$= \sum_{k=1}^{N}\sum_{i=1}^{n}\hat{q}_{ik}\left(\frac{(\varepsilon_{ik}-c_i)^2}{-2\sigma_i^2} - \ln\sqrt{2\pi}\sigma_i - \ln F_{c_i}^{\sigma_i} + \ln Pr(L_i)\right) \tag{12.12}$$

where

$$\hat{q}_{ik} = E(z_{ik} \mid \hat{\mathscr{LP}}) = \frac{\delta(\varepsilon_{ik} \mid \hat{c}_i,\hat{\sigma}_i)\hat{Pr}(\hat{L}_i)}{\sum_{i=1}^{n}\delta(\varepsilon_{ik} \mid \hat{c}_i,\hat{\sigma}_i)\hat{Pr}(\hat{L}_i)} \tag{12.13}$$

From the expression $Q(\mathscr{LP},\hat{\mathscr{LP}})$, our goal is to obtain the optimized values of Pr for the probability distribution of information cells, and the density functions $\delta(\cdot \mid c_i,\sigma_i)$ of information cells.

To find the expression for $Pr(L_i)$, we introduce the Lagrange multiplier λ with the constraint that $\sum_{i=1}^{n}Pr(L_i) = 1$, and solve the following equation:

$$\frac{\partial}{\partial Pr(L_i)}\left[Q(\mathscr{LP},\hat{\mathscr{LP}}) + \lambda\left(\sum_{i=1}^{n}Pr(L_i) - 1\right)\right] = 0$$

or

$$\sum_{k=1}^{N}\frac{1}{Pr(L_i)}\hat{q}_{ik} + \lambda = 0$$

Summing both sizes over i, we obtain $\lambda = -N$ resulting in the following updating formula for the probability distribution of information cells, for $i = 1,\ldots,n$:

$$Pr(L_i) = \frac{1}{N}\sum_{k=1}^{N}\hat{q}_{ik} \tag{12.14}$$

12.4.3 Updating Density Functions of Information Cells

However, it is difficult to obtain the optimized density functions of information cells $\mathbb{L}$ from the expression $Q(\mathscr{LP},\hat{\mathscr{LP}})$. So we try to obtain the sub-optimal values of information cells $\mathbb{L}$ by introducing an auxiliary function $U(\mathscr{LP},\hat{\mathscr{LP}})$:

$$U(\mathscr{LP},\hat{\mathscr{LP}}) = \sum_{k=1}^{N}\sum_{i=1}^{n}\hat{q}_{ik}\left(\frac{(\varepsilon_{ik}-c_i)^2}{-2\sigma_i^2} - \ln\sqrt{2\pi}\sigma_i + \ln Pr(L_i)\right)$$

Due to $-\ln F_{c_i}^{\sigma_i} \geq 0$ we have the following conclusion:

$$U(\mathscr{LP},\hat{\mathscr{LP}}) \leq Q(\mathscr{LP},\hat{\mathscr{LP}}) \tag{12.15}$$

By maximizing the lower bound function $U(\mathscr{LP},\hat{\mathscr{LP}})$ we can obtain the sub-optimal values of density functions $\delta(\cdot \mid c_i,\sigma_i)$ of information cells L_i. Letting

$$\frac{\partial}{\partial c_i}U(\mathscr{LP},\hat{\mathscr{LP}}) = 0$$

and

$$\frac{\partial}{\partial \sigma_i} U(\mathcal{LP}, \mathcal{LP}) = 0,$$

we obtain the formulae:

$$c_i = \frac{\sum_{k=1}^{N} \hat{q}_{ik} \varepsilon_{ik}}{\sum_{k=1}^{N} \hat{q}_{ik}} \tag{12.16}$$

$$\sigma_i^2 = \frac{\sum_{k=1}^{N} \hat{q}_{ik} (\varepsilon_{ik} - c_i)^2}{\sum_{k=1}^{N} \hat{q}_{ik}} \tag{12.17}$$

The above computation of conditional expectation of complete log likelihood function and parameter estimation steps can then be repeated as necessary. Our classification experiments show that updating Eqs. (12.16) and 12.17) are feasible and have a good performance.

12.4.4 Information Cell Updating Algorithm

Given a data set $DB = \{X_k : k = 1, \ldots, N\}$ and a cell number n, the information cellularization algorithm is outlined as follows:

(1) Obtain the prototypes P_i by using k-mean algorithm and assume

$$Pr(L_i(0)) = \frac{1}{n} \text{ for } i = 1, \ldots, n.$$

(2) Compute distances: for $i = 1, \ldots, n$ and $k = 1, \ldots, N$,

$$\varepsilon_{ik} = d_i(X_k, P_i) = \|X_k - P_i\|$$

(3) Initialize $c_i(0)$ and $\sigma_i(0)$ for $i = 1, \ldots, n$ using the following formulae:

$$c_i(0) = \frac{1}{N} \sum_{k=1}^{N} \varepsilon_{ik}, (\sigma_i(0))^2 = \frac{1}{N} \sum_{k=1}^{N} (\varepsilon_{ik} - c_i(0))^2$$

(4) Compute weights: for $i = 1, \ldots, n$ and $k = 1, \ldots, N$,

$$q_{ik}(0) = \frac{\delta(\varepsilon_{ik} | c_i(0), \sigma_i(0)) Pr(L_i(0))}{\sum_{i=1}^{n} \delta(\varepsilon_{ik} | c_i(0), \sigma_i(0)) Pr(L_i(0))}$$

(5) Repeat
   (a) $t = t + 1$
   (b) Update the probability distribution of information cells: for $i = 1, \ldots, n$,

$$Pr(L_i(t)) = \frac{1}{N} \sum_{k=1}^{N} q_{ik}(t - 1)$$

(c) Update density functions $\delta(\cdot \mid c_i(t), \sigma_i(t))$ for $i = 1, \ldots, n$:

$$c_i(t) = \frac{\sum_{k=1}^{N} q_{ik}(t-1)\varepsilon_{ik}}{\sum_{k=1}^{N} q_{ik}(t-1)},$$

$$(\sigma_i(t))^2 = \frac{\sum_{k=1}^{N} q_{ik}(t-1)(\varepsilon_{ik} - c_i(t))^2}{\sum_{k=1}^{N} q_{ik}(t-1)}$$

(d) Compute weights: for $i = 1, \ldots, n$ and $k = 1, \ldots, N$,

$$q_{ik}(t) = \frac{\delta(\varepsilon_{ik}(t) \mid c_i(t), \sigma_i(t)) Pr(L_i(t))}{\sum_{i=1}^{n} \delta(\varepsilon_{ik}(t) \mid c_i(t), \sigma_i(t)) Pr(L_i(t))}$$

(e) Compute objective function $J(\mathscr{LP}(t))$.

(6) Until $|J(\mathscr{LP}(t)) - J(\mathscr{LP}(t-1))|$ is less than a user defined positive threshold.

By applying the above information cellularization algorithm to data set DB, we can explicitly obtain a set of information cells $\mathbb{L}$ with a probability distribution Pr. We can then determine the values $\Delta_{\mathscr{LP}}(X)$ using Eq. (12.7). Hence, if information cell mixture models are applied to a classification problem, we can learn an information cell mixture model for each class, and use Δ decision rule to make classification for any data on the domain Ω.

12.4.5 Learning Component Number of ICMM

Another key issue in the ICMM learning algorithm from a data set DB is the determination of component number n of $\mathscr{LP}$. In this section, we propose a possible method to determine the component number n using the information conveyed by $|\mathscr{LP}|_{DB}$.

According to the current learning algorithm of ICMM, the objective is to minimize the function $\delta_{\mathscr{LP}}(DB)$ given the component number n of ICMM $\mathscr{LP}$. Increasing the component number n we may increase the learning accuracy of ICMM, but also increase the complexity of ICMM. Furthermore, one risk of increasing the component number n may cause the over-fitting problem to the training data set DB and poor generalization capability. The best ICMM should have good learning accuracy for the training data set DB with the least component number n.

$|\mathscr{LP}|_{DB}$ reflects the average number of elements in DB covered by the information cell mixture model $\mathscr{LP}$. In general, we prefer the ICMM having larger $|\mathscr{LP}|_{DB}$. Increasing the component number n may also cause the increase in $|\mathscr{LP}|_{DB}$. This indicates that we can select the component number n according to the value $|\mathscr{LP}|_{DB}$. So the ICMM having sufficient large $|\mathscr{LP}|_{DB}$ and small component number n is the desired ICMM. In the following experiments, we will illustrate the method to determine the component number n in detail.

12.5 Experimental Study

The first example shows the concept learning process of the proposed information cellularization algorithm on a 2-dimensional data set. In this example the data set DB has 140 data points on $[0,1]^2$. The distribution of data set DB is illustrated in Fig. 12.1 .

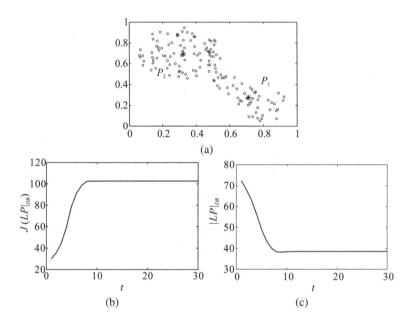

(a)

(b)   (c)

Fig. 12.1 (a) The distribution of the data set DB in $\mathbb{R}^2$, where $P_1 = (0.7119, 0.2770)$ and $P_2 = (0.3241, 0.6929)$. (b) The objective function vs the iteration of information cellularization algorithm. (c) The neighbor number in DB covered by ICMM vs the iteration of information cellularization algorithm

According to this distribution of data set, the number of information cells is then assumed to be 2. We then apply the information cellularization algorithm to this data set DB. After 20 iterations, the objective function $J(\mathscr{LP})$ converges (Fig. 12.1), we finally obtain an information cell mixture model $\langle \{L_1, L_2\}, Pr \rangle$, where the parameters associated with the information cell $L_1 = \langle P_1, d_1, \delta(\cdot \mid c_1, \sigma_1) \rangle$ are $P_1 = (0.7119, 0.2770)$, $c_1 = 0.1458$ and $\sigma_1 = 0.0734$, and the parameters associated with the information cell $L_2 = \langle P_2, d_2, \delta(\cdot \mid c_2, \sigma_2) \rangle$ are $P_2 = (0.3241, 0.6929)$, $c_2 = 0.1777$ and $\sigma_2 = 0.0601$. The probability values associated with information cells are $Pr(L_1) = 0.3341$ and $Pr(L_2) = 0.6659$. In figure 12.1 , we also show the the neighbor number in DB covered by ICMM against the iteration number of the information cellularization algorithm. Roughly speaking, $|\mathscr{LP}|_{DB}$ converges decreasingly to a local minimum. However, the objective function $J(|\mathscr{LP}|_{DB})$

converges increasing to a maximum. This kind of phenomenon may suggest that the functions $J(\mathscr{L}\mathscr{P}|DB)$ and $|\mathscr{L}\mathscr{P}|_{DB}$ have the different properties to control the learning accuracy and generalization capability of ICMM. Actually, on the one hand we should maximize the function $J(\mathscr{L}\mathscr{P}|DB)$ which reflects the likelihood of data set DB generated from the ICMM. On the other hand, we also want to maximize the function $|\mathscr{L}\mathscr{P}|_{DB}$ which reflects the neighbor number in DB covered by ICMM $\mathscr{L}\mathscr{P}$. But increasing $|\mathscr{L}\mathscr{P}|_{DB}$ purely may cause the poor generalization capability of ICMM $\mathscr{L}\mathscr{P}$, which indicates the function $|\mathscr{L}\mathscr{P}|_{DB}$ can not be defined as the objective function of information cellularization algorithm.

Two derived information cells L_1 and L_2 are visualized in Fig. 12.2 . The derived one dimensional density functions associated with information cells, $\delta(\varepsilon \mid c_1, \sigma_1)$ and $\delta(\varepsilon \mid c_2, \sigma_2)$, both of which are normalized normal density functions, are shown in Fig. 12.2 (a). And the corresponding two positive neighborhood functions $\mu_{L_1}(x,y)$ (or $\Delta_{L_1}(x,y)$) and $\mu_{L_2}(x,y)$ (or $\Delta_{L_2}(x,y)$) are both illustrated in Fig. 12.2 (b). In particular, the positive neighborhood function $\Delta_{\mathscr{L}\mathscr{P}}(x,y)$ of the information cell mixture model $\mathscr{L}\mathscr{P}$ is visualized in Fig. 12.2 (c). This function incorporates the information cells and their probabilities, which is a kind of compromise of information cells.

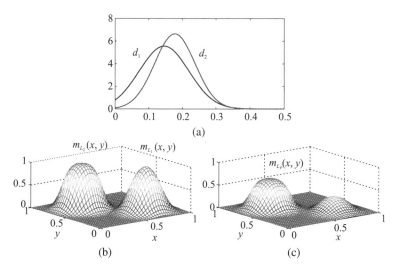

(a)

(b)   (c)

Fig. 12.2   (a) The density functions δ_i of information cells L_i for $i = 1$ and 2, where $\delta_1(\varepsilon) = \delta(\varepsilon \mid 0.1458, 0.0734)$ and $\delta_2(\varepsilon) = \delta(\varepsilon \mid 0.1777, 0.0601)$. (b) The positive neighborhood functions $\mu_{L_i}(x,y)$ of information cells L_i for $i = 1$ and 2, where $\mu_{L_i}(x,y) = \delta_i([d_i((x,y), P_i), +\infty))$ for $i = 1$ and 2. (c) The positive neighborhood function $\Delta(x,y) \triangleq \mu_{\mathscr{L}\mathscr{P}}(x,y)$ of information cell mixture model $\mathscr{L}\mathscr{P}$, where $\mu_{\mathscr{L}\mathscr{P}}(x,y) = \mu_{L_1}(x,y)Pr(L_1) + \mu_{L_2}(x,y)Pr(L_2)$

In order to show the impact of component number n of ICMM $\mathscr{LP}$, we run the information cellularization algorithm by varying the component number n from 2 to 20. From Fig. 12.3 we can see that the neighbor number $|\mathscr{LP}|_{DB}$ covered by ICMM $\mathscr{LP}$ increases as the component number n varies from 2 to 5, and $|\mathscr{LP}|_{DB}$ varies from small when n is bigger than 5. Roughly speaking, $|\mathscr{LP}|_{DB}$ is a monotonic increasing function of component number n, and has an upper bound N. Clearly, $|\mathscr{LP}|_{DB}$ reflects the performance of the learned ICMM $\mathscr{LP}$, and n reflects the complexity of the learned ICMM $\mathscr{LP}$. The optimized ICMM $\mathscr{LP}$ would be a compromise of $|\mathscr{LP}|_{DB}$ and n. In this example, a near optimized ICMM $\mathscr{LP}$ has 5 component numbers.

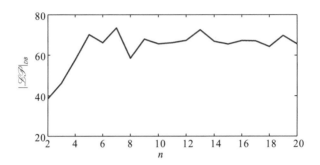

Fig. 12.3   The neighbor number $|\mathscr{LP}|_{DB}$ in DB covered by ICMM $\mathscr{LP}$ against the component number n of $\mathscr{LP}$

The classification problem we have worked with is Iris Plants Database which was created by R.A. Fisher. The data set contains 3 classes of 50 instances each, where each class refers to a type of iris plant. The number of instances in the Iris Plants Database is 150 (50 in each one of three classes), and the number of attributes is 4.

The information cellularization algorithm is then applied to three sub data sets where each one only contains one class. In the algorithm, the involved information cell number is assumed to be 2. Three information cell mixture models $\mathscr{LP}_i$ for $i = 1, 2, 3$ are then obtained, their parameters are listed in Table 12.1 .

After obtaining the information cell mixture models from the iris data set, we then use the decision rule introduced in Eq. (12.9) to make classification. The classification results of the information cell mixture models are compared with the given classes, and discrepancies arising from mismatch between the given classes. For the Iris Plant database, the discrepancies between the actual classes and the achieved classes is very few, and the classification rate is 97.33%.

The second classification problem we have worked with is Pima Indians Diabetes Database which was created by Vincent Sigillito of Johns Hopkins University. The data set contains 2 classes, Diabetes and No-Diabetes. The number

Table 12.1 Information cell mixture models learnt from Iris data sets

		P_i	$\delta(\cdot \mid c_i, \sigma_i)$	$Pr(L_i)$
$\mathscr{LP}_1$	L_1	$(53.7, 38.0, 15.2, 2.8)$	$\delta(\cdot \mid 4.5, 1.3)$	0.3
	L_2	$(48.2, 32.7, 14.3, 2.3)$	$\delta(\cdot \mid 4.2, 2.0)$	0.7
$\mathscr{LP}_2$	L_1	$(63.1, 29.2, 46.1, 14.6)$	$\delta(\cdot \mid 5.6, 2.0)$	0.52
	L_2	$(55.3, 26.0, 38.8, 11.8)$	$\delta(\cdot \mid 5.9, 2.9)$	0.48
$\mathscr{LP}_3$	L_1	$(73.9, 31.3, 62.3, 20.9)$	$\delta(\cdot \mid 6.59, 2.22)$	0.25
	L_2	$(62.8, 29.1, 52.9, 20.0)$	$\delta(\cdot \mid 6.4, 2.7)$	0.75

of attributes is 8, all numeric-valued and the relevant information of Pima Indians Diabetes Database is in Table 12.2 . The total number of instances is 768. we use 512 instances (345 No-Diabetes, 167 Diabetes) to construct the two information cell mixture models: one model corresponds to the No-Diabetes concept C_1, the other model corresponds to the Diabetes concept C_2. We then use 256 instances (155 No-Diabetes, 101 Diabetes) to test the performance of the information cell mixture models.

The information cellularization algorithm is then applied to two training sets where each one only contains one class. In the algorithm, the involved information cell number is also assumed to be 2. Two information cell mixture models $\mathscr{LP}_i$ for $i = 1, 2$ are then obtained, their parameters are listed in Table 12.3 . The classification accuracy for the test data set is 66.7%. We also run the K-NN algorithm to this example and the classification rate for the test data set is 67%. However, compared with K-NN, the information cell mixture models are more concise and transparent.

Table 12.2 Relevant information of *Pima Indians Diabetes Database*

C: C_1, No-Diabetes; C_2, Diabetes					
Attribute	Name	Min	Max	Mean	SD
X_1	Number of times pregnant	0	17	3.8	3.4
X_2	Plasma glucose concentration at 2 hours in an oral glucose tolerance test	0	199	120.9	32.0
X_3	Diastolic blood pressure	0	122	69.1	19.4
X_4	Triceps skin fold thickness	0	99	20.5	16.0
X_5	2-Hour serum insulin	0	846	79.8	115.2
X_6	Body mass index	0	67.1	32.0	7.9
X_7	Diabetes pedigree function	0.084	2.42	0.5	0.3
X_8	Age (years)	21	81	33.2	11.8

Table 12.3 Information cell mixture models learnt from *Pima Indians Diabetes Database* data sets

		P_i	$\delta(\cdot \mid c_i, \sigma_i)$	$Pr(L_i)$
$\mathscr{LP}_1$	L_1	$(3.4, 105.3, 67.6, 17.4, 31.5, 29.5, 0.4, 31.7)$	$\delta(\cdot \mid 49.4, 15.4)$	0.70
	L_2	$(2.7, 129.8, 70.8, 29.5, 227.9, 33.9, 0.5, 29.2)$	$\delta(\cdot \mid 118.7, 80.7)$	0.30
$\mathscr{LP}_2$	L_1	$(4.6, 152.0, 73.9, 33.3, 264.4, 35.9, 0.7, 37.6)$	$\delta(\cdot \mid 139.2, 86.3)$	0.5
	L_2	$(4.9, 136.4, 69.5, 17.2, 26.7, 34.8, 0.5, 36.8)$	$\delta(\cdot \mid 51.2, 14.7)$	0.5

12.6 Summary

The information cell mixture model uses a set of weighted information cells to model a complex concept, where each information cell can be considered as the smallest unit of concept representation with its own prototype(s). The proposed information cell mixture model can be considered as an approximate representation of the disjunction of the underlying information cells, which keeps the transparent structure and operational semantics like the information cells themselves. The positive neighborhood function Δ of the information cell mixture model provides a powerful tool to measure the uncertainty of the underlying concept. More importantly, the information cellularization algorithm developed in this paper gives an iterative procedure to learn the parameters of the information cell mixture model from training data. A direct application of information cell mixture models is the supervised classification, where each class is represented by an information cell mixture model. Another potential application is unsupervised concept learning. Actually the learning algorithm developed in this paper uses an unsupervised way to learn an information cell mixture model from each class. The classification decision is then made by using the Δ decision rule.

References

[1] Lawry J., Tang Y.: Relating prototype theory and label semantics, in: Dubois D., Lubiano M. A., Prade H., Gil M. A., Grzegorzewski P., Hryniewicz O.(Eds.), Soft Methods for Handling Variability and Imprecision, pp. 35-42. (2008).

[2] Lawry J., Tang Y.: Uncertainty modeling for vague concepts: A prototype theory approach. Artificial Intelligence, 173, pp.1539-1558. (2009).

[3] Tang Y., Lawry J.: Linguistic modeling and information coarsening based on prototype theory and label semantics. International Journal of Approximate Reasoning, 50(8), pp. 1177-1198. (2009).

[4] Tang Y., Lawry J.: A prototype-based rule inference system incorporating linear functions, Fuzzy Sets and Systems, 161(21), pp. 2831-2853. (2010).

[5] Sotirov G., Krasteva E.: An approach to group decision making under uncertainty with application to project selection, Annals of Operations Research, 51(3), pp. 115-126. (1994).

[6] Tang Y.: A collective decision model involving vague concepts and linguistic expressions, IEEE Trans. Syst., Man, Cybernetics B, 38(2), pp. 421-428. (2008).